# EUGENICS

MARK H. HALLER

# EUGENICS

Hereditarian Attitudes in
American Thought

RUTGERS UNIVERSITY PRESS
New Brunswick                    New Jersey

# *Preface*

A history of the American eugenics movement provides a means for examining the place of heredity in recent American social thought. In world politics of the twentieth century, the biological doctrines of the Nazis and the victory of Trofim Lysenko over the science of genetics in the Soviet Union are tragic demonstrations that concepts of heredity underlie important social movements. In the fairly recent past, the attitudes of many Americans toward feeble-mindedness, insanity, crime, poverty, immigration, and democracy itself have been expressed chiefly in hereditarian terms. An examination of eugenics involves re-examination of many of the major currents of recent American thought.

While the primary emphasis of the book is upon the social consequences of hereditarian views, those views cannot be divorced from important trends in such fields of biological and social science as genetics, medicine, psychiatry, psychology, criminology, and anthropology. Eugenists have always maintained that their movement involves the application of science to society; necessarily a history of eugenics is a history of science and its social implications.

For assistance in research and writing, I want to express my appreciation, above all, to Professor Merle Curti. He has guided the project from the beginning and has made invaluable suggestions and criticisms throughout. Many others have also been of great help. Professor James F. Crow patiently listened to and answered my many questions concerning genetics and was kind enough to read the chapters dealing most specifically with genetics. Dr. E. Carleton MacDowell went out of his way to assist me in finding my way through the records of the Eugenics Record Office and shared with

*v*

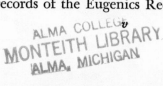

me his reminiscences of many prominent eugenists. At the Training School at Vineland, New Jersey, Dr. Walter Jacob and Dr. Johs. Clausen were very helpful in their comments and in allowing me access to records there. In addition, I wish to express my appreciation to the Social Science Research Council for a one-year grant that permitted me to work full time on the project. Many persons, including the late Mrs. Margaret Wooster Curti, Marc Swartz, Sewell Wright, Charles Rosenberg, and John Tomsich read portions of the manuscript and provided helpful criticism.

To them and to others who have been of assistance I am very grateful.

MARK H. HALLER

*The College*
*University of Chicago*
*January, 1963*

# Contents

# Contents

# EUGENICS

# Chapter I
# Introduction

Eugenics, as an American eugenics leader expressed it, is "the science of the improvement of the human race by better breeding." [1] It is the effort to improve the inborn characteristics of man by the study of human heredity and the application of those studies to human propagation. Eugenists grasped the important fact that a person's hereditary endowment is a major factor in his success and development, and they hoped to breed better people through encouraging propagation by those with desirable traits and through restricting propagation by those with undesirable traits. Primarily the movement was the creation of biological scientists, social scientists, and others with a faith that science provided a guide for human progress. Indeed, during the first three decades of the present century, eugenics was a sort of secular religion for many who dreamed of a society in which each child might be born endowed with vigorous health and an able mind.

Unfortunately, the early eugenists greatly oversimplified the problems of human genetics. Man's genes are not so easily controlled as the eugenists once thought, and the excesses of the early movement brought even the word eugenics into disrepute. But the eugenics movement, concerned as it has been with the nature of man and the role of heredity in shaping man, has played an important part in recent American thought and has raised issues that still seek solution.

Like most ideas, eugenics can be traced at least as far back as the ancient Greeks. Indeed, Plato's *Republic* can be read as a eugenics tract. [2] In its modern guise, however, eugenics was the legitimate offspring of Darwinian evolution, a natural and doubtless inevitable outgrowth of currents of thought that developed from the publication in 1859 of Charles Darwin's *The Origin of Species*. Darwin held that members of a species exhibited numerous small variations and that evolution proceeded through the gradual selection of some and the elimination of other variations through a struggle for existence. If his theory was correct, the key to understanding nature lay in the problem: what caused the variations and in what manner were they passed on to succeeding generations? The attempt to solve these problems led to a widespread interest in the heredity of plants, animals, and man and eventually to the birth of the modern science of genetics.

While evolution focused attention on heredity, it also posed a basic dilemma for students of human society during the late nineteenth and early twentieth centuries. The biological progress of man, the Darwinists claimed, resulted from the selection of the "fit" and the elimination of the "unfit." "We civilised men, on the other hand," as Darwin himself pointed out:

> do our utmost to check the process of elimination; we build asylums for the imbecile, the maimed, and the sick; we institute poor-laws; and our medical men exert their utmost skill to save the life of every one to the last moment. . . . Thus the weak members of civilised societies propagate their kind. No one who has attended to the breeding of domestic animals will doubt that this must be highly injurious to the race of man.[3]

Thus charity, by permitting the survival and propagation of social failures, might be a bar to human progress, increasing the very ills it sought to cure.

Many eugenists had a clear and simple solution to the dilemma. Relying upon the new interest and advances in the study of heredity, they were convinced, during the heyday of the movement, that man's physique, his intellect, and his character were rooted chiefly in heredity. Hence the continued evolution of man might be assured by preventing the unfit from propagating and encouraging the fit to propagate early and often. Through such schemes as marriage restriction, sexual sterilization, or permanent custody of the defective, the eugenists hoped to save society from the burden of the unfit; through financial aid and education in the facts of heredity they hoped to encourage early marriage among the eugenically fit. By elimination of the unfit and the increased propagation of the fit, they would build a better civilization for man.

Eugenics was, of course, but one of many currents stemming from evolutionary thought. Obviously it belonged to the same climate of opinion that produced the conservative social Darwinism associated with the names of Herbert Spencer in England and William Graham Sumner in the United States. Such conservatives found in the dilemma presented by evolutionary thought an excuse for a policy of government *laissez faire*. Unaided by government intervention, they argued, the unfit would succumb to poverty, intemperance, and disease, while the fit would win the economic struggle for survival; and thus the continued evolution of man would be assured.[4] Yet many of those who founded the eugenics movement in America had, on the whole, only limited sympathy with such an outlook. The American movement was in large part the creation of superintendents of asylums for the feebleminded, insane, and alcoholic, of prison wardens and prison physicians, of sociologists and social workers. They were in the forefront of the movement for bigger and better institutions to house and treat the unfortunate classes of mankind. They believed that society had a responsibility to care for the dependent and delinquent but that society had, at the same time, a responsibility to see that such persons did not contaminate the generations to come. Despite the conservative implications of hereditarian thought, eugenics at first was closely related to the other reform movements of the Progressive Era and drew its early support from many of the same persons. It began as a scientific reform in an age of reform.

There is, on the other hand, no doubt that a close connnection often exists between an emphasis upon heredity and a conservative social outlook.[5] From an assumption that men are chiefly shaped by heredity it can be argued that environmental reforms are largely useless and that the class structure of society reflects innate abilities so that those on the bottom are there, not through deficiencies in the social system, but through their own inevitable failures. Similarly, doctrines concerning the innate inequality of races have notoriously served as pretexts for repression of one group by another. Although many of the studies of human heredity upon which the eugenists relied were important scientific advances, others resulted from inaccurate and uncritical scientific and statistical methods, and still others were warped and molded by the social predispositions of men who unconsciously allowed their science to serve their social philosophies. As a result, many strands of eugenics thought were a scientific disguise for conservative, often harsh, indictments of classes and races, and eugenics became, for a time, predominantly a conservative creed.

Because they thought they had found in eugenics a scientific basis for a belief that those from the best race, class, and family should rule and should breed, many eugenists came to feel alienated from the dominant American attitudes. The popular notion that everyone ought to participate in government appeared to them naïve; the American hope that the American environment and education would open opportunities so that even the lowliest could rise represented unscientific sentimentality; and the conviction that social reform and social justice could reduce substantially the sum of human miseries was for such eugenists not merely wrongheaded but outright dangerous. Thus, despite the widespread influence of eugenics upon educated Americans, many eugenists eventually despaired that their views could ever gain mass support. Hence they feared for the future of their own nation; and a movement that began in hope soon culminated in despair.

For convenience's sake, the American eugenics movement can be divided into three stages. The first, from about 1870 to 1905, was a period of preparation during which hereditarian attitudes took root. Many of those concerned with the care and treatment of the dependent and delinquent came to believe that the feebleminded, criminal, insane, epileptic, and pauper were, chiefly or partly, products of their heredity. Hence they hoped that ways would be found to restrict their propagation. At the same time, a few Americans feared the impact of immigrants on American society and began to urge restriction on the grounds of race or national origin. By 1905, as a result, all the ingredients were present so that a formal eugenics movement might be launched.

From 1905 to 1930, then, eugenics entered upon its period of greatest influence. Among students of dependency and delinquency the conviction deepened that the causes of most feeblemindedness and a good proportion of insanity, crime, and pauperism lay in heredity. As a result, the problems of heredity and the prevention of hereditary ills dominated the meetings of the National Conference of Charities and Correction and other reform organizations, and an intensive campaign for permanent custodial care of the feebleminded and for sterilization of many types of defectives was carried on in virtually every state. During the same period, eugenics took on a racist tone when many, fearing that the influx of "inferior" races imperiled the innate capacity of the American people,

found in eugenics the arguments t
tion restriction. This phase of eu
the 1920's when Congress, acceptin
designed to restrict the influx of the
ern and eastern Europe. Eugenics,
and there formed the basis for rese
chologists tested human intelligence
ologists investigated the comparative
cial classes; and biologists wrote on
ples of heredity to man. It was durin
ence that eugenics shifted from a n
nantly, although never entirely, linke
the day to a movement that was predor            ....ugii never entirely, a repudiation of the American reforming tradition.

After 1930 the course of eugenics was rapidly downhill. New developments in such varied fields as anthropology, genetics, mental testing, and psychiatry undercut the scientific basis upon which much of the movement then rested. These studies demonstrated that human heredity was far more complicated than most eugenists had realized and that environmental and cultural factors played a much greater part in man's makeup than earlier eugenists were willing to admit. At the same time, Hitler in Germany demonstrated the uses that might be made of some of the eugenics doctrines. These new developments stripped the eugenics movement of its trappings of science and disclosed that it had been based upon often careless and inaccurate research, that it was permeated by a virulent nativism without basis in fact, and that it frequently mirrored the conservative and reactionary social philosophies of its adherents.

The period since 1930 has therefore been characterized not by legislation, or even by propaganda, but by continued and careful research into the heredity of man. Because the problem of man's genetic future has remained an important one, as the present concern over radioactive fallout amply demonstrates, the eugenics movement did not die. During the last thirty years thoughtful students of human heredity have necessarily considered the applications of their investigations to man's well-being. Today, when rapid advances are being made in all fields of genetic research, a cautious, sober, and scientific eugenics is once more struggling for attention.

# Chapter II

# European Beginnings

### Francis Galton

While eugenics was a natural outgrowth of nineteenth-century
ideas, Sir Francis Galton, F.R.S. (1822-1911), was the revered
founder of the movement. He it was who gave eugenics its name,
established the movement in England, and provided it with much
of its ideology. Galton was a versatile nineteenth-century gentleman
scientist, kindly and proper as an English gentleman should be.
Throughout his life he regularly interrupted his scientific studies
for tours abroad or visits to watering places. Perhaps the key to his
scientific success was that for him statistics were "full of beauty and
interest." [1] His love for numbers led him, when he had nothing else
to do, to count the number of fidgets in an audience or the number of attractive, indifferent, and repellent women he passed on the
street. In his long and distinguished career, Galton led geographical explorations, pioneered in the use of weather maps, made major contributions to psychological testing, discovered statistical tools
of major importance, helped establish fingerprints as a means of
identification, and of course did outstanding work in the study of
heredity. [2]

Galton's genius was, eugenists claimed, an example of what could
be produced by judicious breeding. On his mother's side he was
Charles Darwin's cousin (Erasmus Darwin was their common grand-
father); this accounted for his scientific talent. On his father's side
he descended from a line of stern Quaker businessmen and from
them inherited his fine physical health and a taste for statistics. [3] A
precocious child, Galton learned to read at the age of two and one-

8

half. At the age of sixteen he began to fit himself for the profession of medicine and by 1844, at the age of twenty-two, had completed his medical studies and earned a degree in mathematics from Trinity College, Cambridge. Because his father's death in 1844 made him financially independent, Galton never practiced medicine but instead entered upon a life of extensive travel and gentlemanly ease. By the early 1850's his geographical explorations had earned him election to the Royal Society of Science, and he was soon an active participant in most of the British scientific societies.

With the publication of his cousin's *The Origin of Species,* Galton found the central theme for his future research. Darwin, in his great work, hinted that through the study of evolution "much light will be thrown on the origin of man and his history," but otherwise cautiously left the subject of man alone.[4] Galton, on the other hand, boldly affirmed the importance of evolution in explaining man's past and in plotting man's future. For the remainder of his life he studied heredity and variation in man, and from these studies came his most important contributions to science, as well as the founding of eugenics.

Galton first set himself the task of demonstrating, through a careful study of the pedigrees of famous men, that the mental abilities of man were inherited. His method revealed a somewhat conservative social outlook, for, lacking other standards, he accepted a man's reputation as a measure of his innate ability. "If a man is gifted with vast intellectual ability, eagerness to work, and power of working, I cannot comprehend how such a man should be repressed," [5] he explained. He minimized, therefore, the advantages that family connections and environment might provide in producing several illustrious men in the same family and assumed that, on the whole, the successful possessed innate capacities which the unsuccessful lacked.[6] He believed that mental abilities followed the normal bell-shaped curve of distribution, with persons of average ability grouped in the middle and persons of greater and lesser ability ranging in nearly equal numbers to each side. Galton, no friend to the notion of the equality of man, held that greatly gifted persons were as far above the average as idiots were below it.[7]

In 1865 in an article on "Hereditary Talent and Character" and four years later in a book, *Hereditary Genius,* Galton published the results from his studies of pedigrees of outstanding men. He found that men whose ability and reputation placed them far above the average had a surprisingly large number of relatives of nearly equal ability—a number far greater than could be explained by random expectation. This was true in the case of judges, statesmen, commanders, scientists, poets, clergymen, and even wrestlers of the North Country.[8] Galton collected an impressive array of pedigrees to prove that human abilities were largely inherited, or, as he liked to express it, nature was more important than nurture in man's development. Thus, within six years of the publication of *The Origin of Species,* Galton had arrived at the doctrine that he was to preach for the remainder of his life: that man's character and capacities were primarily shaped by heredity and that the present generation therefore had the power to control and improve the inborn qualities of the many generations to follow.[9] In time this became for him a new ethic and a new religion.

Galton was probably the first to grasp the importance of twins for a study of heredity. In the 1870's he assembled extensive information on eighty pairs of twins. According to Galton, identical twins, whose heredity he rightly assumed to be the same, often displayed remarkable similarity throughout life, not only in details of physical appearance but in temperament as well. The similarities persisted even after the twins separated and lived in varying environments. Fraternal twins, on the other hand, differed—often strikingly—in both appearance and temperament despite the similar environments in which they were often raised. The study of twins provided still another demonstration for him that nature dominated nurture in shaping man.[10]

Convinced that human abilities were inherited, Galton turned to investigations of the wide range of physical and psychological traits among men. He desired to show how greatly men and races differed from each other and thus demonstrate the wide variety of hereditary abilities upon which the next generation might be built. He devised methods for measuring sensitivity to touch and weight, constructed a small whistle to test the upper range at which different persons could hear notes (slightly modified, the "Galton whistle" became standard equipment in psychological laboratories), and undertook remarkable studies in mental imagery that were of great importance in the subsequent development of psychology. When, in 1883, he published the impressive results of his investigation in *Inquiries into Human Faculty,* he became the founder of the psychology of human differences.[11] It was in this book that Galton first used the term "eugenics" to describe the improvement of the human race by better breeding.[12]

Galton was interested not only in individual differences but also in race differences. As a result of his extensive travels, his wide reading in anthropology, and his activities with the Royal Anthropological Institute, he concluded that the ancient Greeks had been the finest of all races. He believed that in his own day the Anglo-Saxons far outranked the Negroes of Africa, who in turn outranked the Australian aborigines, who outranked nobody.[13] Because of the large innate differences between races, Galton felt that a program to raise the inherent abilities of mankind involved the replacement of inferior races by the superior, and he regretted that "there exists a sentiment, for the most part quite unreasonable, against the gradual extinction of an inferior race." [14] In this, Galton set the tone for the racial bias that played an important part in the eugenics movement.

While carrying out these investigations, Galton also found time for extensive research into the laws of heredity. As early as 1865 he rejected the then nearly universal belief that characteristics acquired during the life of the individual could be passed on to the offspring. In this he broke sharply with Darwin and with a long scientific tradition.[15] As long as people believed in the inheritance of acquired characters, there was little need for eugenics; instead, all efforts could be devoted to betterment of present health and education, with the assurance that the improvement would appear in the hereditary endowment of succeeding generations. For a time Galton stood almost alone in rejecting the belief that such reforms could improve the inherited qualities of later generations, and this does much to explain his early espousal of eugenics. It also helps to understand why only after the turn of the century, when the weight of scientific opinion veered toward Galton's ideas, did the eugenics movement achieve organized support.[16]

In the 1880's Galton determined to uncover statistical relationships in heredity, so that the study of heredity, like other sciences, could be reduced to mathematical laws. To collect the necessary data for his book on *Natural Inheritance,* published in 1889, he offered prizes to those who submitted the most accurate family pedigrees containing such traits as height, eye color, temperament, artistic ability, and various diseases. As earlier, Galton found that in each generation many traits tended to follow the normal bell-shaped curve of distribution, but he now set himself the task of analyzing statistically the correlation between the deviation of parents and their offspring from the mean. In studying such traits as height,

Galton found that, as the parents deviated from the mean, their children tended to deviate in the same direction but by only one-third as much. The tendency of children to approach the mean more closely than their parents he named the law of regression, and he expressed the statistical relationship between parents and offspring in terms of what he later called the correlation coefficient.[17] He explained regression by citing the fact that each person inherited not only from his parents but from a long line of ancestors, and the ancestors would on the whole tend to resemble the average of the race.[18]

Although the rediscovery of Mendel's laws in 1900, which began the modern science of genetics, rendered obsolete most of the work that preceded that date, Galton's studies held up remarkably well. He was among the first to reject the inheritance of acquired characters. He pioneered in the use of twins for genetic research. In using the normal curve of distribution and the correlation coefficient, he provided statistical tools that, modified and improved, are still important in genetic studies of many types of traits. But his contributions were accompanied by weaknesses. He greatly underestimated the role of environment in shaping the expression of hereditary abilities. Particularly he underestimated the environmental influences involved in the development of individual personality and of cultural differences among races. At the same time, he overestimated the ease with which man's genetic future could be shaped by judicious breeding. These were weaknesses that characterized not only Galton but the eugenics movement generally.

With the publication of *Natural Inheritance,* Galton won a brilliant disciple in Karl Pearson. The son of a hard-working barrister, Pearson had taken his degree with honors in mathematics at King's College, Cambridge, in 1879. Then came a period of miscellaneous activity. He wrote on German history and philosophy; he studied law and was called to the bar in 1881; he became a socialist and lectured on Marx and Lassalle to revolutionary clubs; and he joined a group of young men and women holding advanced views on sex and marriage. After appointment to the chair of applied mathematics and mechanics at University College, London, he soon established his reputation as a mathematician, while the publication of *The Grammar of Science* in 1893 brought him fame, both with scientists and laymen, as a philosopher of science.[19]

Influenced by Galton and by W. F. R. Weldon, professor of zoology at University College, Pearson began in the 1890's to apply his statistical ingenuity to biological problems. He became convinced that statistics held the key to an explanation of evolution. The study of the percentage of a particular variation within a species, the correlation of variation in one trait with variation in other traits, and the death rates of different varieties would provide the data by which evolution could be demonstrated. In his studies, he sharpened and improved the mathematical tools by which scientists might study nature. His work formed the basis for most subsequent developments in scientific statistics. Yet, in his work, Pearson felt that he was merely extending the methods of Galton, his master, with whom "intimacy ripened into friendship, which grew in closeness with the years." [20]

By 1900 Pearson and Weldon, with Galton's encouragement, had created a new science of biometrics. Unfortunately, the launching of biometrics, with its statistical studies of large populations, occurred just as the rediscovery of Mendel's principles turned most biologists to the study of individual pedigrees and to breeding experiments. The result was a bitter and largely unnecessary antagonism between the biometric school and the dominant Mendelian school of genetics. As Pearson on occasion pointed out, his own researches and those of the Mendelians were complementary. At other times he was sharply critical of Mendelian research. His antagonism toward Mendelian genetics meant that Pearson, the heir to Galton's mantle, was at odds with most other eugenists in both England and America.[21]

As Pearson studied heredity, his social views became increasingly harsh and pessimistic, little in keeping with the socialism he continued to profess. Around the turn of the century, he asked schoolteachers to rank their students from one to five for such traits as vivacity, ability, introspection, popularity, temper, and handwriting. He found the correlations between siblings for these traits to range between .43 and .63 (on a scale in which 1 meant complete correlation and 0 meant no correlation). Since these were about the same as the correlations between siblings for physical traits, which he assumed were hereditary, Pearson concluded that personality and intelligence too were predestined in the germ plasm before birth.[22] Hence he was convinced that heredity determined all and that environment was inconsequential. He estimated that one-fourth of the married couples—mostly the poor and improvident—produced one-half the children of the succeeding generation and feared that civilization was menaced by the fecundity of the poor. He insisted that human progress came only through a struggle of class against class, in which the superior classes won, and through a struggle of race against race, in which the higher races supplanted the lower.[23] Pearson, far more than the genial Galton, linked eugenics in England with conservative and reactionary social attitudes.

### Criminal Anthropology

Galton's interest centered on the role of heredity in producing men of ability. For him, then, the aim of eugenics was primarily to encourage propagation by the better stocks. In this, Galton was not typical of the men who created the eugenics movement. The major impulse that led to eugenics was concern to prevent the burden and tragedy of human defect, and the major preoccupation of eugenists was to control the propagation of the unfit. Eugenics built upon the growing belief during the last quarter of the nineteenth century that back of many defects of man lay the blighting force of heredity.

Among the hereditarian currents in Europe, one of the most interesting and important took the name of criminal anthropology. Criminal anthropology grew from investigations in various of the countries of Europe and exerted wide influence both there and in the United States. It reflected the extreme hereditarian ideas which developed in the wake of evolutionary thought.

As much as any movement can be said to have a beginning, the beginning of criminal anthropology came with the publication of Dr. B. A. Morel's influential *Traité des Dégénérescences* in Paris in 1857. Morel held that alcoholism, criminality, various forms of insanity, epilepsy, and feeblemindedness were different manifestations of a single entity: hereditary degeneration. Degeneration might originate in the first generation through drink, poor working conditions, or other violations of the laws of health and morals. But once established, degeneration passed from parents to children, growing worse in each generation, until it ended in sterile idiocy. Morel and his followers believed that degeneration could be recognized by various physical and psychical abnormalities—the so-called stigmata of degeneration—which included odd, asymmetrical heads, malformed teeth, ears, and jaws, and other deviations from the normal.[24] Because Morel stressed alcoholism as both a cause and result of hereditary degeneration, his conclusions had special impact on the temperance movement in both England and America. More important, the view that the many mental and nervous disorders were varying forms of a degenerate constitution guided most of the research in human heredity until the second decade of the twentieth century.

The center of criminal anthropology was not France, however, but Italy, and its leader was Cesare Lombroso, professor of legal medicine at the University of Turin. Lombroso brought the methods of physical anthropology to the study of criminals, and in 1876 published the results of his investigations in *L'uomo Delinquente* (*Criminal Man*). He examined the criminal brain, measured the criminal skull, investigated the bodily characteristics of the criminal, and studied his habits. While admitting that some committed crimes through force of circumstances or out of sudden passion, Lombroso believed that many criminals were the atavistic products of heredity. Criminals, more often than noncriminals, had traits that resembled savages or animals. The criminal tended to have a primitive brain, an unusual cephalic index [25] (either large like the mongoloids or small like the negroids), long arms, prehensile feet, a scanty beard but hairy body, large incisors, flattened nose, furtive eyes, and an angular skull.[26] Like a savage, the criminal often tattooed himself. According to Lombroso, different types of criminals tended to have different traits. Thieves were characterized by small, restless eyes, thick eyebrows, a crooked nose, thin beard, and narrow, receding forehead. Sex criminals had bright eyes, a cracked voice, blond hair, and a delicate face. Murderers had cold, glassy eyes, a hooked, aquiline nose (like a bird of prey), large cheeks and jaws, long ears, dark hair, and canine teeth.[27] Lombroso believed that the born criminal was a distinct anthropological type of mankind, closely related to other varieties of human defectives.[28]

Other investigators in Italy—most notably Enrico Ferri and Raffaelle Garofalo—added to the doctrines of criminal anthropology. In Austria, Moriz Benedikt, a professor of neuropathology in Vienna, found definite abnormalities in the fissures and gyres of the brains of some nineteen conveniently beheaded criminals. Although Lombroso and other Italian criminal anthropologists increasingly stressed the role of society and environment in the production of criminals, their studies of the hereditary criminal type were best known at least until the turn of the century. It was these works that exerted the strongest influence in England and America.[29]

England produced almost no researchers in criminal anthropology, but a number of distinguished British scientists supported the conclusions of continental investigators.[30] When Her Majesty's Inspector of Prisons asked Galton to study photographs of prisoners to determine whether different facial features were associated with different types of crime, Galton developed a system of composite photography by which many portraits could be blended to form a representative image. He found no proof that the criminal face revealed the type of crime, but did conclude that "fairly distinct types of criminals breeding true to their kind have become established, and are one of the saddest disfigurements of modern civilisation." [31] When, in 1890, Havelock Ellis published his work on *The Criminal,* in which he summarized the findings of criminal anthropologists on the continent, his book served as an introduction to the subject for many in England and America.

These were but a few of the hundreds of investigators in Europe who measured the craniums of the degenerate, described the misshapen faces of the criminal, studied the deformities of the mentally diseased, and recorded the strange habits of the unfit of mankind. Criminal anthropology was, in effect, little more than a scientific version of the old popular belief that criminals could be recognized by their appearance, and was based on many of the same fallacies. It was, after all, quite easy to discover furtive or beady eyes—traits impossible to reduce to objective measurement—in subjects already known to be criminals. It was equally easy to uncover a large proportion of various ill-defined physical stigmata among criminals who were studied with that specific purpose in mind, especially if no comparable group of normal persons was subjected to a similar searching examination. Even if there was some truth to the findings of the criminal anthropologists, the overlap in characteristics between criminals and noncriminals was so great that no theory of a separate criminal type was tenable.

The movement took the name of criminal anthropology because of the interest of the Italians chiefly in criminals and criminal law reform. In a sense, though, the term was a misnomer, for criminal anthropology was concerned with the nature and causes of all classes of human defects. Despite many disagreements, the movement was based on several common assumptions. All agreed that mental aberrations were the result of the physical structure of the brain and body. They agreed that the defective classes were characterized by numerous stigmata, even though they sometimes disagreed on what the stigmata were. Finally, they attributed the defects to heredity. They spoke of morbid heredity, hereditary degeneration, atavism, arrested development, and reversion to type, but whatever the term used—and the terms were often used interchangeably—they agreed that many of the criminal, insane, pauper, feebleminded, and alcoholic were not made but born. So well did the theory of criminal anthropology fit the presuppositions of post-Darwinian thought that for a time it received a respectful and often uncritical reception in Europe and America.

### Eugenics Begins

As the twentieth century opened, various currents of thought, mostly stemming from Darwinian evolution, converged to create a eugenics movement in England. Such respected biologists as Darwin, Alfred Russell Wallace, and E. Ray Lankester had, at one time or another, implied that evolution sanctioned a breeding program for man.[32] Many doctors and students of the feebleminded, insane, and alcoholic gave expert testimony that the defective classes were victims of heredity and should not be permitted to reproduce. Finally, many persons with an amateur interest in science and a concern for social problems—including an odd assortment of noblemen, literary figures, and Fabian socialists—saw in eugenics a way to better mankind or to produce some sort of superman. The eugenists spanned the political spectrum from Tory to socialist; what they had in common was a belief in evolution and a faith that science, particularly genetics, held the key for improving the race of man.

Francis Galton, though now in his eighties and increasingly an invalid, devoted the final decade of his life to the formation of the eugenics movement in England. Repeatedly, in speeches and articles, he defined his eugenics creed. His first and most important statement of a eugenics program was an address on "The Possible Improvement of the Human Breed under Existing Conditions of Law and Sentiment," delivered in 1901 before the Royal Anthropological Institute. Especially in the United States it was influential in crystallizing sentiment for eugenics.[33]

Galton, himself an agnostic, found in eugenics an emotional equivalent for religion. "An enthusiasm to improve the race is so noble in its aim," he declared, "that it might well give rise to the sense of a religious obligation." [34] He foresaw that eugenics might become a sort of national creed, so that law and custom would work together for the improvement of the race. Eugenics must, of course, include compulsory means to limit the breeding of the insane, feebleminded, confirmed criminals, and paupers.[35] But more important, he believed, were means to encourage breeding by the better stock, for if the better stocks bred early enough and often enough, they could soon swamp the descendants of poorer stock. To bring this about, he advocated that capable young men and women be awarded certificates of merit and that, through government or private philanthropy, they be given the financial support necessary to marry young and breed freely. Public opinion, too, Galton hoped, would give recognition to good stock and frown upon marriages of good stock into bad stock. He saw no insuperable barrier to such a development. At various times and in various cultures, polygamy (among Moslems), celibacy (among Catholic priests), and caste marriage (among Hindus) had been accepted standards. Why could not eugenics become a basis for new customs? [36] At any rate, such was the dogma that he preached.

Galton not only defined eugenic orthodoxy but was instrumental in giving the movement permanent organization. One of the first problems was to arrange for research. In 1904, therefore, he offered £1,500 to University College, London, to support a research fellowship in national eugenics for three years, and thereafter continued his support of the National Eugenics Laboratory.[37] At first he personally supervised much of the research, but after 1906, as his health failed, Pearson assumed direction of the laboratory.[38]

In 1907, meanwhile, Montague Crackanthorpe, a lawyer the sound of whose name alone gave distinction to the movement, organized the Eugenics Education Society and persuaded Galton to serve as Honorary President and to take an active part in its program. The Society published the *Eugenics Review* and carried the gospel of eugenics to the educated public. In 1908 the members also lobbied before Parliament to secure adoption of the recommendations of the Royal Commission on the Care and Control of the Feebleminded and to bring British poor laws more into line with eugenic goals. Among those active in the Society were Havelock Ellis, then completing his monumental studies of sex; [39] the Rev. W. R. Inge, a distinguished professor of divinity; David Heron, an associate of Pearson; Dr. Caleb Williams Saleeby, the outstanding propagandist for eugenics in England; Dr. F. W. Mott, a psychiatrist and leading student of heredity in insanity; Dr. A. F. Tredgold, the foremost British expert on feeblemindedness; Edward Nettleship, already respected for his study of hereditary eye diseases; literary figures like George Bernard Shaw and H. G. Wells; socialists like Sidney Webb; and numerous members of the nobility.[40]

Galton's final years were not made any easier by the quarrels and inanities of the motley group enrolled under his banner. George Bernard Shaw embraced eugenics (". . . there is now no reasonable excuse for refusing to face the fact that nothing but a eugenics religion can save our civilization from the fate that has overtaken all previous civilizations"), but embarrassed the cause by his attacks on monogamous marriage. He complained that it was "a national loss to limit the husband's progenitive capacity to the breeding capacity of one woman, or the wife's to an experiment with one father only," and declared: "What we must fight for is freedom to breed the race without being hampered by the mass of irrelevant conditions implied in the institution of marriage." [41] That eugenics involved the abolition of monogamy and the breeding of people like domestic animals was, for most eugenists, a notion to be vigorously combatted.

In addition, Crackanthorpe and Saleeby were temperance enthusiasts and gave the eugenics movement a decided antialcoholic flavor. Saleeby, who wrote his *Parenthood and Race Culture* in 1909 to serve as the basic text for eugenics, emphasized his belief that "race poisons" (like alcohol) damaged the germ tissue and constituted a major danger to future generations.[42] Any disagreements within the Eugenics Education Society, however, were nothing compared to the open warfare between other eugenists and Karl Pearson. Pearson's rejection of Mendelian genetics brought attack and counterattack from eugenists in both England and America. Finally, he sinned unpardonably when, in 1910, he published a statistical study of the children of alcoholics and reported that they differed in no important respect from other children of the same age. For his heresy, he faced the righteous wrath of the temperance movement and was publicly attacked by Crackanthorpe in the London *Times*. Galton found it necessary to write to the *Times* in support of Pearson, who in turn defended himself in several letters and pamphlets.[43]

Despite tribulations, eugenics was now a going concern. Upon Galton's death in 1911, Leonard Darwin, son of Charles, became honorary president of the Eugenics Education Society and directed its activities. In his will Galton left his residuary estate to University College to endow the Galton Professorship of Eugenics, complete with a laboratory. Pearson was tendered the professorship and accepted. Under him the Eugenics Laboratory published memoirs, a lecture series, and, after 1925, the *Annals of Eugenics*. As the first professor of eugenics, Pearson gave his enthusiasm, his statistical genius, and his penchant for controversy to the cause of eugenics until his own death in 1936.

By the time Galton died, eugenics was fast becoming a world movement. In Great Britain the Eugenics Education Society, centered in London, had branches in Birmingham, Liverpool, Southampton, Manchester, Hashemere, Glasgow, and Belfast, with other branches in the several Dominions. In the United States the establishment of the Eugenics Record Office at Cold Spring Harbor on Long Island in 1910 provided a center for eugenics research and propaganda. In Germany an Internationale Gesellschaft für Rassen-Hygiene was formed in Munich in 1910, with Galton as honorary president and Dr. Alfred Ploetz, editor of the six-year-old *Archiv für Rassen- und Gesellschafts-Biologie,* as acting president. The members, drawn mainly from Germany and Scandinavia, pledged themselves to improve their own spiritual and physical health, to submit to medical examination before marriage and refrain if pronounced unfit, and to watch over the racial well-being of their children.[44] Thus eugenics in Germany began its sad history that, under the Nazis, would justify wholesale sexual sterilization and then euthenasia for the allegedly unfit and would provide part of the justification for the slaughter of four to six million Jews. Other eugenics organizations sprang up in Scandinavia, France, Austria, Italy, Japan, and South America. Because of the international interest in the subject, the Eugenics Education Society in 1912 sponsored a highly-publicized International Congress of Eugenics in London, attended by over eight hundred scientists and social scientists throughout the world.[45] Thereafter eugenists in various countries attempted to continue their co-operation and held additional international congresses in New York in 1921 and 1932.

The rapid spread of the movement was not due entirely, often not chiefly, to the direct influence of Galton, for in each country various currents of thought, mostly with roots in Darwinian evolution, had prepared the way for the reception of eugenics doctrine. In each country the movement took on somewhat different characteristics and followed a different course. The eugenics creed was eagerly imported into the United States, for instance, because a demand had already been created. The growing emphasis on heredity among educated Americans had fostered a climate of opinion that made a movement like eugenics almost inevitable.

## Chapter III

# Dependents and Delinquents

In 1874 Richard L. Dugdale, a slightly built, chronically ill merchant from New York City, toured the jails of rural Ulster County on an inspection trip for the Prison Association of New York. He was surprised to find six relatives all being held in jail at the same time, and he determined to trace the history of the family in the hope that he might lay bare the causes of crime and pauperism. His decision to do so was part of a split life that he had led for some time: working as a merchant chiefly to earn money to pursue an interest in social problems, an interest symbolized by his membership in numerous societies ranging from the New York Sociology Club to the American Free Trade League.[1]

Dugdale managed to trace the family back to Max, a colonial frontiersman, and to two of Max's sons who married into a family of six sisters of uncertain origin. He culled his information on the Jukes, as he called the descendants of these sisters, from poorhouse records, prison and court files, and the memories of old residents. Doubtless the nature of his sources, plus the fact that he had no information on any Jukes who had escaped the degrading environment of the ancestral habitat, swelled the total of derelicts and failures he found in the family. Despite such crudities, however, Dugdale assembled such impressive and frightening family histories that the Jukes study became the most influential American work on heredity during the nineteenth century.[2]

In five to six generations of the family, Dugdale unearthed 709 Jukes or persons married to Jukes, of whom eighteen had kept brothels, 128 had been prostitutes, over 200 had been on relief, and over seventy-six had been convicted criminals. He estimated that the total cost to the public, through relief, medical care, arrests and imprisonment, and other expenses, was $1,308,000.[3] He found that branches of the family revealed characteristic types of failure, one branch being so given to crime, for instance, that he labelled its founder Margaret, the Mother of Criminals. Although hereditarians used the sad tale of the Jukes to support their case, Dugdale himself was careful to balance heredity and environment. Repeatedly he pointed out that, while children might inherit tendencies to crime, sensuality, and pauperism, the environment in which they were raised almost inevitably reinforced the traits. "The tendency of heredity," he stressed, "is to produce an environment which perpetuates that heredity: thus, the licentious parent makes an example which greatly aids in fixing habits of debauchery in the child." For this reason, Dugdale looked to environment for reform since "where the environment changes in youth, the characteristics of heredity may be measureably altered." [4] His major recommendation was that children of pauper and criminal parents be removed from their degrading surroundings and be given industrial training so that they would learn a vocation and acquire habits of work.[5]

In a generation that eagerly read Darwin and applied evolution to politics, theology, ethics, anthropology, and many other fields, Dugdale's study, in both Europe and America, became basic to discussions of heredity and environment in the shaping of man. On the whole, hereditarians managed to appropriate the Jukes to their own uses, despite Dugdale's disclaimers. For them the lesson of Dugdale's tale was clear: if the original parents of the Jukes had been prevented from breeding, the state would have been spared much crime, prostitution, disease, and pauperism, and the taxpayers would have saved $1,308,000. Those who advocated schemes to prevent reproduction by the unfit argued that, in the long run, theirs was both a scientific and an economical approach to social problems.

An awareness of the role of heredity was not, of course, the exclusive possession of the generation that followed Darwin. Deeply ingrained in the Christian tradition was a belief that the iniquities of the fathers were visited upon the sons. Feeblemindedness and insanity had commonly been attributed to some dark ancestral taint. Temperance crusaders were already convinced that alcohol destroyed the bodies and minds of parents and their children. For most people, in fact, it was simply axiomatic that traits of character and body were chipped off the old block. Darwin's theories, nevertheless, intensified the interest in heredity and caused many social thinkers, by the 1870's, to recast their ideas in evolutionary terms.

The role of heredity in producing the unfit—the pauper,[6] alcoholic, insane, feebleminded, epileptic, and criminal—was a major problem for those charged with their care in the decades following the Civil War. Yet science provided little reliable guidance in the study of heredity, and many of the scientifically accepted notions of the day now seem almost incredible. Some believed, for example, that in rare instances a child conceived in a later marriage might inherit characteristics of the husband from an earlier marriage.[7] There was, too, an exaggerated belief that the attitude of parents at the time of sexual intercourse exerted hereditary influence on the child and that the experiences and thoughts of the mother during pregnancy could work strange changes in the unborn infant. (One mother read Swedenborg during her pregnancy. "When the child came," she reported, "it was such a comfort to me; the child seemed to be a natural mystic. When quite young it evinced a passion for metaphysical thought. . . ." [8]) More important were the vague ideas signified by the term atavism, a term sometimes used to indicate an inheritance from a grandparent or some other fairly distant relative but more often to mean an inheritance from the savage stages of man's evolution.

Finally, the assumption that acquired characters were inherited was hardly doubted until the 1890's and guided almost all research in human heredity until the twentieth century. The belief in the inheritance of acquired characters was a basis for both optimism and pessimism. On the one hand, since improvements in body and mind during one generation could strengthen the body and mind of the next generation, reformers saw no bounds to the possible improvement and evolution of the human race.[9] On the other hand, deterioration of body and mind could also be passed from generation to generation and thus families, even nations, could gradually deteriorate into crime, insanity, pauperism, disease, and idiocy. So long as a belief in the inheritance of acquired characters prevailed, there was little basis for a clash between those who stressed heredity and those who stressed environment. Even the hereditarian, although he might desire to prevent propagation by the defective, would also have to admit that environmental reforms could strengthen the innate qualities of future generations. During the nineteenth century, in fact, there existed the odd situation that a belief in the importance of heredity might strengthen a person's determination to secure environmental reforms, since such reforms would improve not just the present but also succeeding generations.

In the study of human heredity, scientists and medical men in the late nineteenth century were convinced that various mental aberrations were pathological conditions. That is, criminality, insanity, feeblemindedness, pauperism, alcoholism, and many diseases were thought to be closely related and to have their origin in defective or unstable organization of the brain or nervous system. The defective constitution could be inherited, so that idiocy or inebriety in one generation might, proteanlike, appear as prostitution, or cancer, or eccentricity in a succeeding generation. Under such a theory, it was simple to ascribe nearly all forms of delinquency and defect to heredity, for few persons could present a family tree that was free from suspicion of hereditary weakness.

At the time, there were basically two methods by which human heredity was investigated. One method, like Dugdale's study of the Jukes, was to trace the recurrence of certain traits through several generations of a single family. The other was to take a special group, like the inmates of an insane asylum, and determine how many had ancestors with similar traits. Such a study would yield a conclusion that, for instance, 30 per cent, or 60 per cent, of insanity was caused by heredity. Obviously both of these methods were guilty of the ancient logical fallacy of *post hoc, ergo propter hoc.* After all, the discovery of a trait in both parent and offspring no more proved that the trait was inherited than that it was environmental. Without controlled studies and without critical statistical methods, the countless investigations of human heredity during the period lacked scientific conclusiveness.

Despite the inconclusiveness, the emphasis upon heredity so fitted the tenor of the times that few pointed out the rather obvious fallacies involved. The easy acceptance of a hereditary explanation for human failures came in large part from the unconscious biases of the college-trained, middle-class physicians and social workers charged with the care of the socially inadequate. As they searched for the causes of the burden of the defective and delinquent, they found that the insane were largely incurable, the feebleminded proved to be untrainable, criminals returned to their lives of crime, alcoholics clung to their bottles, and the poor seemed often to prefer a life of indolence and want. Unable to believe that a normal person could fall into such ways of living, they became convinced that such persons were born with a fatal flaw. Hereditarian thought thus became closely associated with a fatalistic attitude toward possibilities of cure or reform, although there was no logical reason why an inherited ailment should be any more incurable than one that was acquired. At any rate, such biases, at a time when scientists were showing increasing interest in heredity, led to the acceptance of the studies as convincing demonstrations that heredity played a crucial part in the failure of man.

## Institutional Cases

The closing decades of the nineteenth century were times of rapid change and mounting tensions in the United States, a period of industrialization and labor strife, of the growth of cities and slums, of racial conflicts and adjustments in the South in the wake of the Civil War, and of an increasing influx of immigrants who brought a variety of ethnic, religious, and economic problems. Many troubled Americans—journalists, clergymen, politicians, social reformers, professors, as well as quacks of all sorts—probed the causes of, and sought solutions for the poverty, tensions, and failures. They reported the not-too-secret corruption of political machines, the power of the trusts and the needs of labor, the unbelievable crowding and misery of the slums, and the social problems created by the growing stream of immigration.

Among those who probed the causes of human failure were members of a growing number of professions engaged in caring for the dependent and delinquent. In the period following the Civil War, almshouses—into which were gathered the aged, the sick, the insane and feebleminded, the drunk, the vagrant, and the orphaned—remained a blot upon American welfare methods. But recognition of the need for separate care brought, in the more progressive states, rapid construction of reformatories for juveniles, a more extensive prison system for criminals, hospitals for the alcoholic, and asylums for the insane, feebleminded, and epileptic. Many states gradually took over responsibility from the counties and, through state boards of charity, inspected and supervised public charitable institutions. In the cities, during the same years, organized charity created the need for full-time investigators and administrators. The result was the appearance, virtually for the first time, of a number of new professions: social workers to investigate the families of the poor, psychiatrists for the mentally ill, trained prison wardens and prison physicians, and medical men experienced in the care of the feeble-minded, epileptic, and alcoholic.

In the decades following the Civil War, members of the new professions organized numerous professional societies and founded journals to exchange information on their specialties.[10] Increasingly they centered upon heredity as a major factor in the burden of dependency and delinquency. From such persons, the experts in their fields, came the theories and impulses that first led to eugenics.

Foremost among those who laid the basis for the American eugenics movement were the custodians of institutions for the feeble-minded. In a way this was rather odd, for in 1870 only seven states provided institutions for the feebleminded, the institutions had but 1,000 inmates, and the oldest institution had existed just slightly more than twenty years.[11] From the beginning, though, heredity was assigned the major role in the cause of feeblemindedness. In 1848 Samuel Gridley Howe, the early teacher of the feebleminded in Massachusetts, reported that of 359 congenitally feebleminded persons investigated by him, all but four had resulted from the sins of the parents:

> . . . one or both of the immediate progenitors of the unfortunate sufferers had in some way widely departed from the normal condition of health, and violated natural laws; this is to say, one or the other or both of them were very unhealthy or scrofulous, or they were hereditarily disposed to affections of the brain, causing occasional insanity, or they had intermarried with blood relatives, or they had been intemperate, or had been guilty of sexual excesses which impaired their constitutions.[12]

In the post-Civil War period, all available information seemed only to add to the proof that feeblemindedness was overwhelmingly a problem of heredity.[13]

What gave the problem particular urgency was a growing conviction that feeblemindedness was not only hereditary but was a substantial menace to society. By 1884 Dr. Isaac N. Kerlin, the influential superintendent of the Pennsylvania Training School for Feeble-Minded Children at Elwyn, wondered: "How many of your criminals, and prostitutes are congenital imbeciles?" Many investigators, after visits to almshouses, came away convinced that all sorts of illegitimacy and depravity could be traced to persons with weak minds in strong and oversexed bodies. By the 1890's there was a stereotyped picture of the typical lives of the feebleminded. As children they dropped out of school early, the boys to enter upon a life of squalor and vice, the girls to become the easy prey of depraved men and boys. "One perverted feeble-minded woman can spread throughout a community an immoral pestilence which will affect the homes of all classes, even the most intelligent and refined." Occurring in clusters of interrelated families, living in poverty and dirt, given to loose marital habits, they presented a problem that demanded action to control them and prevent propagation.[14]

The first institutions for the feebleminded, just before the Civil War, were organized on educational lines in the optimistic faith that feebleminded children might be trained to assume a place, however modest, in the everyday work of the world. Because of this, the institutions accepted primarily the most promising youths. Yet experience soon seemed to demonstrate that most of them could not be prepared for the responsibilities of the outside world. By the period after the Civil War the institutions faced a dilemma: should they retain the feebleminded upon reaching maturity and thereby deprive other children of the opportunity for training, or should they release them to find their places in the jails and poorhouses of the state? Those charged with the care of the feebleminded soon saw that the answer was to provide custodial departments and colonies for the adult feebleminded and for the physically deformed who were not accepted in the earlier institutions.[15]

New York State, prodded and persuaded by Josephine Shaw Lowell, took the lead in custodial care. Mrs. Lowell was born in Massachusetts of distinguished New England ancestry and was raised in New York. In 1863 she married Col. Charles Russell Lowell (nephew of the poet), accompanied him to his army camp, and there nursed the sick and wounded until, in the following year, her husband was killed in action. Widowed before the age of twenty-one, she returned to New York City and, since she was financially independent, threw herself into charity work—as a supporter of the Freedmen's Association, as a founder of the Visiting Committee of Bellevue and other hospitals, and as a worker in the State Charities Aid Associations. In 1876 Governor Samuel J. Tilden appointed her the first woman member of the New York State Board of Charities.[16]

On her numerous inspections of the state's institutions, she observed that many women, periodic guests in almshouses and jails, gave birth repeatedly to illegitimate children who inherited the weak wills and strong passions of their parents. "What right," she asked her fellow reform workers, "had we to permit them [the children] to be born of parents who were depraved in body and mind?" [17] In 1877 she used her position on the State Board of Charities to begin a crusade for reformatories to house delinquent and vagrant girls under age thirty whenever they were arrested or gave birth to their second illegitimate child. Even if reform failed, the state would be practicing the wisest economy, for—as the study of the Jukes had shown—the cost of hereditary pauperism would be greater than the cost of keeping the young women in the reformatory. After 1880 the State Board backed her, and she lived to see three reformatories for women in New York.[18]

Side by side with the delinquent girls in the almshouses, she found feebleminded girls, almost invariably licentious and the source of numerous defective offspring. Custodial care was necessary for two reasons, she believed: to protect the unfortunate women and to protect society from the burden of their progeny. In 1878, as a result of her urging, New York appropriated the money to open an asylum in Newark for the custodial care of feebleminded women of childbearing age. The new asylum was an important precedent, for it was the first separate custodial asylum in the country and the first effort by a state to cut off the hereditary taint of feeblemindedness—the first important recognition of eugenics principles by a state.[19]

By the 1880's the necessity for custodial care of the feebleminded, to prevent the propagation of defective offspring and to remove them from the jeers of the world and the poverty and degradation of jails and almshouses, was standard doctrine among those charged with their care. Ernest Bicknell, secretary of the Indiana State Board, spoke for many when he warned that "feeblemindedness descends from parent to child as no other defect does" and claimed: "It is impossible to calculate what even one feeble-minded woman may cost the public, when her vast possibilities for evil as a producer of paupers and criminals, through an endless line of descendants is considered." [20] The standing committee on the feebleminded of the National Conference of Charities and Correction, after its formation in the mid-1880's, yearly demanded custodial care; and the same theme was the burden of virtually every presidential address before annual meetings of the Medical Officers of American Institutions for Idiotic and Feeble-Minded Persons.[21]

The attitude toward the insane, like the attitude toward the feebleminded, changed from optimism before the Civil War to pessimism following the war. In the reforming ferment of the 1840's, those who urged extended care of the insane promised that, through proper treatment, a large percentage could be cured. Asylum superintendents, to prove the worth of their asylums, competed to surpass each other in statistics of cures, until some were reporting success for as many as 97 per cent of their cases.[22] But gradually, as asylums become increasingly burdened with the care of the incurable insane, the conviction mounted that insanity was largely incurable. More accurate statistical methods indicated that no more than 20 or 25 per cent were in fact being cured.[23] It was in this period that asylums had the look of great stone prisons whose forbidding exteriors and crowded wards symbolized the lack of hope for those who entered their walls. As early as 1865, New York passed an act establishing Willard Asylum to care exclusively for the incurable, and during the remainder of the century other states adopted various systems to meet responsibilities in caring for both the curable and incurable insane.[24]

During this period, most psychiatrists (then known as alienists) agreed that insanity was the result of physical malfunction of the brain or nervous system and rejected the notion that its roots lay in a moral or emotional disturbance of the individual. Both the insane and the sane experienced moral and emotional crises, but the presence of a physical lesion divided the insane from the sane. In searching for the causes of insanity, therefore, psychiatrists performed autopsies to find the elusive lesions of the brain.[25] Naturally, since insanity was caused by a physical lesion, it might be inherited like any other physical trait:

> A person of average healthy constitution to begin with will not become insane from any of the ordinary vicissitudes of life; and, on the other hand, a person with inherited instability of nerve-structure may become insane from apparently slight causes. In other words, a majority of cases of insanity are due to two causes, hereditary predisposition on the one hand, and one or more exciting influences on the other.[26]

As one doctor told the National Conference of Charities and Correction, "the laws of heredity, so universal in their application, from the simplest cell upward through all gradation of organic life, make no exception here." [27]

In the nineteenth century, the lack of statistics made it difficult for psychiatrists to estimate the role of heredity as a cause of insanity. They were reduced to statements that heredity was "without contradiction" the most important cause, or that "hereditary tendency has more effect, is a more potential agency in the production of insanity, than all other causes put together." [28] About the turn of the century, however, several studies indicated that between 30 and 40 per cent of the insane in asylums had family histories suggesting a hereditary basis for the mental illness, and this became the accepted figure.[29]

The poor prognosis for insanity and the emphasis upon heredity caused many psychiatrists to consider means for preventing propagation by the insane. During the 1880's several physicians experimented with removal of the ovaries as a method of alleviating certain forms of insanity among women. Although primarily curative in purpose, the operation obviously prevented procreation, and one psychiatrist as early as 1882 predicted: "I am, indeed, not sure that in the progressive future, it will not be deemed a measure of sound policy and of commendable statesmanship to stamp out insanity, by castrating all the insane men and spaying all the insane women." During the 1890's, however, the practice largely ceased because of the generally unsatisfactory results of the operation as a cure of insanity.[30]

Nevertheless, as the twentieth century neared, many psychiatrists stressed that, because a large proportion of the insane were incurable, prevention was of primary importance. They urged that the facts of heredity be made clear to the public and that children born into unstable families be raised with special care to prevent the onslaught of mental illness. A few even supported asexualization of the insane and most agreed on the need for laws to restrict their marriage.[31]

The medical attitude toward alcoholism paralleled in many ways the attitude toward insanity and feeblemindedness. When a number of physicians formed the American Association for the Study and Cure of Inebriety in 1870, they adopted as principles that "inebriety is a disease" and that "the constitutional tendency to this disease may be either inherited or acquired." [32] They held that alcohol, by attacking the nerve centers, rendered its victim unable to master his longing for the bottle or to maintain his mental stability. Such a condition, the doctors argued, required neither prayer nor exhortation, but medical treatment. The degenerative effects of alcoholism passed to descendants in a variety of manifestations,

. . . exhibiting insanity in one, epilepsy in another, intemperance in a third, idiocy in a fourth, hypochondria in a fifth, hysteria in a sixth, and so on . . . , each generation increasing in numbers, and contributing in a direct ratio to the filling of our jails, penitentiaries, inebriate asylums, insane retreats and poorhouses.[33]

Alcoholism took its place among that cluster of physical and mental aberrations that were closely related and rooted in heredity.

Dr. Thomas D. Crothers, superintendent of the Walnut Hill Asylum, in Hartford, Connecticut, and editor of the Association's *Quarterly Journal of Inebriety* from its founding in 1876 until his death in 1918, was a dominating figure in the movement to recognize and treat alcoholism as a medical problem. In the 1880's, he studied a random sampling of one hundred chronic cases that came to him in Hartford and found that in over 50 per cent of the cases, alcoholism lurked in the ancestry and that, in another 30 per cent, some other degenerative disease existed in the family. "If heredity is the cause, directly and indirectly, of over eighty per cent of all inebriety," he concluded, "its study is by far the most important of all temperance studies, and everyone interested in the means for the prevention and cure of inebriety should turn to heredity and its laws, for here the solution of this evil can be found." [34]

Little wonder, then, that the direful hereditary effects became a major part of the indictment of alcohol among those fighting for temperance and prohibition. For a short time in the mid-1880's, the Women's Christian Temperance Union published a *Journal of Heredity* (reprinting excerpts from Galton's writings). Indeed, the influence of alcoholism on heredity and heredity on alcoholism was simply taken for granted by scientists and social reformers, who assumed that nearly every physician

> has his story of experiences with premature births and still-born children—frightful infant mortality, puny physiques, convulsions, idiocy, epilepsy, early drunkenness, crime, and premature death as a direct result of alcoholism on the part of the parents and especially of mothers.[35]

Victory over intemperance promised a better life not only for the present but for future generations as well.

One man—that man an immigrant from Scotland named Alexander Graham Bell—stood at the center of discussion of hereditary deafness. As a young man Bell studied anatomy and physiology at University College, London, assisted his father in his profession as a teacher of elocution, and adapted his father's system of "visible speech," in which symbols represented the different voice sounds, to the training of the deaf. After his arrival in America in 1870, Bell attracted wide attention through his work for the education of those shut out from the world of sound. His own wife, whom he married in 1877, was deaf. After his invention of the telephone and his subsequent financial success, he founded the Volta Bureau in Washington, D. C., to study the deaf and educate the public.[36]

In 1884 Bell published an important paper "On the Formation of a Deaf Variety of the Human Race," in which he analyzed statistics he had gathered on the heredity of deafness. A large proportion of the deaf, he found, came from families in which deafness could be traced; in fact, both normal and deaf members of such families had considerably more than their share of deaf offspring. Quite naturally, the congenitally deaf were more likely to have deaf children than those whose deafness stemmed from accident or disease.[37] He feared that, in time, a distinct deaf variety of the human race might result from the continued intermarriage of the deaf. In youth they were taught together and learned sign language so that they could communicate with each other; as adults they often banded together in clubs. "Indeed," Bell declared, "if we desired to create a deaf variety of the race, and were to attempt to devise methods which should compel deaf-mutes to marry deaf-mutes, we could not invent more complete or more efficient methods than those that actually exist and which have arisen from entirely different and higher motives." [38]

In speeches and articles, Bell publicized his findings and recommendations. He advocated that, as much as possible, the deaf be educated in schools with normal students and that there be more emphasis upon speech rather than sign language, so that the deaf would not be forced into association only with the deaf. He advised the deaf that, in choosing a spouse, they should use the family and not the individual as a guide: the deaf, if they married, should always select hearing persons from hearing families, for where several members of a family were deaf, "there you have proof that a tendency to deafness exists *in the family*." Finally, he suggested that laws might well be passed to forbid the marriage of two congenitally deaf persons or of two persons from families with more than one deaf member.[39]

Although Bell's reputation lent weight to his conclusions, they did not go unchallenged. Several American teachers of the deaf doubted the validity of his statistics and feared that his views were helping to revive a feeling that the deaf, as a group, were indesirable members of society. That many of the deaf, too, were not overly happy was shown at the National Convention of the deaf in 1889 when the president declared: "We must settle forever the sensational alarm concerning 'the formation of a deaf variety of the human race': not with assertions only, but by an array of evidence that will cause Prof. Bell to haul down the danger signal he has hoisted, and free us from the incubus of what is becoming a widespread public prejudice." [40] As a result of the controversy, Bell offered the support of the Volta Bureau to Edward A. Fay, editor of the *American Annals of the Deaf*, so that he could carry out a painstaking study of all available statistics on the heredity of deafness. In his report of 1898 on *Marriages of the Deaf in America*, Fay confirmed most of Bell's conclusions. [41]

What is interesting is how close Bell and Fay, in their emphasis upon the importance of family characteristics and upon the deaf marrying into hearing families to overcome the defect, came to the Mendelian concept of dominant and recessive traits. Certainly their studies were the most respectable of the nineteenth-century studies of human heredity in the United States. And it was perhaps fitting, therefore, that Bell became one of the most respected, if not one of the most zealous, participants in the American eugenics movement.

## Paupers and Criminals

By the 1870's many of those working among the poor began to think of the lowest classes as hereditary losers in the struggle for existence. They were the unfit, who were often allowed to survive and breed through indiscriminate and disorganized charity.

For many American charity workers, in fact, the depression of 1873 was a lesson in the failures of unorganized relief. Charles Loring Brace, who had labored long and hard for the poor boys of New York City and who had been so fascinated by evolution that he read and re-read *The Origin of Species* thirteen times, reported that during the depression winter of 1873-74 those connected with charity work had warned against indiscriminate giving to the poor. But the warnings went unheeded, with the result that tramps converged on New York, many poor families abandoned their jobs, and many laborers lost the habit of steady industry. Charity had fostered a spirit of pauperism that "degrades all that is manly and self-respecting in a human being, and destroys all habits of industry and self-support." If left uncorrected, Brace warned, "a community of paupers, transmitting pauperism to children of like character, would soon become one of the most degraded and miserable on the face of the earth." He advised that charity, to avoid such a pitfall, be as much as possible connected with labor and be given only after investigation.[42]

The charity organization societies established in many American cities in the late 1870's and 1880's, although they drew upon the philosophy and example of the London Charity Organisation Society, founded in 1869, had their origin in the need to solve American problems of relief. The mission of C.O.S. was to bring order out of chaotic charity and to administer a scientific philanthropy that would strengthen the impoverished and help them to rise out of their poverty. Although the societies desired to aid all who stood in real need, they also desired to make that aid unpleasant enough so that it would not become habit forming. Hence, they were active in efforts to suppress beggary and vagrancy and to coordinate the public and private charity work of the city. To prevent fraud and to refer the poor to the proper agency, the societies kept family records of the needy, a practice that led to the family case-work system and modern social work.[43]

In many cities the C.O.S. workers faced what seemed to them the direful workings of heredity. During the formative period of the New York C.O.S., established in 1882, the guiding figure was Josephine Shaw Lowell, already quite convinced of the importance of heredity from her visits to almshouses and jails. Pauperism was, she felt, the result of a physical or moral degeneration of the individual, to which charity was often a contributing cause since "no man can receive as a gift what he should earn by his own labor without a moral deterioration." Public relief, instead of pauperizing the individual, should aim at reform; it should be "surrounded by circumstances that shall not only repel every one, not in extremity, from accepting it, but which shall also insure a distinct moral and physical improvement on the part of all those who are forced to have recourse to it—that is, discipline and education should be inseparably associated with any system of public relief." While all have a right to live, "yet the community has a right to say that incompetent and dangerous persons shall not, so far as can be helped, be born to acquire this right." [44] In her writings and speeches, Josephine Shaw Lowell was a major spokesman for the C.O.S. movement in the United States.

In Indianapolis, the Rev. Oscar C. McCulloch, a liberal Congregational minister far more interested in social problems than in theology, was the guiding power in the formation of the Charity Organization Society. On a visit for the society in the fall of 1877, he discovered an impoverished family—an old blind woman, her son, his wife and child, a sister with two children—huddled in a small, unheated room. Influenced by Dugdale's recent study, McCulloch traced their ancestry and found that they were part of a large family with a long history of crime, disease, and prostitution. The members of the Tribe of Ishmael, as he called the family, were irredeemable: "Of this whole number, I know of but one who has escaped, and is to-day an honorable man," McCulloch reported. "I have tried again and again to lift them, but they sink back." [45] He believed the origin of the family could be traced to convict laborers shipped to the colonies during the seventeenth century and that the family had survived and multiplied largely through the aid of public relief and private charity.[46] Soon the Tribe of Ishmael took its place with the Jukes as a horrible example of the tragedy and expense from ignoring heredity in the lives of men.

This is not to suggest that heredity dominated American attitudes toward poverty or excluded other interpretations in the late nineteenth century. Many who went to school to C.O.S. found that the interplay of many factors was involved in forcing individuals and families below the poverty line. Most of those who came in contact with poverty through residence in social settlements and institutional churches or learned the lives of the poor through muckraking journalism were far more likely to indict the social system than heredity. Yet there were common elements in the way many Americans approached the problem of poverty and pauperism. Pauperism was viewed as a degeneration of the individual, like parasitism in nature. Degeneration often stemmed from social conditions—from business fluctuations, accidents, unhealthy working conditions, or low wages. There were, however, other causes that arose within the individual himself: disease, intemperance, sensuality, senility, insanity, or hereditary weakness. Amos Warner, in his classic study, *American Charities,* a book that in its many editions became a standard text on poverty and charity, cited the investigations of Galton, Dugdale, McCulloch, and Bell and concluded: "Observations more than ordinarily careful show that more varieties of bodily and mental weakness are transmitted from parent to child than is ordinarily supposed." [47] In the late nineteenth century, when so many thought in evolutionary terms, it was only natural to divide man into the fit and the unfit.

The study of the criminal was governed by the same sorts of investigations and assumptions that governed the study of other forms of social inadequacy. Dugdale's investigation of the Jukes, after all, had been undertaken as an inspector for the New York Prison Association. By the 1870's many prisons, in their annual reports, listed heredity or inherited depravity among the causes that brought a man to the prison door. Medical men, especially, conceived that crime was a disease, that the causes of criminal action lay in the physiology of the brain, and that, as Dr. Oliver Wendell Holmes, in his famous essay, "Crime and Automatism," declared, "in most cases crime can be shown to run in the blood." There was a growing tendency to see criminality as a pathological condition, one of the many manifestations of an inherent weakness that might also take the form of insanity, alcoholism, feeblemindedness, or pauperism.[48]

At the same time, however, the major emphasis of prison administrators and prison reformers in the 1870's and 1880's was environmental. At their various conferences, they were chiefly occupied with such problems as preventive work among juveniles, reform of the prisons, and advocacy of the indeterminate sentence.[49] Faith in the reform of the criminal heart was so strong that when Zebulon R. Brockway, warden of the world-famous Elmira Reformatory, suggested in 1884 that one-half of the prisoners were incorrigible, often because of heredity, he received little support from his colleagues. One reformatory superintendent said he did not like to think of anyone as incorrigible; others declared, on religious grounds, that there were none who could not be saved.[50] Not until the introduction of criminal anthropology during the 1890's did heredity become a major problem for American criminologists.

## Better Breeding

The late-nineteenth-century emphasis upon heredity produced several interesting sidelights. Later eugenists, in fact, regarded the short-lived Institute of Heredity, established by Loring Moody in Boston about 1880, to be the first eugenics organization in the United States. Moody had been active for some time in various social reforms, but the writings of Galton and others convinced him that most reforms were merely palliative because they did not strike

at the hereditary roots of social ills. The purpose of the Institute
of Heredity was to collect books and pamphlets on health and heredity and to spread scientific information through lectures and publications. Chiefly Moody hoped to educate parents, and he warned
of the dire effects upon the unborn child if parents were sinful,
sensual, or unhealthy, or if they drank—especially preceding copu-
lation.[51]

Another peripheral movement—and one that eugenists were not
so eager to call their own—was the scientific breeding practiced by
the Oneida Bible Communists. Established in 1848 under the dominating leadership of John Humphrey Noyes, the community at
Oneida, New York, became the most successful of the nineteenth-
century communitarian experiments in America. The Bible Communists called themselves Perfectionists, for they believed that
moral laws were for the unregenerate and that those, like themselves, who had attained perfection in Christ were above the law.
Unwilling to restrict their love, they practiced "complex marriage,"
a system that was barely, if at all, distinguishable from free love;
this they combined with "male continence," a method of contraception in which the male in sexual intercourse stopped short of
orgasm.[52]

Noyes read Galton in the 1860's and found him strong in theory
but weak in practice. "When he comes to the point where it is
necessary to look beyond his theory to the duties it suggests," Noyes
complained, "he subsides into meekest conservatism." Noyes saw
that what was needed was scientific propagation, or stirpiculture,
for ". . . every race-horse, every straight-backed bull, every pre-
mium pig tells us what we can do and what we must do for man." [53]
Outside the Oneida community monogamous marriage was a bar
to scientific breeding, but within the community conditions were
ideal. In 1869, therefore, he had fifty-three of the young women
and thirty-eight of the men sign a pledge to participate in an experiment to breed healthy Perfectionists by matching those most
advanced in health and perfection. The women pledged:

1. That we do not belong to *ourselves* in any respect, but that we
*do* belong first to *God,* and second to Mr. Noyes as God's true representative.

2. That we have no rights or personal feelings in regard to child-
bearing which shall in the least degree oppose or embarrass him in his
choice of scientific combinations.

3. That we will put aside all envy, childishness and self-seeking, and

rejoice with those who are chosen candidates; that we will, if necessary, become martyrs to science, and cheerfully resign all desire to become mothers, if for any reason Mr. Noyes deem us unfit material for propagation. Above all, we offer ourselves "living sacrifices" to God and true Communism.[54]

In the next ten years, the experiment produced fifty-eight children, at least nine fathered by Noyes himself. According to Dr. Theodore Noyes, the founder's son, the health of the children was far above normal.[55] Unfortunately for the cause of scientific breeding, however, dissatisfactions among the Bible Communists and pressures from outside brought the dissolution of the community in 1880. Like most of the American communitarian experiments, its influence was not great.[56]

These were, of course, merely sidelights. The important fact was that, by the 1890's, Americans active in the study and treatment of the dependent and delinquent increasingly found in heredity a major cause for those mental aberrations that cost the nation so much in the maintenance of asylums, prisons, and poor relief. They marshaled family studies and statistics impressive in demonstrating that degenerate ancestry revealed itself inevitably in alcoholism, insanity, feeblemindedness, and epilepsy, even criminality and pauperism. Naturally such an emphasis led to pleas that the unfit be prevented from propagating their kind. The campaign for custodial care of the feebleminded was the most important result, but the attack by charity organization societies on indiscriminate giving, the warnings of temperance advocates, the advice that Bell gave the deaf —all represented the same concern.

In the nineteenth century, however, the medical and scientific emphasis upon hereditary defect was confined chiefly to the growing and influential body of experts. There was little organized effort to educate the public and hardly any appeals to the voters in behalf of programs to prevent propagation of the unfit. But the extent of vague and general hereditarian assumptions cannot be measured simply by the history of scientific studies, for those studies were a part of a larger acceptance of social Darwinian ideas among educated Americans. The assumption that man's progress in the past had resulted from selection of the fit and elimination of the unfit and the justification of a free and competitive economy on the grounds that such a system allowed the fit to succeed and the unfit to succumb to poverty and disease were attitudes that spread well beyond the bounds of those acquainted with scientific studies of heredity. Thus, when the eugenics movement arrived in the twentieth century—when researches in heredity increased and when societies initiated extensive campaigns to educate the public and secure specific eugenics reforms—the movement built not only upon a specific background of medical and scientific hereditarian assumptions but upon a general background of Darwinian social thought.

# Chapter IV

# Prelude to Eugenics, 1890-1905

By the mid-1890's the emphasis upon heredity mounted in intensity and produced a two-pronged attack on the threatened hereditary contamination of the American stock. On the one hand, as a result of a growing belief in the heredity of many forms of dependency and delinquency, a campaign began to secure laws for marriage restriction and asexualization of the unfit.[1] On the other hand, the late nineteenth century witnessed the development of a phobia that soon permeated American thought and, by the 1890's, brought the beginning of a campaign for immigration restriction to shield American blood from "inferior" racial traits. These developments constituted a prelude to eugenics, for as yet the word eugenics was not in use and the two movements—that against the socially unfit and that against the racially unfit—were almost wholly separate and distinct. One result of the eugenics movement would be to unite the two into a single self-conscious crusade.

## Criminal Anthropology

A major factor in intensifying American emphasis upon heredity and increasing the demand for marriage restriction and asexualization was the impact of the European school of criminal anthropology. By the early 1880's, Morel's theory of hereditary degeneration and Benedikt's studies of the criminal brain exercised influence in the United States. By the late 1880's, the theories of Lombroso and the Italian school received occasional mention and shortly became something of a fad among American students of crime and mental disease.[2]

In its stress upon heredity and upon a physical basis for mental aberrations, criminal anthropology provided reinforcement for assumptions that were already widely accepted. Criminal anthropology had, however, the additional advantage of suggesting methods for studying physical and psychical anomalies of the defective and delinquent. As a result, it became an important guide for research in the decade and a half after 1890. The brains of criminals, imbeciles, and the insane were the special province of physicians; but virtually anyone—criminologist, psychologist, doctor, minister, or charity worker—could measure skulls and search for stigmata of the hair, palate, jaws, teeth, limbs, and fingernails.

An important result of criminal anthropology was that it undermined for some persons a faith in the possibility of reforming the defective classes and thus strengthened a belief that heredity and incurability were inseparably linked. The grim lesson of criminal anthropology was that a murderer was an atavistic beast whose behavior could no more be changed than his atypical brain, that a pauper's dependency was as incorrigible as his deformed jaw and teeth. Criminal anthropology, in the name of science, would banish sentimental faith in reform and prescribe that those whose failures were inherited and incurable should be forbidden to propagate. Thus, with the introduction of criminal anthropology, the hereditarian emphasis for the first time directly questioned some of the basic assumptions of the American reform tradition.[3]

The concepts of criminal anthropology had a vogue far beyond the confines of experts in criminology. Jack London in many of his popular novels and Frank Morris in such novels as *McTeague* and *Vandover and the Brute* employed atavism and degeneration to explain character. McTeague, in the novel *McTeague,* had a crazed alcoholic as a father and a drudge as a mother, while he himself exhibited definite atavistic stigmata ("his head was square-cut, angular; the jaw salient, like that of a carnivora"). Indeed, Max Nordau, in his widely read book, *Degeneration,* went so far as to blame the decadence of the arts in western civilization upon degeneration of the artists—as could be seen in the emotionalism of Wagner's music, the "filth of Zola's art," the egomaniac obscurities of Nietzsche, and the visual derangement of impressionistic painting. The new esthetic movements drew their following from fiery, unbalanced men who "act as, in consequence of the diseased constitution of their brain and nervous system, they are compelled to act." In line with Lombroso's belief that genius was akin to degeneracy, Nordau held that an examination of the ancestry of such artistic figures would show a background of hereditary disease.[4] These were but a few of the ways in which criminal anthropology passed into popular literature and thought.

A handful of Americans were so overwhelmed by criminal anthropology that they demanded immediate and far-reaching measures to stamp out degenerate families. In his book, *Prisoners and Paupers* (1893), Henry M. Boies, an expert on penology of the Pennsylvania State Board of Public Charities, declared it to be "established beyond controversy that criminals and paupers, both, are degenerate: the imperfect, knotty, knurly, worm-eaten fruit of the race." He urged that criminals and defectives be segregated or castrated and that others, ranging from tramps and alcoholics to the cancerous and scrofulous—as well as their children and grandchildren—be forbidden to marry. Even more alarmed was W. Duncan McKim, whose book, *Heredity and Human Progress,* published in 1900, was the climax of extremism. For him the scientific proof was overwhelming that "heredity is the fundamental cause of human wretchedness." In degenerate families could be found "insanity, idiocy, imbecility, eccentricity, hysteria, epilepsy, the alcohol-habit, the morphine-habit, neuralgias, 'nervousness,' St. Vitus' dance, infantile convulsions, stammering, squint, gout, articular rheumatism, diabetes, tuberculosis, cancer, deafness, blindness, deaf-mutism, color-blindness," and other forms of degeneracy. Charity, as the history of the Jukes demonstrated, was futile in the struggle against human degeneration. The only solution was to prevent the unfit from propagating, and "the surest, the simplest, the kindest, and most humane means for preventing reproduction among those whom we deem unworthy of this high privilege, is a *gentle, painless death.*" He found very few who would support his solution.[5]

The chief impact of criminal anthropology was, of course, upon American criminology, and in that field attitudes ranged from wholehearted acceptance to outright rejection. The most enduring influence was to create an awareness of a need for careful laboratory study of the criminal. Many prison physicians, impressed by criminal anthropology, recognized that they had a special opportunity to search for the physical and psychical stigmata of degeneration. Among prison physicians, Dr. Hamilton D. Wey at the world famous Elmira Reformatory in New York was particularly insistent and influential in urging laboratory study of criminals.[6] Such ideas became so generally accepted that, when Charles R. Henderson, an ecclesiastical sociologist at the University of Chicago, urged in a report in 1900 that prison laboratories be extended and strengthened, his report received the enthusiastic endorsement of the National Prison Association. On the national level, Arthur MacDonald, as specialist on the abnormal classes for the Bureau of Education, pressed Congress to establish a national laboratory for studying the criminal, pauper, and defective classes.[7]

University psychologists and sociologists also found stimulation in criminal anthropology. George E. Dawson, a fellow in psychology under G. Stanley Hall at Clark University, tested criminal anthropology in an influential study of sixty delinquent boys and girls in Boston. He discovered that several of the boys had high cephalic indexes (mongoloid) and one had a low index (negroid); all of the girls had "abnormal" cephalic indexes. In addition, 30.8 per cent of the boys and 42.3 per cent of the girls had asymmetrical faces, while 38.6 per cent of the boys and 34.6 per cent of the girls had deformed palates. Several delinquents had bullet heads ("so much in evidence at police courts"), and one boy was web-footed between his second and third toes. Dawson concluded that such degeneration was largely hereditary, for over 80 per cent of the boys and 45 per cent of the girls had intemperate parents, of whom many had been inmates of prisons and asylums.[8]

While some criminologists were convinced by criminal anthropology, the dominant attitude was an acceptance with reservations. As chaplain at San Quentin, August Drähms in 1900 published *The Criminal* (with a highly favorable introduction by Lombroso). Drähms believed that there existed instinctive criminals, whose "biological, moral, and intellectual equipments are the results of hereditary entailment from prenatal sources," and that sexual appetite, avarice, and a tendency to theft, homicide, and pauperism could be inherited. Yet he also pointed out the inconsistencies of criminal anthropology: that studies of the criminal brain brought conflicting opinions because there was no agreement on what constituted a normal brain; that Lombroso found criminals to have large ears and others found small ears; that Lombroso thought the criminal tended to be tall and others thought him short.[9] Charles R. Henderson was even less convinced than Drähms. He held that the instinctive criminal was only one of many types; hence he argued that "it is easy to prove that only a part—perhaps a small minority —of the total prison population are seriously defective. Of most offenders, we may say with confidence that they are not 'victims' of heredity." [10]

There were, in addition, criminologists who firmly rejected criminal anthropology, especially its fatalistic implications. Some attacked the research methods of criminal anthropology. They suggested that criminal anthropologists were prejudiced by seeing men shaven and in prison garb. They stressed what even the advocates of criminal anthropology had to admit: that because many confirmed criminals bore no stigmata and many honest citizens did, criminal anthropology was of no practical value in separating the criminal from the noncriminal.[11]

Foremost among the opponents was Frederick H. Wines, secretary of the Illinois State Board of Charities, perhaps the most respected of American criminal reformers, and a man deeply convinced that the criminal heart could be reformed. "I do not believe in inherited crime any more than I believe in the imaginary criminal type," he told the members of the National Prison Association in 1898. "One may be born with a physical and mental constitution which predisposes him to crime," Wines admitted. "But so much greater is the influence of environment than that of heredity, in the formation of character, that proper training may and often does correct this predisposition." [12] Others, too, stressed the power of environment to mold heredity. "While there are those born with a predisposition to crime, yet under proper conditions they do not develop into criminals, or may be reformed after they have become such," a minister declared. And he added: "Old mother Jukes and her criminal progeny have committed vastly more crimes in the hands of the hereditarians, than they ever committed in actual life." [13] Yet it is important to note how far even the critics of criminal anthropology went in ascribing a hereditarian basis to crime while rejecting the fatalistic implications.

Superintendents of asylums for the feebleminded, already well advanced in their concern for heredity, did not need the promptings of criminal anthropology; still they could not avoid its influence. Among those charged with the care of the feebleminded, Dr. A. W. Wilmarth was the most ardent champion of criminal anthropology. Born in Massachusetts in 1855 of an old New England family and graduated from Albany Medical College in 1879, he became assistant superintendent in the Pennsylvania Training School for Feeble-

Minded Children at Elwyn in 1883. There, with the encouragement of Isaac N. Kerlin, Wilmarth began the study of the retarded brain, and in innumerable autopsies found a variety of abnormalities, many similar to those that Benedikt had found in the criminal brain.[14] Like his colleagues, Wilmarth believed that heredity was the major cause of feeblemindedness, and he became one of the most active speakers in favor of marriage regulation and asexualization. When, in 1897, Wilmarth was named head of the State Home for the Feeble-Minded in Chippewa Falls, Wisconsin, he had performed more autopsies on the brains of the feebleminded than any other man. In Wisconsin he became a wheelhorse of the eugenics movement.[15]

As the twentieth century opened, a steadily increasing emphasis upon the menace of the feebleminded kept the students of the feebleminded in the vanguard of the movement for asexualization or permanent custodial care. Walter E. Fernald of Massachusetts, already honored as the leader among institutional superintendents, issued a classic statement in a description of the feebleminded to the National Conference of Charities and Correction:

> The adult males become the town loafers and incapables, the irresponsible pests of the neighborhood, petty thieves, purposeless destroyers of property, incendiaries, and very frequently violators of women and little girls. It is well known that feeble-minded women and girls are very liable to become sources of unspeakable debauchery and licentiousness which pollutes the whole life of the young boys and youth of the community. They frequently disseminate in a wholesale way the most loathsome and deadly diseases, permanently poisoning the minds and bodies of thoughtless youth at the very threshold of manhood. Almost every country town has one or more of these defective women each having from one to four or more illegitimate children, every one of whom is predestined to be defective mentally, criminal, or an outcast of some sort.

Fernald saw a close connection between Lombroso's theory and his own. "Is there not more than a close resemblance between the imbecile and the instinctive criminal?" he asked. "Is not the typical instinctive criminal of Lombroso a typical adult imbecile of middle or high grade?" [16]

So complete was the acceptance of this conception of feeblemindedness that when Martin W. Barr, chief physician at Elwyn, published in 1904 the first comprehensive work on feeblemindedness in a generation, he repeated and emphasized all the stereotypes concerning heredity, the menace of the feebleminded, and the necessity for permanent custodial care and asexualization.[17]

A major influence of criminal anthropology was to convince many American physicians of a need for marriage restriction and asexualization. Whatever psychoanalysts might say concerning the motivation of those who seemed possessed by a compelling urge to castrate the unfit, physicians stated their motives in medical terms. In the studies of Benedikt and Lombroso lay the evidence that criminals and other misfits were hereditary victims of their own degenerate brains and bodies. They were, therefore, a medical problem and asexualization was a kind of preventive medicine. For three decades after 1890, in speeches before medical societies and articles in medical journals, a rapidly increasing chorus of doctors declared that surgery could be a practical aid in solving the problems of dependency and crime.[18]

Until the late 1890's, the only means of asexualization was removal of either the testes or ovaries. Such an operation not only prevented propagation but also had important physical and psychological effects on the victim. Because of this, many doctors advocated asexualization not only to halt breeding of the unfit but also to act as a cure and as a deterrent. By removing sexual passion, it would cure sexual crimes and prevent robbery and suicide when committed out of love of woman. ("The murderer is likely to lose much of his savageness; the violator loses not only the desire, but the capacity for a repetition of his crime, if the operation be supplemented by penile mutilation according to the Oriental method," one doctor explained.) [19] The fierce criminal would become mild and could become a useful member of society as a clergyman, choir singer, or dry nurse.[20]

Equally important would be the value of castration as a deterrent. "The loss of sexual capability as a mark of manhood is so utterly abhorrent to all men," Dr. Robert Boal explained, "that it would be avoided if possible by all individuals not hopelessly insane." [21] (Castration had special appeal to many as a means of controlling the alleged increase of rape by southern Negroes, particularly since lynching and capital punishment had apparently failed to do so.) [22] Physicians often expressed disdain for the sentimental opponents of asexualization. "In the consideration of such a vital question as the management of the criminal class," one warned, "the sentimentalist and his natural ally, the preacher, have joined hands on the question, and to them the world has looked for reformation for which it has waited in vain." [23] Thus a substantial proportion of the medical profession added its prestige to the campaign for asexualization.

During the 1890's, then, criminal anthropology had an important impact upon American attitudes toward the defective and delinquent. It guided a share of the research into the origins of the unfit, helped undermine a belief in the ability of society to cure and reform them, and reinforced the emphasis upon heredity that had developed in the preceding decades. The impact of criminal anthropology was such that, when the campaign for asexualization got under way, criminals and the feebleminded were the ones most often mentioned as proper candidates for the surgeon's knife.

### Beginning the Legislative Battle

By the mid-1890's students of the unfortunate classes were generally agreed upon a need for laws to forbid such persons to marry. Those who also advocated asexualization were weaker in numbers but strong in conviction. Marriage restriction was less extreme, for the states had long regulated both age and consanguinity of couples intending to marry. About one-half the states, in fact, already had laws that declared void the marriage of an insane or feebleminded person—not on eugenic grounds but on the grounds that such persons were unable to make a contract. The problem, therefore, was to strengthen such laws, to win their adoption in additional states, and to secure adequate enforcement.[24]

In 1896 Connecticut became the first state to regulate marriage for breeding purposes. A law of that year provided that "no man and woman either of whom is epileptic, or imbecile, or feebleminded" shall marry or have extra-marital relations "when the woman is under forty-five years of age," and set a minimum penalty of three years' imprisonment for violation.[25] Connecticut was immediately extolled as an example for other states to follow, and many legislatures discussed bills to forbid marriage to a variety of persons: the feebleminded, insane, syphilitic, alcoholic, epileptic, and certain types of criminals. Kansas in 1903, New Jersey and Ohio in 1904, and Michigan and Indiana in 1905, joined the ranks of states with eugenic marriage laws.[26]

Even while advocating such laws, many supporters held out little hope that they would prove effective. The unfit of society would not, in their breeding habits, be bound by laws, even when efforts were made to enforce the laws. "The waifs and strays, the vicious and lawless, and above all the unrecognized, unsuspected defectives in all ranks of society it is powerless to reach," was a common judgment.[27] That was why many were convinced that the protection of society demanded the enactment of laws for the asexualization of the unfit, for only such a program could effectively destroy the power to taint future generations.

On the asexualization front, action preceded legislation. In the mid-1890's Dr. F. Hoyt Pilcher, superintendent of the Kansas State Home for the Feeble-Minded, castrated forty-four boys and fourteen girls under his charge. His was the first effort at systematic asexualization in the United States for eugenic purposes—appropriately enough begun in an asylum for the feebleminded. Because his actions were without legal warrant, public opinion soon forced him to stop, but not before he had established a reputation as a heroic pathfinder. The Board of Trustees of the institution pointed out that all great scientific advances had met criticism at the outset: "Those who are now criticizing Doctor Pilcher will, in a few years, be talking of erecting a monument to his memory." In a presidential address before the nation's institutional superintendents, Martin W. Barr was happy that "the courageous attitude of Dr. Pilcher, of Kansas, as pioneer, strong to face ignorance and prejudice, has already had its good effect." [28]

Part of the justification of Dr. Pilcher's action was the beneficial results, physical and mental, that were claimed for the operation.[29] In 1905 Dr. Barr, to rally sentiment for castration, reported what he considered to be the fine effects on some eighty-eight youths, ages fourteen to twenty-two. "In every case, there was marked mental and physical improvement, the children growing stout, and acquiring large frames. There was no hair on the pubes or face, and the cheeks became round and prominent; indeed they resemble large women." Among the cases was a "sexual pervert of the most pronounced description, who would solicit women on the road, and was extremely vulgar in every way . . . and is now languid in movements, and has developed a most excellent soprano singing voice, and has improved in temper and habits." [30] However praiseworthy some may have found these results, certainly the public could never be brought to support asexualization when it had such far-reaching effects.

What was needed was a simple surgical procedure that would render the patient sterile without affecting the internal hormones of the ovaries or testes. By the turn of the century, such operations were available. Salpingectomy—the cutting and tying of the fallopian tubes—was developed in the nineteenth century as a means to sterilize women who were forced to have children by Cesarian operation. By about 1897 the operation had been tested and was well-known. Since it involved opening the abdomen, the operation was about as serious as an appendectomy. To render the male sterile, vasectomy—the cutting and tying of the *vas deferens* through a slit in the scrotum—was developed in Europe during the 1890's. The operation could often be quickly and easily performed in a doctor's office.[31] With the introduction of these two operations, it was possible to urge sterilization for eugenic reasons alone, without the necessity of defending the radical effects of the earlier operations that had shocked public opinion. One of the chief problems, in fact, was to make clear that sterilization did not destroy the enjoyment of sex or alter the internal hormones.

Dr. Harry Sharp, physician at the Indiana Reformatory in Jeffersonville, introduced vasectomy into the United States. In 1899 a nineteen-year-old inmate who masturbated some four to ten times daily asked Dr. Sharp to castrate him to break the habit. (To understand the request, one should remember that competent medical opinion of the day attributed dwarfism, idiocy, rotting teeth, tuberculosis, early death, and a general decline of the human race directly to the "secret vice.") [32] Instead of castration, Dr. Sharp performed vasectomy. Within three weeks, the youth apparently ceased to masturbate, grew healthier, and improved in school work, but had no loss of sexual desire. Sharp was encouraged and began to accommodate all comers until, at the end of a year, he had operated on seventy-six youths without a single accident or unfavorable symptom. "It was then," he later reported, "that it occurred to me that this would be a good method of preventing procreation in the defective and physically unfit." [33]

Sharp became an insistent advocate of sterilization to ease the burden of the defective and delinquent. "Shall we permit idiots, imbeciles, and degenerate criminals to continue the pollution of the race simply because certain religionists teach that 'marriages are made in heaven' and that the 'function of procreation is divine?'" he asked. "To me these are the most damnable heresies." [34] Galton's investigations, Sharp argued, demonstrated that heredity applied to both the mental and physical life. He called on his fellow men of science to labor before legislatures to secure the necessary laws.

Others, too, saw the advantages of the new operation and began to urge it as a solution to the problem of the defective and delinquent.[35] They were well-armed for a thirty-year assault upon state legislatures to secure sterilization laws.

The assault had, in fact, already begun. In 1897 a bill for asexualization of the feebleminded and certain criminals was introduced into the Michigan legislature, discussed, and finally defeated. At the same time, Dr. DeForest Willard of Philadelphia, a member of the board of the Pennsylvania Training School for the Feeble-Minded, began agitating the question of asexualization in Pennsylvania, with the active encouragement of Dr. Martin W. Barr. In 1901 and again in 1905, a bill "for the Prevention of Idiocy" passed the Pennsylvania legislature, but failed to secure approval from the governor.[36]

The failure in Pennsylvania permitted Indiana to pass the first sterilization law in the United States. There Dr. Harry C. Sharp, following his own advice, organized the fight for the law. In 1905 he encouraged W. H. Whittaker, superintendent of the Indiana Reformatory, to introduce a bill into the legislature. That year, unable to win a unanimous report from the Committee on Reformatories, its supporters allowed the bill to die in committee. In 1907 another bill passed and "was signed by Governor J. Frank Hanly, whose administration has been noted for its efforts at race purity and civic righteousness." The bill made mandatory the sterilization of confirmed criminals, idiots, imbeciles, and rapists in state institutions when recommended by a board of experts.[37]

With the law on the books, Dr. Sharp dubbed sterilization the "Indiana Idea" and boasted: "I am proud that Indiana is the first State to enact such a law, and that the Indiana Reformatory is the pioneer in this work." Yet, had he known the meager results that such laws would have in his own state and in the United States, he might not have been so exultant.[38]

### Prelude to Racism

Between 1870 and 1900 educated Americans took giant strides toward a fairly wide acceptance of varying forms and degrees of racism. Before the Civil War, the lack of a well-developed racist philosophy in the Western world and a general belief that all men descended from Adam and Eve retarded the growth of race concepts. Only among those defending Negro slavery from increasingly bitter attack did specific biological theories of race become at all impor-

tant. In the post-Civil War period, however, the general background
of evolutionary thought and the writings of European racists provided a climate of opinion that nurtured race thinking. Although
the general concept was imported, the motives and emotional tone
of American racism were home grown. The American scene largely
determined the important choice of which races, so-called, were to
be praised and which to be condemned. Out of anxieties and dislocations within American society came expressions of a vague but
virulent racism that influenced ever wider segments of the American public.

Educated native Americans came increasingly to identify themselves and their values with the Anglo-Saxon race. In England the
Anglo-Saxon myth had a long history, and in America before the
Civil War had grown increasingly in favor as a way of defining
American principles of free government. The Anglo-Saxons, it was
held, were an exceptionally restless, industrious, and creative people. Their love of liberty and respect for law originated among
Teutonic tribes in the forests of Germany and from there spread
with the Anglo-Saxons to England. That same love of liberty caused
the peoples of northern Europe to accept Protestantism while more
servile peoples of southern Europe remained under the dominion
of Rome. Love of liberty, in the blood and bone of the Anglo-
Saxon, created the New England town meetings, fired the War for
Independence, and reached fruition in the American constitution.
The Anglo-Saxon interpretation virtually dominated the writing of
American history as the century closed and, at the same time, was
widely publicized and popularized.[39]

Doctrines of racial inferiority first achieved widespread support
in their application to peoples of color. In the South, even before
the Civil War, a conviction that the Negro was a separate and inferior creation had become fairly common. As the idealism of the
Civil War wore off, many northerners came to assume that the
corruption and mismanagement of southern reconstruction govern-
ments demonstrated an innate incapacity of Negroes for government. Physicians and social workers were appalled by an apparently
rapid increase of crime, insanity, and disease among the freedmen.
Reports from observers, both northern and southern, reinforced a
stereotype of the sensual, happy-go-lucky, immoral Negro unable to
adapt to a complex Anglo-Saxon civilization.[40]

In the generation that followed Darwin, what more logical explanation than that the Negro had followed a separate evolutionary

course from the white man and was closer to the simian and savage stage of development? The broad, flat nose, the slanted profile of the Negro face, and the smaller average skull capacity—so it was argued—placed the Negro closer to the anthropoids. By 1900 the race hatred of uneducated Americans merged with the racism of the educated to create a climate that acquiesced in fastening second-class citizenship upon Negro Americans.[41]

Before the Civil War there was already scientific support for a condemnation of marriage between the white and colored races and much speculation that the mulatto was a relatively sterile and short-lived hybrid. The scientific racism of the late nineteenth century led a number of publicists, writing "from a purely scientific view-point," to assure the public that miscegenation was the road to racial degeneration. Racial greatness required that the Anglo-Saxon keep his blood uncontaminated; otherwise the United States, like the na-tions of Latin America, would "drag the ball and chain of hybrid-ism." [42]

Attitudes toward the Negro were part of a larger concept which also rejected other peoples of color. Faced with a growing Chinese immigration after the Civil War, the west coast launched a vigorous political resistance, supplemented by burnings and lynchings, that resulted in exclusion of Chinese laborers after 1882. In the twen-tieth century, the immigration of Japanese to the west coast brought renewed tensions and violence that were only temporarily allayed by the 1907 Gentleman's Agreement under which Japan voluntarily halted emigration to the United States. In the same period, discus-sion of the "yellow peril"—the racial danger from the population explosion in the Orient and the growing military might of Japan —occupied both the popular press and scholarly magazines. So per-vasive did racist doctrines become that when, as a result of the Spanish-American War of 1898, America assumed the "White Man's burden" in the Philippines, both proponents and opponents of the new policy couched their arguments in these terms. A minor but persistent theme in all these discussions was the need to preserve the inherent vigor of white America from adulteration.[43]

The first step toward applying the stigma of racial inferiority to European immigrants was to promulgate a belief that immigrants were different from native Americans and that their customs, mor-als, and living standards prevented their assimilation. The next step, then, would be to find that the traits which made immigrants dif-

ferent were innate and that they did not assimilate because, biologically, they could not.

Many Americans in the late nineteenth century feared that the
immigrants were bearers of un-American and radical creeds—of an-
archism, socialism, and communism, of strikes and labor violence.
The bloody strikes of 1877, the Haymarket riot of 1886, and industrial strife of the 1890's fed the growing fears. Another element of
distrust was the traditional anti-Catholicism of many Protestant
Americans alarmed by the rapid growth of the Catholic Church,
which was largely an immigrant church. Periodic anti-Catholic out-
bursts culminated in the extremes of the American Protective Association of the 1890's. Americans who longed to heal the cancerous
sores of American society often felt that the immigrants blocked
their way: as supporters of the corrupt city bosses; as the drinkers
whose votes protected the liquor interests; as the ones whose low
standards of living and odd habits of sanitation contributed to the
blight of the slums; and as a group whose poverty and crime threatened to swamp the prisons and to increase enormously the outlay
for poor relief. An erosion of the traditional American welcome of
the immigrant occurred as old-stock Americans competed with immigrants for jobs, watched immigrants climb to positions of social,
political, and economic influence, and feared that the future of
America belonged not to their own children but to the children of
aliens.[44]

Yet in the 1880's the growing tensions did not destroy a faith in
the nation's ability to assimilate the alien throngs. A few might warn
that the nation could not permit the view to go "uncontradicted
that we are the natural cess-pool for the reception of the human offal
and rubbish of the entire world." Worshippers of Anglo-Saxonism
knew, however, that the Anglo-Saxon was the greatest race because,
like all great races, it was a mixed race. Americans had the authority of both Charles Darwin and Herbert Spencer that the American
nation was likely to be the finest of all because its people were an
amalgam of the most restless and intelligent blood of Europe. The
universal belief in the inheritance of acquired characters supported
a faith that American institutions could mold the immigrant so that
his child might inherit the traits of an Anglo-Saxon, might, in fact,
become an Anglo-Saxon.[45]

The alarmed mood of many Americans toward the end of the
1880's was perhaps best reflected by Richmond Mayo Smith, an old-
stock American and Columbia University professor, whose book,

*Emigration and Immigration,* published in 1890, became a Bible to immigration restrictionists. He detailed the social, economic, and moral failures of the immigrants and insisted that the United States had the right and duty to restrict the flow. Yet he could still maintain that "mixed races are the strongest" and predict hopefully that "the American people of the future will be a race composed of many different elements, and it is possible that this mixture will produce a people possessing the best characteristics displayed by these various elements." [46]

The 1890's, however, witnessed the emergence of a nativism that rejected the optimism and confidence of earlier years. The first major impetus came from Francis A. Walker, distinguished Civil War general, economist, statistician, president of the Massachusetts Institute of Technology, and a man deeply disturbed that over five million immigrants poured into the United States from 1880 to 1890. As director of the census in 1870, he had noticed a declining birth rate among Americans of native stock. When the census of 1890 showed a continuation of the trend, he felt he knew why: Americans of native stock shrank from bringing children into the world to compete with the lower standards of immigrants. If the birth rate of the native stock from 1790 to 1830 had continued through the century and if there had been no immigration, the population of the United States in 1890 would have been about what it was. Thus immigration "amounted not to a reenforcement of our population, but to a replacement of native by foreign stock." Walker put into figures the fear that already gnawed at many Americans of native stock, and his conclusion was increasingly discussed until it became a minor phobia in American thought.[47]

The next step toward nativism came with the discovery that the source of immigration was gradually shifting from northern Europe to southern and eastern Europe. By 1896 the so-called new immigration—Italians, Greeks, Turks, Slavs, Magyars, and Russian and Polish Jews—for the first time outnumbered old immigrants from Ireland, England, Scotland, Germany, and Scandinavia. After 1899 the tide rose sharply so that in 1907 the new immigration reached its record peak of nearly one million. The new immigrants differed enough from the old so that the differences were easy to exaggerate and stereotype. They tended to have a peasant background and a high rate of illiteracy, to be members of Catholic, Greek Orthodox, or Jewish faiths, to talk in unfamiliar languages, to wear odd clothes, and to have strange and sometimes swarthy appearances. As a result, some Americans began to argue that the new immigrants were a different race from the northern European stocks that had first mingled their blood to create the American type and that, being different, they could not be assimilated without permanent injury to the racial strength of the nation.[48]

To support this conclusion, American nativists invoked racial doctrines that had recently begun to conquer European thought. For over a generation physical anthropologists had been attempting to classify "races" by innumerable measurements of the skull and other traits, often with the implicit or explicit assumption that shapes and sizes of the skull were accompanied by particular race personalities as immutable as the skulls themselves. In *The Races of Europe* (1899), William Z. Ripley, professor of sociology at the Massachusetts Institute of Technology and lecturer in anthropology at Columbia University, provided the standard source by which European racial concepts passed to American publicists. Ripley neatly divided Europe into three races: Nordics, Alpines, and Mediterraneans, each with its own history and now blended in varying proportions to form the modern races of Europe. The tall, blond, dolichocephalic (long-headed) Nordics dominated in northern Europe; the stocky, brown-haired, brachycephalic (round-headed) Alpines in Central Europe; and the dark-haired, slender, dolichocephalic Mediterraneans in Italy, Spain, and North Africa. While Ripley attributed racial differences to social conditions, geography, and heredity, he placed sufficient emphasis on heredity so that his distinctions could be borrowed with a clear conscience.[49]

In the spring of 1894, a group of young Harvard graduates formed the Immigration Restriction League to spearhead a drive for a reduction of the immigrant influx. Leaders of the League were Robert DeCourcy Ward (whose mother was a Saltonstall) and Prescott F. Hall, both of the Harvard class of 1889. Ward, who became convinced as an undergraduate that the major social problems in American society were rooted in immigration, divided his time between the teaching of climatology at Harvard and the work for restriction. Hall, a lawyer with a passion for science, Wagnerian music, and German philosophy, became so obsessed with the work of the League that, despite his frail health, his life's work centered mainly on immigration restriction. The League soon exercised considerable influence.[50]

Even before formation of the League, some categories of immigrants were forbidden admission. As a result of requests from

state legislatures and charity workers, Congress in 1882 excluded
known criminals, lunatics, idiots, and persons likely to become public charges. Polygamists and persons suffering from loathsome or
dangerous contagious diseases joined the excluded list in 1891, to
be followed by epileptics, beggars, prostitutes, and anarchists in
1903. Such laws received support of the League, but League members knew, too, that such laws could halt only a trickle in the
stream of immigration.[51]

Primarily the League placed its hopes on a bill to exclude all
adult immigrants unable to read or write a language. Henry Cabot
Lodge, a proper Bostonian and powerful Republican, a scholar in
politics whose Ph.D. dissertation under Henry Adams at Harvard
described the glories of Anglo-Saxon law, was political sponsor for
the statute. As early as 1891 Lodge had warned his fellow Congressmen that they did not fully appreciate the threat from the
fact that "immigration of people of those races which contributed
to the settlement and development of the United States is declining in comparison with that of races far removed in thought and
speech and blood from the men who have made this country what
it is." When he introduced the League's bill in 1895, many business groups and labor leaders, alarmed by three years of economic
depression, endorsed it as a means to restrict the flow of immigration. But the bill's sponsors valued it chiefly because it would not
only restrict but select—it would discriminate most against the new
immigration and thereby protect the blood of the nation from the
contamination of "inferior" racial strains.[52]

In 1896 the bill passed with overwhelming support, only to meet
the veto of Grover Cleveland. But the victory of William McKinley
and the Republicans in the election of 1896 did not mean victory
for restriction. Returning prosperity, growing opposition to the
bill from organized immigrant groups, and the exhilarating victory
over Spain in the War of 1898 restored the nation's confidence.
Although the law was repeatedly introduced and was favored by
Theodore Roosevelt as President, not until the last year of William
Howard Taft's administration was another President confronted
with the bill.[53]

Before a movement bearing the name eugenics had begun in the
United States, then, the stage had been set. By the mid-1890's a
number of educated Americans were becoming aware of the seem-
ing threats to the quality of the national stock. On the one hand,
an increase in asylums, prisons, and poor relief revealed, as never

before, the enormity of the task of caring for the dependent, delinquent, and pauper. Already influential voices had issued the call for custodial care, restriction of marriage, and sterilization. On the other hand, the stream of immigration into the country caused many Americans to feel threatened, threatened that the future of their own nation might not belong to their own kind. In an atmosphere of nativism, an educated minority had already rejected the tradition of America as an asylum for the poor and oppressed and, on frankly biological grounds, called for immigration restriction. Only the catalytic effect of the eugenics movement in England was needed to transform these impulses into an indigenous crusade for eugenic reform.

# Chapter V
# Genetics and Eugenics

By 1915 no one could write about eugenics without mentioning the remarkable growth of the movement in the previous five to ten years. By then anyone up-to-date on the newest in social thought could identify Francis Galton, was worried about the "menace of the feebleminded," and feared the tragic results of a birth rate by which the lower classes contributed more than their share to future generations. Indeed, eugenics had many of the characteristics of a fad: joked about in newspapers, lectured about before women's clubs, introduced into the college curriculum, and supported by the inevitable lunatic fringe. The eminence of those who supported eugenics and the influence of its assumptions, however, made it far more than a fad. An emphasis upon race and heredity in shaping man and man's society was basic to American thought during the early decades of the century.

Both the word eugenics and the movement were importations that arrived with the twentieth century. From 1901, when Galton gave his speech on "The Possible Improvement of the Human Breed under Existing Conditions of Law and Sentiment," to 1904, when the National Eugenics Laboratory undertook research, to 1908, when the Eugenics Education Society initiated a propaganda campaign, a handful of Americans watched the new movement with interest. They soon regarded themselves as eugenists and sought to transfer the movement to their own nation. Whether a person was a psychiatrist concerned with preventing propagation by the insane or feebleminded, a psychologist studying human intelligence and its inheritance, or a Boston Brahmin worried about the effect of alien races upon American stock—all saw themselves now as part of a world movement to improve the inborn nature of man. The British influence, in short, created a movement where before there had been a number of diffuse currents of thought.[1]

The British movement served not only as a catalyst but also as a source of doctrine for American eugenists. (Even in the nineteenth century, of course, students of science in America knew of Galton's work through his articles and books.)[2] For the early eugenists, Galton's study of hereditary genius and Pearson's contention that moral and intellectual traits followed the same laws as physical traits provided the most satisfactory evidence that man's mind as well as his body could be improved by better breeding. Equally important, Galton's many thoughtful statements on the goals of eugenics, on its ethical and religious implications, and on the need to work through the cultivation of public support were quoted like scriptural texts by American eugenists. In a very real sense, Galton was doctrinal father of the movement in America.

With the establishment of the Eugenics Record Office at Cold Spring Harbor on Long Island in 1910, the formal organization of eugenics in the United States was undertaken. The Eugenics Record Office influenced both research and propaganda, and provided the chief link between the American movement and the world movement. To understand the founding of the Office, however, it is first necessary to understand the development of modern genetics.

## Human Genetics

The modern science of genetics had its inception in the late 1880's and 1890's when August Weismann of Germany questioned the age-old belief in inheritance of acquired characters. Weismann, like Galton earlier, rejected inheritance of acquired characters because of dissatisfaction with many of its implications. But Weismann went beyond Galton in providing a specific biological alternative to explain heredity.

Previous theory had held that the germ plasm, which determined the heredity of the offspring, was molded and changed during the life of the individual, so that what happened to the individual could affect the traits that he would pass on. Weismann, on the other hand, propounded his theory of the immortality of the germ plasm, his belief that the germ cells, bearing the germ plasm, were independent of the body cells and independent of changes that might occur to the body. Specifically, he held that the hereditary determiners were lodged in the chromosomes of the germ cells. Each germ cell potentially contained two types of substances, which in the embryo separated to become the germ cells and body cells of the developing individual. While individuals might be shaped by the environment, germ cells passed from generation to generation unaltered; and thus acquired characteristics obviously could not be inherited.[3]

Weismann's theory triggered a long debate in biology between neo-Lamarckians, who defended the inheritance of acquired characteristics, and neo-Darwinians, who rejected it. Weismann's theory ran so counter to all that was then believed that most physicians and many biologists at first doubted it or rejected it outright. "Now, if there is any principle in inheritance which has appeared self-evident and not requiring any demonstration at all," Henry F. Osborn, the eminent paleontologist declared, "it is that acquired characters *are* inherited." [4] Much evidence was cited in favor of the old theory: of mice that had their tails cut off until, after seven generations, a tailless bred was produced; of guinea pigs which, after a brain operation, bred epileptic young; of dwindling little toes in man through the wearing of shoes; or of a father who sat before the fire twiddling his thumbs and knocking his nails together and whose sons inherited the same habit.[5] Because further experimentation failed to confirm these and similar evidence, most biologists by the early 1900's acknowledged the victory of the neo-Darwinians; and gradually thereafter the new view passed to other scientists and laymen.

An important reason for the resistance to Weismann's theory was its implications for human progress. The theory was advanced at a time when the optimism of many social reformers was based on a faith that betterment of man in one generation might be passed on and result in betterment of all coming generations. Amos Warner, in his widely read *American Charities,* succinctly stated the dilemma that faced the reformer: "If acquired characteristics be inherited, then we have a chance permanently to improve the race independently of selection, by seeing to it that individuals acquire characteristics that it is desirable for them to transmit." But if Weismann be correct, "our only hope for the permanent improvement of the human stock would then seem to be through exercising an influence upon the selective process." [6] A final victory for neo-Darwinians meant that social reform could not improve the inherited qualities of man and that only a program of breeding could do so.

For the first time there was ground for a split between hereditarians and environmentalists. The disproof of the inheritance of acquired characters was, therefore, a major episode on the road to the acceptance of eugenics.

While the controversy between neo-Lamarckians and neo-Darwinians was in full force, there occurred an event that marked the beginning of modern genetics. About 1900 three European biologists, including Hugo de Vries of Holland, independently rediscovered Gregor Mendel's laws of heredity and also discovered the obscure paper of 1865 in which the Austrian monk had recorded the results of his famous experiments with peas. Like many great scientific advances, Mendel's experiments were extremely simple and the resulting laws equally so. He merely crossbred different types of peas, followed specific traits through several generations, and in each generation *counted* the number of progeny with each trait. The simple ratios that he discovered begin any modern text of genetics and are basic to an understanding of all twentieth-century developments in the study of heredity in plants, animals, or man.

Essentially Mendel discovered that the determiners of inherited traits (later called genes), occur in pairs, one gene in each pair deriving from each parent. If a person receives the same gene from each parent (making him homozygous), then he will develop the trait and will pass on the gene to each of his offspring. But a person may receive a different gene from each parent (making him heterozygous). In that case one of the genes may be dominant and the other recessive, that is, one of the traits may appear and the other be submerged. The gene for albinism in man, for instance, is recessive. Hence the gene may pass from generation to generation without the trait appearing until such time as both parents pass the gene on to the same offspring. (Whenever two parents are heterozygous carriers, then the chances are one in four that a particular offspring will be albino.) A dominant trait, on the other hand, will appear in each offspring that receives the gene and will not skip a generation. If the parent carrying the trait is homozygous, each of his children will be affected; but if he is heterozygous, only one in two will receive the gene.[7]

At first Mendelian genetics turned biologists to breeding experiments and the study of pedigrees in an effort to find simple Mendelian ratios for innumerable traits of plants and animals. Soon it became evident, however, that most traits were too complex to be traced to the action of a single gene, and geneticists began the painstaking process of unraveling the way in which the development of various traits of an organism resulted from the interaction of genes with each other and with many environmental influences. Eventually, biologists and biochemists devoted themselves to the still more basic study of the specific biochemical action by which genes could control the process of growth and change, for here lay the key to life itself.

Although Mendelian genetics won rapid acceptance, its application to man was unfortunately by no means easy, and most advances in genetics have come from the study of the humble corn, fruitfly, bread mold, and bacteria. For several reasons man is an unsatisfactory animal for genetic research. The number of children per mating is too small to reveal Mendelian ratios, and man lives such a long life, with so many years between generations, that it is difficult to follow a trait through several generations. Besides, the geneticist cannot experiment by arranging the types of matings that he would like to study. Finally, although many traits in man have been found to follow simple Mendelian laws, most traits, including the most important, are a product of complex interrelations among the genes and the many environmental factors that shape the working of the genes.

An expanding interest in genetics at the turn of the century led directly to the first organization of the eugenics movement. The American Breeders' Association—formed in 1903 by agricultural breeders and university biologists—provided the chief center for encouragement of Mendelian research in the United States. At its second meeting in January, 1906, the Association set up numerous committees on specific breeding problems. Among them was a Committee on Eugenics "to investigate and report on heredity in the human race" and "to emphasize the value of superior blood and the menace to society of inferior blood." This was the first group in the United States to advocate eugenics under the name of eugenics.[8]

Indeed, the membership of the Committee was a *Who's Who* of the founders of the eugenics movement in America: David Starr Jordan, its chairman, a prominent biologist and Chancellor of Stanford University; Alexander Graham Bell, famous with the public as an inventor but famous among eugenists for his sheep breeding and his study of hereditary deafness; Charles R. Henderson, a University of Chicago sociologist, well known in all reform circles and a respected student of crime and poverty; and Luther Burbank, who remained something of an anomaly in the movement because he retained a belief in the inheritability of acquired characteristics. Other members included Roswell H. Johnson, geologist and later a professor of eugenics; Vernon L. Kellogg, a biologist at Stanford University; and William E. Castle, the Harvard geneticist. But the most important member was Charles Benedict Davenport, whose name dominated, for good or ill, the early eugenics movement.

## Eugenics Record Office

Davenport, the eighth of eleven children of Amzi Benedict Davenport, was born in 1866 in Stamford, Connecticut. His father was a Puritan of Puritan stock, proud enough of his ancestry to publish genealogies carrying the family back to the Davenports of early New England and then on back in England to the Norman conquest. Stern and demanding, he had little Charles work in his New York real estate office in the winter and on their farm near Stamford in the summer, and during odd moments gave the boy most of the early schooling he received. When the boy was nearly fourteen, his father permitted him to attend Brooklyn Polytechnic Institute, where after four years he graduated at the head of his class and, after two years more, received a B.S. in civil engineering. Shortly thereafter, he determined to study biology at Harvard, and there, living frugally, he earned a B.A. and Ph.D. He then served as a Harvard instructor in biology until, in 1899, he became an assistant professor at the University of Chicago.[9]

Davenport's early isolation left him with a premature seriousness and with vague feelings of inferiority that made him ill at ease and sensitive to criticism. "To the end of his day," a colleague wrote, "he remained a lone man, living a life of his own in the midst of others, and feeling out of place in almost any crowd." Yet he combined his insecurity with a remarkable organizing capacity, an ability to make contact with influential people, to secure their cooperation and backing in an enterprise, and to fire others with his own enthusiasm. His boyish frame mirrored the boyish enthusiasm of the man, and his enthusiasms, more than anything else, guided his research and activities.[10]

While at Harvard Davenport was an ardent believer in the statistical study of nature developed by Galton and Pearson. In the late 1890's he was already in correspondence with these men, and his book, *Statistical Methods* (1899), introduced Pearson's methods to America. In the early 1900's, on a visit to England, he met both Galton and Pearson. Although Davenport knew these men when they were launching the eugenics movement in England, his own enthusiasm for eugenics was not aroused this early. For a time relations between Davenport and Pearson were cordial, but Davenport's sensitivity to criticism and his espousal of Mendelian genetics soon made the men bitter critics of each other's work.[11]

When the Carnegie Institution of Washington was incorporated in 1902 to further scientific research, Davenport threw himself enthusiastically into an intensive two-year campaign to persuade the Institution to establish a biological experiment station, with himself as director. His persistence paid off in 1904, and his position as director of the Station for Experimental Evolution at Cold Spring Harbor on Long Island brought him power and prestige, and lent great weight to his pronouncements when he became a dedicated eugenist.[12]

At first doubtful concerning Mendel's laws, Davenport became an enthusiastic supporter. At Cold Spring Harbor he put his staff to work on a variety of problems in cytology and breeding, while he himself undertook breeding experiments with snails, mice, houseflies, moths, sow bugs, trout, cats, canaries, chickens, and sheep. Yet, ironically, shortly after he won his battle to direct a biological experiment station, he became interested instead in tracing in man those same simple Mendelian ratios that geneticists were finding in plants and animals. In 1907, with his wife, he began to publish on the heredity of eye, skin, and hair color in man and therewith entered upon his eugenics career. His work in experimental genetics flagged, and he now initiated plans to make Cold Spring Harbor a center for research in human genetics and for propaganda in eugenics.[13]

At this time, Davenport became secretary of the Committee on Eugenics of the American Breeders' Association and immediately expanded its activities. In 1909 he organized committees to encourage the study of human heredity in universities and institutions. Alexander Graham Bell, a friend of Davenport's, naturally headed a committee on deaf-mutism. Henry H. Goddard of the Training School at Vineland, whose work with mental testing and heredity of feeblemindedness gave him a central place in the eugenics movement, and Walter E. Fernald of Massachusetts, the most distinguished American student of feeblemindedness, joined a committee on feeblemindedness. A committee on insanity boasted Adolf

Meyer, a leading psychiatrist, Elmer E. Southard, the brilliant young psychiatrist of the Boston Psychopathic Hospital, and Aaron J. Rosanoff of the Hospital at Kings Park in New York. A committee on inheritance of mental traits included Robert M. Yerkes, the Harvard psychologist, Edward L. Thorndike, psychologist at Columbia University, and Frederick Adams Woods, a biologist at the Massachusetts Institute of Technology. Among members of a committee on criminality were Charles R. Henderson, sociologist at the University of Chicago, and William Healy, whose investigations revolutionized the study of the criminal mind. A committee on epilepsy included Everett Flood and David F. Weeks, both institutional superintendents. Finally, Prescott F. Hall and Robert DeC. Ward, leaders of the Immigration Restriction League and classmates of Davenport at Harvard, assumed control of a committee on immigration.[14] Through the committees Davenport provided a remarkable stimulus for research in human genetics, and placed himself in a position of leadership.

Davenport aspired to make Cold Spring Harbor a center for the growing interest in eugenics and hoped some great philanthropist might see the value that lay in such a goal. "Vastly more effective than ten million dollars to 'charity' would be ten million dollars to eugenics," he told the American Breeders' Association. "He who, by such a gift, should redeem mankind from vice, imbecility and suffering would be the world's wisest philanthropist." [15]

Unwilling to wait for philanthropists to come to him, Davenport approached Mrs. E. H. Harriman and converted her to the cause. ("She often said," Davenport later explained, "the fact that she was brought up among well-bred race horses helped her to appreciate the importance of a project to study heredity and good breeding in man.") In the spring of 1910, Mrs. Harriman purchased eighty acres of land on a hill above Cold Spring Harbor near the Station for Experimental Evolution, and there, under the Committee on Eugenics, the Eugenics Record Office began operations on the first of October. Davenport was resident director, while Harry H. Laughlin, a Princeton graduate and a teacher of agricultural breeding at a Missouri normal school, became superintendent.[16]

The Eugenics Record Office developed rapidly as a center for the American eugenics movement. A summer school, established the first year and continued through 1924, trained a total of 258 eager young men and (mostly) women to be eugenics field workers. The students learned the principles of heredity from Davenport himself, studied methods of collecting family histories, and took field trips to visit outstanding defective families of the Jukes sort and to see at firsthand inmates in asylums for the feebleminded, epileptic, and insane. Some of the field workers remained with the Eugenics Record Office; others were sent out to asylums and reformatories, where they gathered family histories of the inmates. Through its field workers the Record Office influenced countless surveys and studies of the role of heredity in man.

The Office, too, urged private individuals to prepare and submit their family histories.[17] For young people facing marriage and for others with personal heredity problems, the Office offered heredity counseling—thus anticipating by thirty years the heredity counseling clinics in operation today. At the Eugenics Record Office the data collected from field workers and private individuals were assembled, catalogued, and filed. The materials were the basis for numerous monographs by Davenport and others on the heredity of man. Finally, the Eugenics Record Office, for purposes of education and propaganda, had an extension division that provided a lecturer to speak before women's clubs, churches, and fraternal societies.[18]

Mrs. Harriman was the chief source of funds—and she was something more: a friend and confidante for Davenport in his crusade for eugenics. By 1918 she had given $246,832.82 to the enterprise. Desiring to place the Office on a permanent basis, she offered the buildings and grounds, plus $300,000 endowment, if the Carnegie Institution would assume control. In 1918 the Institution accepted the offer, and three years later consolidated the Eugenics Record Office and the Station for Experimental Evolution into a single Department of Genetics under Davenport's direction.[19]

Davenport, then, was a pioneer in the study of human genetics, and he had the facilities and support to create a world center for painstaking and important investigations in the heredity of man. That he did not do so was a tragedy resulting largely from his own scientific methods and temperament.

## Research

Among geneticists, during the first two decades of the twentieth century, there was a generally uncritical approach in the application of Mendelian genetics to man—a tendency to draw conclusions from unusual and striking pedigrees, a certain naïveté in assuming that most traits, both mental and physical, probably had a simple Mendelian explanation, and an easy faith that led them, through lack of critical statistical controls, to find Mendelian ratios where none existed. At first Davenport was out of step chiefly in the enthusiasm with which he fell into common errors, but as other geneticists generally grew more critical, his uncritical approach seemed farther and farther out of place, until eventually he had drifted away from the mainstream of American genetic research. As a result, despite his thirty-five years of investigations into human heredity, his name was linked to almost no studies that proved to be of permanent value.

No doubt Davenport's failure derived largely from the fact that he had the temperament of a reformer and the social philosophy of an extreme conservative. Because of his temperament, he saw in eugenics a cause that could bring much good to man and often urged action before the evidence was in. Because of his philosophy, he sought in eugenics confirmation for his conviction that man was bound by heredity and could be little affected by religion, education, or reform.[20] In public and private, he belittled reform and reformers. Before a group of psychiatrists he told the story of a man who found a bitter gourd and carefully watered it and tended it to make it delicious. "This man was a trustee of an insane asylum," he concluded. "Nobody else, I feel sure would spend so much time in trying to improve the characteristics of an organism without knowing anything at all about its origin and hereditary potentialities." To him, even poverty meant innate incapacity of the individual and, for this reason, Davenport advised the National Conference of Charities and Correction that social reform was futile; "the only way to secure innate capacity is by breeding it." [21]

Because he believed that man was what his genes had made him, Davenport assumed that nearly any trait of man that could be named could be traced directly to a gene. The handy *Trait Book*, given to the eugenics field workers to guide them in recording important hereditary characteristics in family pedigrees, listed everything from eye color, feeblemindedness, and insanity to personality traits like inadventuresomeness, unconversationableness, matter-of-factness, occupational interests, and reading habits.[22] Davenport not only assumed such traits to be hereditary, but for him heredity usually meant simple Mendelism. A single test was often enough for him to determine whether a trait was dominant or recessive: if a trait generally did not skip a generation, it was dominant, while if it often skipped a generation, it was recessive. He then pooled the offspring from several matings to determine whether the offspring

conformed to expected Mendelian ratios. All too often, his treatment showed carelessness or what appeared to be outright manipu-
lation.

So convinced was Davenport of the power of heredity that he attempted to explain human personality in simple Mendelian terms.
In his widely quoted book, *Heredity in Relation to Eugenics,* published in 1911 and gratefully dedicated to Mrs. Harriman, he explained that mechanical skill, artistic and musical ability, shiftless-
ness, and bodily energy were simple recessive traits.[23] As data poured
in to the Eugenics Record Office, he studied in some detail personality traits involved in antisocial and criminal behavior. Nomadism
(the wandering impulse) was clearly a hereditary trait, Davenport
felt, because such racial groups as Comanches, Gypsies, and Huns
were nomadic. He searched pedigrees for examples of nomadism:
tramps and vagabonds, traveling salesmen, railroad workers, and
boys who played truant or ran away. Since the trait showed mostly
in men, he concluded that it must be sex-linked and recessive, passing from mothers to half of their sons. In other pedigrees he studied
violent temper and deduced: "The fact that the tendency to out-
bursts of temper does not skip a generation indicates that it is a
positive or dominant trait." In an investigation of the Nam family—
a family group similar to the Jukes—Davenport decided that lazi-
ness was dominant, love of alcohol and shyness recessive, and licen-
tiousness strongly hereditary, although the Mendelian inheritance
was not clear.[24] He argued that the clustering of various of these
antisocial traits in a single family could explain the existence of subnormal and criminal family groups. Such studies represented the
extent to which Davenport would apply Mendelian laws to man.

## Insanity and Feeblemindedness

The traditional view of mental disease, hallowed by the endorsement of the major psychiatrists of the nineteenth century, was that
different mental abnormalities were varying manifestations of a general inherited weakness. A form of insanity in one generation might
be followed by feeblemindedness, criminality, alcoholism, tuberculosis, or eccentricity in succeeding generations. By the twentieth
century, however, there began to be a recognition that these conditions involved a wide variety of biological patterns, little if at all
related, and that their heredity should be studied separately.

For one thing, Emil Kraepelin, the great German psychiatrist, formulated a new diagnostic terminology for mental illnesses, basing his terminology upon the entire course of the disease and not upon prominent symptoms that might be present upon a patient's admission to an institution. Among the many disease entities, he distinguished and named the common functional psychoses: manic-depressive psychosis and dementia praecox (later often called schizophrenia). Paranoia, often regarded as a form of schizophrenia, had already been identified. In the 1890's Kraepelin's terminology was introduced into the United States by Adolf Meyer and became the basis for the terminology still in use.[25] Psychiatrists, during the same period, were achieving victories in differentiating various organic mental diseases. The Wassermann test confirmed the long suspicion that general paresis was syphilis of the brain; cretinism was traced to an endocrine disorder; other mental illnesses were found to result from arteriosclerosis, tumors, and birth trauma.[26]

At the same time, various studies, especially in Europe, indicated that descendants or siblings of a person with a functional psychosis were likely to have the same psychosis if they also became mentally ill. In other words, relatives of a manic-depressive, if they also suffered from mental disease, were very likely also to be manic-depressive even though schizophrenia was a more common disease. Such findings suggested that the psychoses were not varying manifestations of inherited weakness but rather separate biological entities with differing genetic bases.[27]

Unfortunately the studies of human heredity done under Davenport's friendly guidance tended to continue the old theory under Mendelian auspices. All sorts of mental diseases, quirks, and eccentricities were lumped together and traced to the action of a single gene, despite the fact that the conditions were biologically unrelated or not biological conditions at all.[28]

In the field of insanity, the research of Dr. Aaron J. Rosanoff, working with eugenics field workers and using Davenport's advice, was the most important. Rosanoff assumed that there existed a "neuropathic make-up." This catchall, although it excluded those insanities due to syphilis, tumors, or other causes not necessarily hereditary, did include various types of feeblemindedness, epilepsy, eccentricity, psychoses and neuroses of all sorts, and even persons labeled "easy going, is somewhat odd" or "religious recluse, nun in convent." [29] The neuropathic make-up consisted of such a splendid variety of traits that the field workers had no difficulty in assembling long and impressive pedigree charts. By molding the charts to the demands of Mendel's laws, Rosanoff concluded that the neuropathic make-up was definitely a simple recessive trait.[30]

Investigation of hereditary feeblemindedness centered at the Training School at Vineland, New Jersey, under the direction of Henry H. Goddard. In 1910, the year Davenport established the Eugenics Record Office, Goddard already had field workers traveling through New Jersey to search out and record the family histories of the children at Vineland. After contact with Davenport, he soon began to test the Mendelian inheritance of feeblemindedness and, with the publication of *Feeblemindedness, Its Causes and Consequences* in 1914, marshaled his evidence that most feeblemindedness was a simple recessive trait. (That meant that two feebleminded parents would have only feebleminded children.) Of the 300 cases for which he had information, he felt that 19 per cent were environmental, caused by injury before or during birth, by diseases such as spinal meningitis, or by falls and blows to the head. For another 2.6 per cent he could find no cause whatsoever. The remaining cases, which included all ranges of intellect and many types of bodily development, he regarded as hereditary. His book was packed with hundreds of pedigrees and his proof buttressed by pooling over 1,500 offspring to demonstrate Mendelian ratios.[31]

While such studies made a strong impact, they also met the criticism they deserved. Abraham Myerson summarized many of the criticisms of Davenport and his coworkers when he declared: "Their efforts seem to me to be directed not so much to discover the laws of the transmission of insanity as to fit the facts to Mendelian theory." [32] He attacked especially the tendency to find a common genetic basis for all sorts of traits of widely differing biological bases. Others pointed out that environment played an important part in such traits as nomadism or insanity and that a peculiar sort of naïveté was necessary to assume that the presence of such a trait proved the presence of a gene as its cause. Still others objected to the method of collecting pedigrees, for the field workers recorded simply the presence or absence of a trait. Yet human intelligence, for instance, ranges from idiocy to genius, and only by arbitrarily dividing mankind into normal and feebleminded could a simple Mendelian explanation be found. By requiring the field workers to record the presence or absence of traits, Davenport, Goddard, and others were, in effect, already assuming the Mendelian inheritance which they were purportedly attempting to prove.[33]

In England several members of the Eugenics Education Society seized upon the American work as definitive guides to eugenic policy and taunted Pearson's Laboratory of National Eugenics for failure to make equally startling discoveries. Pearson, on the other hand, considered the American Mendelian studies absurd as science and a danger to the growth of eugenics. His fellow worker, David Heron, prepared a bitter criticism in which he not only attacked the methods but showed how Davenport and other Americans had manipulated their data to reach their conclusions. Unfortunately the criticism had little influence on Davenport, for he did not take criticism well.[34]

While many of Davenport's specific findings faced criticism, they were part and parcel of an intense interest in heredity that ushered in the eugenics movement after 1910.

Very few accepted Davenport's conclusion that personality traits followed simple Mendelian laws, but deeply ingrained in the eugenics faith was a conviction that man's intelligence, personality, and morality were directly controlled by heredity. Early eugenists were convinced that, through selective breeding, man could produce progeny who were musically or scientifically talented, moral or licentious, conservative or radical, wise and farsighted or frivolous and obtuse. Davenport believed eugenics could breed an ideal president or general and pointed to the Barrymores as the natural product of parents who were traveling actors. Most American eugenists accepted the Adamses, Lees, and Edwards as American families with outstanding inborn traits; the Jukes and Ishmaels as examples of the mingling of inferior genes. Such a belief fired their confidence that eugenics might remake the world.[35]

Although only a few psychiatrists accepted the hypothesis that the inheritance of insanity followed simple Mendelian ratios, most psychiatrists intensified their concern over heredity after 1910. The American Medico-Psychological Association appointed a committee on applied eugenics whose report in 1913 was greeted with enthusiasm by the assembled psychiatrists.[36] The National Committee for Mental Hygiene, first organized in 1909 and soon boasting branches in many states, placed eugenics among the methods by which it would aid in the study, prevention, and cure of the nation's mentally ill. Its executive committee numbered among its members such eugenists as Davenport, Jordan, Lewellys F. Barker, Walter E. Fernald, Irving Fisher, Elmer E. Southard, and Robert M. Yerkes.[37]

Among the students of the feebleminded, already predisposed to a hereditarian outlook, even those who took no stand on the Mendelian inheritance of feeblemindedness used Goddard's book as proof that two-thirds to four-fifths of all feeblemindedness had its origin in the germ plasm. After 1910 the use of mental tests for diagnosis, combined with investigations of depraved and feeble-minded families, created a widespread myth of the menace of the feebleminded. A major goal of the eugenics movement was to control the menace and thus save the nation from its burden of defective genes.

## Organization

From the activities centering at the Eugenics Record Office, the eugenics movement spread in many forms across the nation. Nearly every college and university had one or more professors inspired by the new creed. Some colleges established special courses in eugenics, but primarily eugenics entered the curriculum through courses in biology, genetics, sociology, or psychology. By 1914 Harvard, Columbia, Cornell, Brown, Wisconsin, Northwestern, Clark, and Utah Agricultural College offered courses devoted in whole or in large part to eugenics. In 1912-13 Roswell H. Johnson, who had been a student of Davenport's at Harvard and later did research for a while at Cold Spring Harbor, began a course on eugenics at the University of Pittsburgh. At the Massachusetts Institute of Technology Frederick Adams Woods lectured on eugenics. A number of texts for college courses appeared. In 1911 William E. Kellicott, professor of biology at Goucher College, published *The Social Direction of Evolution: An Outline of the Science of Eugenics,* and in 1916 Michael F. Guyer, zoologist at the University of Wisconsin, brought out his popular *Being Well-Born: An Introduction to Eugenics.* Two years later Roswell Johnson and Paul Popenoe collaborated on *Applied Eugenics,* the best comprehensive treatment published in the early years of eugenics.[38]

In the popular lecturer and writer, Albert E. Wiggam, eugenics found one of its most effective publicists. During 1917 alone, he gave eighty-six speeches about eugenics on the Chautauqua circuit. With him he carried family record blanks from the Eugenics Record Office and thereby helped the Office to build its file of pedigrees. He also told of the heredity counseling available from the Record Office, with the result that by 1924 the Record Office had to stop the service because the load had become so great. In the 1920's, in addition to his lectures, Wiggam wrote numerous popular books and articles on science in general and eugenics in particular.[39]

After 1910 eugenics societies sprang up across the country, usually with professors prominent among the officers and members. There was a Eugenics Education Society of Chicago, a St. Louis Eugenics Education Society, a Eugenics Society in Madison, Wisconsin, a Minnesota Eugenics Society, a Eugenics Society in Utah, and a section on eugenics of the Commonwealth Club in San Francisco. In Battle Creek, Michigan, Dr. John H. Kellogg, influenced by Davenport and Irving Fisher, founded and endowed the Race Betterment Foundation. The Foundation held highly publicized Race Betterment Conferences in 1913, 1914, and again in 1928, where prominent men from many fields of study reported on heredity and other phases of public health and hygiene. Besides such organizations for propaganda, many scientific societies, too numerous to list, had committees on heredity and eugenics.[40]

The most important local organization was the Galton Society of New York, of which Davenport was founder and first president. Its prestige arose from the eminence of the men who gathered at its luncheons and dinners to hear papers and discuss the problems of race and heredity. Among the members were Henry F. Osborn, the distinguished paleontologist of the American Museum of Natural History; Madison Grant, the nation's most influential racist; Lothrop Stoddard, the second most influential racist; Edward G. Conklin, Princeton biologist; Ellsworth Huntington, a Yale geographer; Edward L. Thorndike, the Columbia University psychologist; and such other prominent scientists as John C. Merriam, F. A. Woods, E. A. Hooton, and Raymond Pearl. These distinguished men served as leaders and guides within the eugenics movement.[41]

The Eugenics Research Association, begun in 1913 as a conference where eugenics field workers and others active in the study of human heredity could share their problems and discoveries, was the most important organization to unite eugenists nationally. In 1916 Davenport and Laughlin began a monthly *Eugenical News* as a clearinghouse for the activities of the Eugenics Record Office and as the official organ for the Eugenics Research Association. Eminent men in many fields, united by their interest in heredity, became members of the Eugenics Research Association and participated in its annual conferences at Cold Spring Harbor, so that it became the chief organization for encouraging and coordinating the study of human genetics in America.[42]

Davenport and his friends also provided the chief link between the American movement and world eugenics. The American consultative committee for the First International Eugenics Congress, held in London in 1912, consisted of Davenport and such familiar names as Bell, Castle, Henderson, Meyer, Woods, Aleš Hrdlička, and Vernon L. Kellogg. When a second Congress was scheduled for New York City in the fall of 1915, Davenport served on the executive committee that planned the meeting. He helped persuade Bell, whose world-wide fame and long white beard would lend prestige, to be honorary president, and Henry F. Osborn to serve as president. When the war forced cancellation of the Congress, a new committee, with Davenport as chairman, laid plans for a Congress in New York in the fall of 1921.[43]

Out of the Second International Congress arose an International Committee on Eugenics, with representatives from each nation, that met annually in Europe to discuss eugenics problems and arrange for the next International Congress. Usually Davenport or one of his friends represented the United States at these meetings.[44]

Out of the Congress, too, came the formation of an Ad Interim Committee to guide and promote American propaganda for eugenics. The chairman was Irving Fisher, a conservative Yale economist with an interest in public health and prohibition, whose contact with Davenport had created a great enthusiasm for eugenics. (In 1913, after a visit to Cold Spring Harbor, he wrote Davenport: "I almost wish I were doing the very kind of work you are doing there; for it is surely the greatest work in the world today. It will be a great satisfaction even to push at the tail of the cart.") Nearly all of the important American eugenists were on the Committee, but because its interests were more in propaganda than in research, Fisher rather than Davenport was its guiding genius. In a series of tortuous moves, the Ad Interim Committee became the Eugenics Committee of the United States of America in 1922, which in turn began in 1923 to organize the Eugenics Society of the United States of America, a name shortened in 1925 to the American Eugenics Society. This Society was then, and remains still, the most important center for eugenics education in this country.[45]

All of these activities represented efforts to spread the eugenics creed in general form. More important still were the societies and individuals who were devoted to specific eugenic goals and reforms —those laboring for segregation of the feebleminded, for sexual sterilization of the unfit, for birth control, or for restriction of immigration. When such activities were added to the general propaganda for eugenics, the total amount of organizing, educating, publishing, propagandizing, and lobbying for eugenics in the two decades after 1910 was considerable indeed.

All in all, Davenport's place in the eugenics movement is difficult to assess, for he was a strange mixture of scientist and advertiser. As an organizer, he led the movement. He it was who founded the Eugenics Record Office, encouraged others to unravel the threads of human heredity, and spurred the formation of societies and committees to spread the eugenics creed. As a scientist, however, his influence was less happy, for the eventual repudiation of his research by other scientists often brought repudiation of the movement of which it was a part. In addition, his extreme hereditarian bias led him to draw into leadership men who shared his biases but often lacked his scientific interest. Thus he contributed not only to the rapid spread of interest in eugenics but also to a type of eugenics that was often extreme in its emphasis upon race and heredity. Perhaps it was inevitable that the eugenics movement was largely the creation of true believers—men convinced that only in eugenics lay the road to human progress.

# Chapter VI
# Eugenics Orthodoxy

Eugenics in its early years exerted a broad influence upon American thought as a sort of scientific reform among the many other reforms of the Progressive Era. Like other reform currents, it arose from a generation of research into the causes of the social ills that beset the nation. Like them, its appeal was often felt by those who prided themselves in keeping abreast of recent developments in the study of social problems. As Charles R. Van Hise, president of the University of Wisconsin and a leader among conservationists, put it:

> We know enough about agriculture so that the agricultural production of the country could be doubled if the knowledge were applied; we know enough about disease so that if the knowledge were utilized, infectious and contagious diseases would be substantially destroyed in the United States within a score of years; we know enough about eugenics so that if the knowledge were applied, the defective classes would disappear within a generation.[1]

Eugenics played a part in shaping the movement for peace, prohibition, and birth control. It influenced the actions of those who labored in behalf of programs for the care of the nation's paupers, delinquents, insane, and feebleminded and the prevention of conditions that produced these unfortunates. Naturally, many attacked the assumptions or specific programs of eugenics, as, indeed, they did other reforms. But an era searching for the causes of human ills, emphasizing the care of the unfortunate, intent upon using government to improve the present and future generations, could not very well reject the offerings of eugenics—especially considering the eminence of those who sponsored it.

The period of reform that preceded World War I was, in fact, remarkably diverse and in many ways quite pragmatic. Eugenics had appeal because it was a "scientific" reform. Its emphasis upon heredity was not out of keeping with the attitudes of many of the middle-class American who took part in the reforming impulse. Indeed, it helped them to explain the disappointing incorrigibility of many delinquents and paupers and the incurability of many of the insane; the failure of such persons to respond to environmental reforms was taken as evidence that their problem was hereditary. Thus many reformers saw no inconsistency in working one day on a committee that campaigned for tenement house reform and another day on a committee that worked for sexual sterilization. Both provided avenues toward the improvement of American society.

Within the reform movement, those most strongly influenced by hereditarian doctrines were such persons as physicians, psychiatrists, social workers, members of state boards of charity, and others whose direct responsibility was with persons who, through crime or illness, became wards of the state for care and cure. Those least influenced were residents of settlement houses, sympathizers with labor organizations, and others who were primarily concerned with the general problems arising from industrialization and urbanization. Nor should it be thought that only reformers were hereditarian. Educated men of both liberal and conservative temperaments were far more conscious of race and heredity in the early twentieth century than are their counterparts today.

## The Eugenics Creed

Eugenists soon presented a comprehensive dogma to explain man's past and prescribe policies for his future. In their own jargon, they divided social reform into two parts: "eugenics" (the improvement of man's innate capacity) and "euthenics" (the reform of man's environment). Eugenists commonly asserted that eugenics and euthenics should work together for the betterment of man but often added that eugenics, because it resulted in a permanent improvement of the human race, was the fundamental reform. Eugenics itself had two sides: "positive eugenics" and "negative eugenics." The purpose of negative eugenics was to prevent propagation by the "cacogenic," those likely to have defective or undesirable offspring, while the purpose of positive eugenics was to increase propagation among the "aristogenic," who carried outstanding qualities in their genes. Hence the overwhelming concern of eugenists was with the birth rates of various groups, classes, and races of the population, for these birth rates determined the hereditary qualities of succeeding generations.

In man's history, many eugenists saw race and heredity—the birth rates of the fit and unfit—as the forces that shaped political and social developments. The mysterious fall of Rome, for instance, was not so mysterious when one examined the genes of its citizens. Those concerned with social class could argue that Rome declined when its best citizens went off to war and left its worst behind to beget succeeding generations. Those concerned with race, on the other hand, stressed that Rome was inundated by immigrants and slaves from the many corners of the empire; what lay behind the economic and social decline was "the fact that the people who built Rome had given way to a different race." In either case, the decline of Rome resulted from the poorer hereditary quality of its people.[2]

The qualities of the genes, according to the early eugenists, revealed themselves in subsequent history. The middle ages were dark because the most intelligent and holy lived as celibate priests and the most creative were killed off by wars and religious persecution. Spain fell from its days of glory because the nation scattered its most vigorous stock in the new world (where, unfortunately, it was of little help since it was diluted by mixture with inferior races). Even the United States showed the varying effects of good and bad stock. New England's Puritans, endowed with stern consciences and a love of learning, carried such traits with them as they spread west and stamped the character of the nation, while Cavaliers of Virginia produced the great statesmen who molded the nation's institutions. The colonial criminals and indentured servants, on the other hand, peopled the hills of Tennessee and Kentucky and produced the Ishmaels of Indiana.[3]

Pursuing such analysis to its extreme, Frederick Adams Woods, a lecturer in biology at the Massachusetts Institute of Technology and a confirmed and conservative follower of Galton, worked out a hereditarian philosophy of history that showed history to be "really but a branch of biology." With incredible naïveté, he presented detailed proof that members of the royal families of Europe were chiefly what their heredity made them. He further showed that, in nation after nation, the political and economic development reflected the character of the ruling monarch. Obviously, if the genes determined the monarch and the monarch determined history, then "the master key of history is heredity." He drew the natural lesson that in all societies the most important resource was the genes of the few leading families.[4]

In the American birth rate of their day, eugenists saw every reason for alarm. An undoubted fact was that the over-all birth rate in America, as in most of the western world, had declined precipitously during the nineteenth century. According to census figures, there had in 1800 been 976 children under five years of age for every one thousand women of childbearing age, but a century later the number had fallen to 508.[5] Many Americans grew alarmed over the falling birth rate, dubbed it race suicide, and feared that the nation faced a dangerous loss of power.[6] In the 1890's Theodore Roosevelt was already lecturing his fellow Americans that, if a people permitted a low birth rate, "then that race is not only fated to extinction but it deserves extinction." "A race is worthless and contemptible," he inveighed, "if its men cease to be willing and able to work hard and, at need, to fight hard, and if its women cease to breed freely."[7] Roosevelt's strident warnings found sympathetic response from many Americans.

To eugenists, however, Roosevelt's statements were adolescent rantings.[8] The issue was not quantity of offspring but quality. And the declining birth rate, they argued, was dangerous because it seemed most marked among the educated and well to do. Hence eugenists argued that those of least genetic worth produced the most children and those of greatest genetic worth produced the fewest. Yet eugenists had, in fact, few figures to prove that the birth rate was as calamitous as they feared (and almost no evidence that classes differed significantly in genetic endowment).

Assuming that native stock was better than immigrant stock, eugenists confirmed their fears with evidence of the falling birth rate of the native stock. They noted that the average American mother before 1700 probably bore as many as 7.37 children, but her descendant in the decade after 1870 bore only 2.77 children. "Unless a radical change is effected very soon," they warned, "the stock that founded this nation and which nurtured it through the grave perils and trials of the formative period, will soon have vanished from the face of the earth."[9] More convincing evidence, however, lay in a declining birth rate of college graduates in the nineteenth century, so that early in the twentieth century college graduates were no longer replacing themselves. Every four Harvard and Yale men raised up but three sons as replacements. Little more than one-half the graduates of women's colleges even married at all.[10] In addition, in a study of American scientists, J. McKeen Cattell found that they averaged only seven-tenths of a son apiece to transmit their names and abilities.[11] Eugenists blamed the declining birth rates not on biological infertility but on purposeful restriction in the number of offspring from a desire for a life of greater ease and freedom. The figures boded ill for the future of America and showed that a major mission of eugenics would be to educate the better stocks in their duty to race and nation.[12]

Naturally such an exaltation of good stock meant a surplus of ancestor worship within the eugenics movement. Many eugenists were only too smugly aware of the Puritan forebears and outstanding men adorning their own family trees. David Starr Jordan praised patriotic societies and agreed with their assumption, "well justified by facts, . . . that revolutionary fathers were a superior breed of men, and that to have had such names in our personal ancestry is of itself a cause for thinking more highly of ourselves." [13] (He had such names in his personal ancestry.) Many eugenists took a scientific interest in those families that had contributed through the years to make the nation great—the Edwards and Dwight families of scholars and college presidents; the Lees of Virginia for military leadership; Adams, Lowell, and Randolph for statesmanship; Agassiz for science; Astor and Morgan for business and finance.[14] Just as Galton had "proved" that genius in England and Europe was hereditary, so Frederick Adams Woods showed, by a study of the Hall of Fame, that American genius ran in families.[15]

Eugenists foresaw national degeneration not only from the falling birth rate of the talented few but also from what they believed was the growing incidence of feeblemindedness, insanity, crime, and pauperism. The statistical evidence, however, was far from certain. Superficially, the problem was simple. The census returns, which recorded the numbers in institutions and asylums, showed a steady and often rapid increase in proportion to the population as a whole. Since the states were building and expanding their prisons, hospitals, and asylums, however, the census returns provided no answer to the question: To what extent, if at all, did the increase in institutional population indicate a real increase in crime and mental disease? While the question was simple, the detailed and ingenious statistical interpretations were neither simple nor conclusive.[16]

Eugenists, along with many other Americans, nevertheless were generally convinced that the nation faced a rising tide of crime and mental disease. Indeed, with the growing complexity of modern civilization and the large numbers of children spawned by the "worthless" classes of society, what could be more logical? Increase or no increase, the development of state asylums and hospitals and the growth of professions to deal with the defective and delinquent brought home as never before the enormity of the problem and the cost of treatment. Viewing the direction of the nation's birth rate, the President of the University of Arizona could draw no other conclusion but that one must be "an optimist indeed who can see in our trend toward race degeneracy . . . anything other than a plight in which the race must find its final destiny in trained imbecility." [17]

Several eugenists toyed with possible government schemes to reverse the trend of the birth rates by granting financial advantages to couples with children and thus encourage the prudent and farsighted to breed more freely.[18] But most agreed that there was no effective way, in a democratic society, to make the fit reproduce at a faster rate except through the slow process of education. Alexander Graham Bell stated the problem succinctly, if a bit pretentiously: "The individuals have power to improve the race, but not the knowledge of what to do. We students of genetics possess the knowledge but not the power; and the great hope lies in the dissemination of our knowledge among the people at large." Young people had to be taught the importance of heredity so that they would choose their mates from good stock and would have instilled in them a desire to rear up children for the good of the nation.[19]

The education of citizens in their duties as parents was in line with Roosevelt's call for larger American families, and by 1910 he had framed his plea to bring it into line with eugenics (even admitting that criminals should be sterilized). In private he wrote Davenport, "Some day we will realize that the prime duty, the inescapable duty, of the *good* citizen of the right type is to leave his or her blood behind him in the world; and that we have no business to permit the perpetuation of citizens of the wrong type." And in public he affirmed, "The great problem of civilization is to secure a relative increase of the valuable as compared with the less valuable or noxious elements in the population. This problem cannot be met unless we give full consideration to the immense influence of heredity." [20] But demands that good stock must breed, even when made by a vigorous and popular ex-President, could not bring it about.

Considering the impossibility that eugenists in America would ever be granted an opportunity to arrange marriages among young people, they devoted considerable attention to the moral and scientific justification of a positive breeding program. Most troubling was the criticism that mankind needed variety and that eugenics was a class movement to breed chiefly the upper classes. Whatever truth may have lain in the charge, most eugenists repeated Galton's answer that eugenics would accept the best from all classes. Other critics claimed that eugenics would prevent the breeding of geniuses (like Alexander Pope or Lord Byron) who were from degenerate stock or were themselves physically defective, or they charged that eugenics would breed monstrosities, men who were all body but no brains or men who were all brains but no morals.[21] Such criticisms, eugenists felt, arose from a failure to understand that generally good qualities were correlated, that sound health, a fine mind, emotional stability, and excellent morals tended to occur in the same persons. It was this that inspired in eugenists a faith that their creed could greatly improve the nature of man.[22]

## Doubts and Doubters

The rapid growth of eugenics provoked moral and scientific objections from several persons disturbed by the deterministic and pessimistic implications of much of the eugenics creed. The religious view that man's personality could be regenerated by conversion and the course of his life changed through training and prayer was not easily reconciled with the view of some eugenists that personality and morality were expressions of ancestral genes. One lady of a religious turn of mind expressed her objections in a poem entitled "Eugenics," describing a youth as he gazed at his family pedigree:

> The chart before him lay, wherein to see—
> Defeat and failure as his ancestry,
> Weakness and pain as his heredity.
> He bowed his head in bitter agony
> Feeling himself unworthy utterly.
> Then light, through black despair,
> Shone piercingly.
> "They have forgot my brother," whispered he,
> "Jesus, Who died for others on the tree,
> and my great father God, who strengthens me." [23]

Just such feelings kept countless Americans from responding to the doctrines of eugenics.

To a general religious distrust of eugenics, the Catholic Church added theological objections of far-reaching significance. Because the Church condemned as sinful such practices as contraception and sexual sterilization, many church leaders feared the consequences of eugenics and rejected entirely its biological judgments. The possibility or even probability that a child would be born hereditarily defective or deformed, according to Catholic doctrine, was no excuse for state interference with the right to marry or to bear children. The Church looked on a child not as a physical organism but as a soul sent from God;

> she counts the earthly existence of a helpless cripple, a chronic invalid, or a mental weakling intrinsically good, and she knows that all such persons are capable of a life of eternal happiness face to face with God. Consequently her viewpoint is infinitely removed from that of those practical atheists who measure the worth of a subnormal person by the same standard that they apply to a dog or a horse.[24]

Because eugenics was nearly irreconcilable with Catholic teaching, many Catholic clergy and laymen entered the lists against it. A prominent Catholic physician of Philadelphia, in fact, went so far as to claim that it was "doubtful whether physical defects, disease, and degeneracy can, in a biological sense, be transmitted from parent to offspring" and that the children of a chaste and loving couple were "bound to be good." [25]

Eugenists, aware that their creed met resistance in religious circles, defended the compatibility of religion and eugenics. A psychologist at the Hartford School of Religious Pedagogy, for instance, argued that salvation of the world would eventually come through development of higher types of individuals and noted that Christ himself demonstrated what eugenics might accomplish, for "He came from a stock of priestly and prophetic men." [26] Among the clergymen themselves, the more liberal and reform-minded tended to be most sympathetic with eugenics. (The Liberal Ministers Association of New York, composed of social gospel sympathizers, had a eugenics committee headed by the Rev. Dr. John Haynes Holmes, whose credentials as a reformer were above reproach.) [27] Such ministers were most likely to be aware of recent trends in the study of crime, insanity, and feeblemindedness and therefore most likely to support the programs of eugenists.

Some sociologists and psychologists, few in number but influential in their views, attacked eugenics orthodoxy on sociological grounds. Here the attacks came primarily from men who early came to fear the largely conservative uses to which the eugenic concept of human nature and society might be put.

Chief among such critics was Lester F. Ward, perhaps the most important of America's early sociologists and a man of wide learning in science as well as sociology. Ward's sociology was dedicated to a defense of social reform and a criticism of those aspects of social Darwinism that justified *laissez faire* or the *status quo*. For this reason, he feared the belief in innate class differences, since such a belief often excused inequalities between the classes and thwarted efforts to extend protection and opportunities to individuals in the poorer classes.[28]

Ward admitted that men varied widely in innate biological ability and accepted as proven Galton's contention that genius was largely inherited.[29] At the same time, he maintained that inherited ability was equally distributed among all classes and that the "lower classes of society are the intellectual equals of the upper classes." He distinguished between biological heredity and social heredity—the latter being the transmission of accumulated knowledge and technology from generation to generation—and held that in man's progress social heredity was the more important. The lower classes, he contended, did not differ from the upper classes in the distribution of native ability but only in their lack of access to the social heritage. The great aim of government, therefore, should be to extend equality of education and opportunity to all its members and classes. Ward stressed the malleability of human personality, and had confidence in education and reform as means to human progress.[30]

Hence Ward did not despair that the lower classes outbred the upper classes, for he had faith that

> so far as the native capacity, the potential quality, the "promise and potency," of a higher life are concerned, those swarming, spawning millions, the bottom layer of society, the proletariat, the working classes, the "hewers of wood and drawers of water," nay, even the denizens of the slums—that all these are by nature the peers of the boasted "aristocracy of brains" that now dominates society and looks down upon them, and the equals in all but privilege of the most enlightened teachers of eugenics.[31]

Ward's contention that eugenists overlooked the possibilities latent in the less favored classes were fully justified, but his belief that the classes were equal in ability was the faith of a democrat and reformer, a faith with no more to back it than the opposite faith of those he attacked.

Others developed further the distinction between biological and social heredity. They pointed out that man's progress, during recorded history, had not come through greater inborn ability but through the slow and painful accumulation of social organization, scientific and technological skills, and an increasingly rapid control over the environment. A pretension of eugenists to further social progress primarily through biological improvement of man resulted from a naïve and narrow understanding of human society. There was no reason to believe, such critics declared, that education and environmental reforms would not continue, as in the past, to be the major road to social progress.[32]

J. McKeen Cattell—who was, incidentally, a president of the Eugenics Research Association—stressed that a belief in heredity should not stifle efforts to extend education and opportunity. He admitted that, if innate ability determined completely what an individual could accomplish, then there was little room for social reform; but he argued that "such an extreme position, though it is approached by men with so much authority as Sir Francis Galton, Professor Karl Pearson, Dr. F. A. Woods, Dr. C. B. Davenport and Professor E. L. Thorndike, is untenable." For some time to come, extending education and opportunity would be the best means of improving civilization. "The number capable of exhibiting genius is limited, but many of them are lost through lack of opportunity. It is our business, it should be our principal business, to improve our civilization by giving opportunity to those who are fit, while at the same time investigating conditions which will give us a better race." [33]

## Fads and Movements

Despite the rapid growth of eugenics and the many respected scientists and social reformers who adhered to it, eugenists often felt unwanted and misunderstood. They complained that the press treated eugenics as a bizarre fad or a scheme for breeding people like farm animals. A particular problem was to make clear that eugenics was concerned with heredity alone and to disentangle eugenics from the myriad of other schemes, legitimate and crackpot, to produce healthier and happier children. Such varying causes as sex education, sanitation, prenatal culture, prevention of venereal disease, and pure milk for babies took the name of eugenics. In Ohio a Practical Eugenic Movement, with a membership of over 7,000, distributed a magazine on *Practical Eugenics* to discuss sex hygiene, temperance, care of babies, personal health, and the evils of tobacco. Eugenics even found adherents among astrologers who promised to plot the best times for the conception of particular types of offspring.[34]

Eugenists had special difficulty disentangling their movement from crackpot fads for sex reform. The first American periodical to bear the name of eugenics, in fact, was the *American Journal of Eugenics,* edited in 1907 by Moses Harmon, whose long white hair and shaggy beard gave him the look of an Old Testament patriarch. The journal advertised books and pamphlets on socialism, Marxism, phrenology, vegetarianism, prostitution, and sex. ("If you want literature on Eugenics, Freethought, Economics, or any other advanced subject," one advertisement read, "I would be pleased to receive your order.") Primarily the journal advocated teaching the facts of sex and contraception to produce finer offspring and to save the young from perversion, venereal disease, abortion, and the white slave trade. Many contributors suggested that monogamous marriage should be re-examined and abolished so that breeding might be eugenic and man might satisfy his need for liberty in sexual expression. After eight issues, the magazine was declared unmailable under the so-called Comstock law; and Moses Harmon abandoned publication, convinced that scientific discussion of eugenics was impossible under American law.[35]

Shortly afterward, the American Social Hygiene Association united many persons dedicated to the rapidly growing belief that sex education rather than prudery and secrecy could best prepare young persons for life. The respectability of the movement was attested by the fact that Charles W. Eliot, president emeritus of Harvard, was honorary president, and such figures as Jane Addams, R. Fulton Cutting, David Starr Jordan, Julius Rosenwald, and William Welch were honorary vice-presidents. One phase of the movement was to encourage education in the facts of heredity as part of a youth's preparation in choosing a mate and planning a family. "Eugenics," one leader explained, "will destroy that sentimentalism which leads a woman deliberately to marry a man who is absolutely unworthy of her and can only bring disease, degradation, and death." Eugenics thus became a minor part of an expanding movement for education in the facts of sex.[36]

In addition to its influence on the movement for sex education, the eugenics creed played a part in many of the reform efforts of the Progressive Era. As the nation moved toward its unfortunate ex-

periment with prohibition, for instance, the nineteenth century indictment of alcohol as a cause of hereditary defect intensified. The
indictment now took an up-to-date form, however, since vague references to inheritance of acquired characteristics were no longer scientifically respectable. The new theory, which went by the name of
blastophthoria, was that alcohol in the blood might directly damage
the germ cell in such a manner that subsequent offspring would be
hereditarily deformed.[37]

Although proponents of such a view were naturally embarrassed
by Karl Pearson's finding that children of alcoholics differed in no
important respect from children of normal parents, they argued that
the weight of scientific evidence contradicted Pearson. Several investigators found that the feebleminded often had alcoholic parents,
while from Switzerland came reports that a large proportion of
feebleminded children there were born nine months after the grape
harvest, Carnival, or some other debauch. In laboratory experiments, furthermore, some scientists found that alcoholized rats and
guinea pigs had a large proportion of defective offspring. Although
subsequent experiments have failed to confirm these findings and
geneticists now reject such views, they had wide medical and scientific support in the United States until well into the 1920's. As a
result, many a scientist agreed that "abstinence is one of the principles of human eugenics, that new science that is just being born." [38]

Eugenics in America also served the cause of peace by combat-
ting the biological arguments for war that had made a deep impression in Europe and had found some support in the United States.
Darwin's doctrine of the struggle for existence and survival of the
fittest had become a justification for a belief that war was natural,
inbred in man, and that out of the destruction of war came human
progress through survival of those nations and races which proved
themselves most fit. This philosophy of force gave biological sanction to militarism, the soldierly virtues, and the slaughter of battle.
Such a philosophy deeply pained those Americans whose dedication
was to peace.[39]

Chief among those who took issue with this brand of Darwinism
was David Starr Jordan, a distinguished educator, outstanding biologist, and respected leader in the American peace movement. While
carrying on zoological researches, he had remained a man of catholic
tastes and wide reading, an accomplished speaker, teacher, and
writer. In 1884 he became president of Indiana University, the
youngest university president in the country, and in 1891 he ac-

cepted a similar position at Stanford University to guide that university through its early struggles. Jordan was proud of his Puritan forebears and his own conscience was Puritan, although his religion was a scientific skepticism. War he found morally abhorrent. He opposed America's entrance into the Spanish-American War, joined the anti-imperialist crusade in the war's aftermath, and worked against America's entry into the First World War, for he believed that the economic interests of the East, in control of the banks and press, "promoted it for selfish purposes." [40]

Jordan framed a biological indictment of war and popularized his views in speeches, articles, and books. Far from bringing progress, he declared, war led inevitably to the deterioration of those nations that waged it. In the *Human Harvest,* dedicated to his brother who had died while a soldier in the Civil War, he argued that Rome had been a proud republic until she entered upon a policy of conquest and scattered her best blood throughout the empire. Then the sons of stableboys, slaves, and camp followers became the new citizens of Rome, and soon there came the rise of the mob and of emperors who ruled the mob. Similarly, the degeneration of Spain followed inevitably when that nation sought glory through empire and sent her most valiant men to the new world. The decline of France began in Europe when Napoleon hurled her finest manhood against the Russian army and the Russian winter, only to have them slaughtered.[41] After a study of the eugenic effect of the Civil War upon the southern states, Jordan decided America itself had not escaped the scourge. He placed the southern loss at 10 per cent of the white population and declared that, on the whole, the better stocks saw the most fighting and suffered the severest losses.[42]

Darwinism, then, was not a justification for war but an argument for peace, for war did not mean victory of some vague entity called nation or race; it meant the slaughter of individual combatants, often the choicest stock from both sides. "War's real tragedy lies not in wrecked cathedrals, filled graves, or gutted treasure boxes," Irving Fisher explained. The tragedy of war was "its waste of germ plasm." Most American eugenists, as well as many in England, agreed that prevention of war was a eugenic good.[43]

The birth control movement, launched by Margaret Sanger in 1914, was one that eugenists could not ignore. They already had reason to believe that contraception, in the late nineteenth century, played a major role in a tragic decline of birth rate among the educated and well to do. Obviously the birth control movement, by spreading knowledge of contraceptive methods to still other classes, could exert a significant influence on the birth rate of the future and therefore on the genetic quality of the future.

Davenport would have had no difficulty in tracing the personality of Margaret Sanger, *nee* Higgins, to a hereditary source. Her father, an immigrant from Ireland, had been an artist, socialist, single taxer, phrenologist, and agnostic; and Margaret in many ways followed in his footsteps. After training as a nurse and marriage to William Sanger, an artist and architect, she moved among radicals and anarchists of New York City—John Reed, William Dudley (Big Bill) Haywood, Alexander Berkman, Emma Goldman, and Rose Pastor Stokes—and in talks with them developed some of her early ideas on birth control. As a nurse, she frequently went among the poor of the slums and ministered to women who, in unbelievable poverty, brought child after child into the world. She found that the women rebelled against the repeated pregnancies that destroyed their own health and introduced unwanted children to a life of poverty and early death. Yet many a mother, in her ignorance, could only "resign herself hopelessly to the irresponsible procreation of children without number, or submit that toil-worn, exhausted, fatigue-ridden body of hers to the ministrations and clumsy mutilations of the quack abortionist." When the poor begged her for the secret by which educated women prevented pregnancy, she was unable to tell, for she did not know.[44]

When she set out to learn the methods and effects of contraception, she found in America little information to answer her questions. Since 1830 when Robert Dale Owen published his *Moral Physiology,* there had been advocates of contraception. By the late nineteenth and early twentieth century, however, the movement was largely in the hands of obscure and radical sex reformers of the Moses Harmon type. The exceptions—like Dr. Abraham Jacobi, the grand old man of American medicine and a confirmed eugenist—were few in number.[45] Margaret Sanger's quest for knowledge sent her several times to Europe, where she came in close contact with Havelock Ellis, Marie Stopes, and the British Neo-Malthusians.[46]

The birth control movement in the United States dated from 1914 when Margaret Sanger adopted the term "birth control," advocated it in a periodical entitled *The Woman Rebel,* and began distribution of her pamphlet on *Family Limitation* to give contraceptive advice. The fight she faced was not so much against the ignorance of the poor as against the laws that classed information on contraception with obscenity. The Comstock law, passed by Congress in 1873 at the urging of young Anthony Comstock and the Society for the Suppression of Vice, prohibited the mailing of contraceptive devices, or information on contraception, or information where or from whom such knowledge might be obtained. The prohibition made no exceptions for medical journals or textbooks. Twenty-four states, following the federal precedent, had obscenity laws that variously banned advocacy of contraception, imparting of contraceptive information, or possession of contraceptive devices.[47]

Nor were the laws the only source of opposition. Among physicians, the ones most directly concerned since it would fall to them to advise on contraception, birth control at first encountered indifference and sometimes hostility. Many religious persons opposed the movement because they held birth control to be immoral or feared that the spread of contraceptive knowledge would undermine the morals of youths who would no longer fear the consequences of illicit relations.

Chief and most unyielding among the opponents of birth control stood the Catholic Church. According to Catholic doctrine, the purpose of the generative faculty was the procreation of children, and when through contraception the faculty was used so that it could not attain its natural end, then the individual was guilty of sinful perversion. Neither danger to the mother's health through pregnancy nor the possible production of defective offspring were adequate excuses. In such cases the parents had open to them "chaste abstention from marital intercourse." (In the Papal encyclical of 1930, *Casti Connubii*, the Catholic opposition was confirmed.) The Church, as a result, took the lead in many states in urging enforcement of laws against contraception, in resisting amendment of the laws, and in attempting to prevent discussion of birth control. From members of the Church, too, came some of the most complete and bitter criticisms of both birth control and its advocates.[48]

The early years of the birth control movement were times of struggle and frequent defiance of the law. The Post Office suppressed *The Woman Rebel* shortly after it appeared. Later the police closed the birth control clinic that Mrs. Sanger set up in New York City, the first such clinic in the nation. She, her husband, and her sister all served time behind bars, and her sister engaged in a highly publicized hunger strike as protest against imprisonment. Gradually, however, the movement gained stability and organization. In 1915, under Mary Ware Dennett, the National Birth

Control League began its campaign, through education and lobbying, to change the laws rather than break them. After a triumphant nationwide tour by Mrs. Sanger in 1916, local Birth Control Leagues brought added support and strength. In time many Protestant leaders, physicians, scientists, and other molders of opinion rallied to the movement.[49]

Eugenists were divided in their attitude toward the movement. Some, like Davenport, had a deep distrust for both birth control and its advocates, and had little desire to link their scientific movement with the radicalism and sensationalism of birth control. "If it is desirable for us to make a campaign in favor of contraception," Paul Popenoe confided to Madison Grant, "we are abundantly able to do so on our own account, without enrolling a lot of sob sisters, grandstand players, and anarchists to help us." [50] Besides, eugenists were already troubled because birth control was practiced most by those who should practice it least. And many feared that the spread of birth control information would only compound the evil by causing the more intelligent members of the artisan and laboring classes to join the educated classes in a low birth rate. In a face-to-face encounter with Davenport in 1925, Mrs. Sanger was unable to shake his belief that birth control was a eugenic danger. (In her autobiography she described him as follows: "Professor Davenport used to lift his eyes reverently and, with his hands upraised as though in supplication, quiver emotionally as he breathed, 'Protoplasm. We want more protoplasm' "—showing that her imagination was a good deal stronger than her grasp of genetics.) [51] Many eugenists continued to believe that the real need was to persuade the better stocks to have more children, not to encourage additional industrious and farsighted parents to have fewer.[52]

More typical of eugenics sentiment, however, were those prominent eugenists who enrolled in the birth control movement because they saw in it possibilities for eugenic good. When Margaret Sanger called the First American Birth Control Conference in 1921 in New York, with the purpose of making birth control scientific and respectable, such respected and scientific eugenists as Adolf Meyer, Aaron J. Rosanoff, Roswell H. Johnson, and Clarence C. Little participated. (Indeed, Little, a Harvard man who had served for a short time as assistant director under Davenport at Cold Spring Harbor before becoming president of the University of Maine and then of the University of Michigan, directed the American Birth Control League after 1925.) Other eugenists who supported the movement in the 1920's included Edward A. Ross, Lothrop Stoddard, Leon J. Cole, University of Wisconsin geneticist, Edward M. East, a Harvard geneticist, and Raymond Pearl, who had once studied with Pearson in England and became professor of biometry and vital statistics at Johns Hopkins. Although several of these men were interested in birth control primarily as a weapon to combat a danger of world overpopulation, by the early 1920's they had given birth control a decided eugenic coloring.[53]

At the 1921 Conference and again at the 1925 International Birth Control Conference in New York City, Roswell H. Johnson, one of the eugenists most active in the birth control movement, secured adoption of eugenics resolutions in order to reassure those eugenists who felt alienated from the movement.[54] At the same time, Margaret Sanger began increasingly to speak like an orthodox eugenist. From the beginning she had urged birth control for those with presumed hereditary ailments like insanity and epilepsy. By the 1920's she advocated sterilization for the unfit, pointed to the Jukes as the sort of tragedy that birth control might halt, and stated that "it is a curious but neglected fact that the very types which in all kindness should be obliterated from the human stock, have been permitted to reproduce themselves and to perpetuate their group, succored by the policy of indiscriminate charity of warm hearts uncontrolled by cool heads." [55]

Birth control and eugenics, then, were two closely related movements. Birth control advocates used eugenics as a source of arguments and as a method of attracting scientific support; eugenists, on the other hand, became aware that in birth control they had a weapon with which to manipulate the birth rate for eugenic purposes.

## Impact

While such movements as sex education, peace, prohibition, and birth control reveal the wide influence of eugenics upon American thought, they were but sidelines to the major eugenics activities. Chiefly eugenics made its mark through the influence of three different but somewhat overlapping groups. First were the psychiatrists, psychologists, and social reformers interested primarily in the prevention of crime, mental illness, and disease. They provided the principal eugenics impulse, which grew out of the nineteenth century concern with hereditary defect, and resulted in an intensive campaign for custodial care and sterilization of the unfit. For many of them, their involvement in eugenics was but one of many activities for civic betterment in which they engaged.

A second group consisted of those alarmed by the new immigration that poured into the nation as the new century opened. Mostly old stock Americans, proud of their heritage and heredity, such racists feared that the new immigrants lacked the biological endowment to adopt to American culture and democracy. Because their concern was with America's genetic future, they found support for their program in the assumptions of the eugenics creed.

Finally, a third group, represented primarily in the nation's universities, were principally interested in research into human genetics. Although they often described the implications of their research for social action, they did not always enter the fray directly.

Among eugenists there were not only differences in interest but also in sense of urgency. Some spokesman for the early eugenics movement accepted the eugenics creed in its entirety, and demanded an immediate program of eugenics to avert a crisis. Often, upon biological bases, they built a social philosophy that was largely elitist and reactionary. They emphasized the role of a few distinguished families in providing the leadership of American society and they regretted that most of their fellow citizens derived from stock innately unable to manipulate ideas or to manage their affairs with industry and prudence. Their philosophy was steeped in pessimism. The fact that the lower classes outbred the upper classes and the inferior races outbred the nobler races could mean only that civilization would crumble and fall as mankind moved toward intellectual and moral imbecility. Such views were a logical outcome of the hereditarian concepts that created the early eugenics movement.

Other eugenists, doubtless a majority of the vocal adherents in the early period, opposed or ignored such extreme and pessimistic implications. They argued that scientific knowledge did not yet justify radical action of any sort and perhaps never would. Even Davenport, on numerous occasions, emphasized that "for a long time yet our watchword must be investigate." The moderates feared that public reaction against legislation, especially sterilization, would bring the movement into disrepute before it had even started. "True eugenics is, at present, in less danger from its avowed enemies than from those who masquerade as its friends," a distinguished eugenist wrote. "Hasty and ill-advised legislation is preceding not only the cultivation of public opinion, but also that solid foundation of demonstrable fact which alone would justify law-making." [56] There remained always in the movement balanced men of science whose espousal of eugenics was nothing more than a legitimate concern for the genetic future of the nation.

On the whole, those whose political views were harshly reactionary and racist were the more willing to accept extreme hereditarian views; those with greater sympathy for reform and a democratic heritage found most to criticize in the research and interpretations that led to extremism. As the conservative implications of the eugenics creed became clearer and as new developments in genetics cast doubt on the extremists' position, the fears of the moderates increased and so did their alienation from the movement. While eugenics at first had a broad impact on American thought, after World War I it spoke increasingly for men of the right.

By the 1930's the eugenics crusade lay in wreckage, its scientific character sadly compromised. By then it was only too clear that the movement had been built on slipshod genetics and uncritical racism and that the vaunted scientific basis of the movement all too often reflected political prejudices. In the 1930's, therefore, a scientific reconstruction of eugenics began, but a distrust of the political motives and scientific objectivity of eugenists continued to haunt the movement—and still haunts it today.

# Chapter VII

# Myth of the Menace of the Feebleminded

In 1911 Henry H. Goddard, psychologist at the Vineland Training School for the feebleminded in New Jersey, reported his results from testing juvenile delinquents with the new Binet intelligence test. Of fifty-six wayward girls between the ages of fourteen and twenty, who were out on parole in New Jersey, the tests revealed that only four were not feebleminded—the rest were "clearly mental defectives, and could be made, or could have been made, had they been taken early enough, happy and useful in an institution for the feebleminded." That same year he studied one hundred juveniles chosen at random in the detention home in Newark and found sixty-six per cent to be "distinctly feeble-minded." [1] He drew the obvious conclusion that a large proportion of crime resulted from feeblemindedness. Goddard, it must be remembered, was a leading expert on the feebleminded and was already noted for the introduction of intelligence tests into the United States.

Indeed, from 1910 to 1920 a myth of the menace of the feebleminded became a major force in American social thought. The myth had its origin in several developments that increased public awareness of the feebleminded and exaggerated the dangers they presented. When, in the 1890's, several states began enforcement of compulsory school laws, the backward and feebleminded children kept in school hindered the work of education. The result was the gradual establishment of special schools and classes, so that by 1913 at least 108 cities made some sort of provision for educating those with retarded minds.[2] After 1910, when the Binet intelligence tests came into use, the tests indicated that perhaps 1 to 3 per cent of the population was feebleminded. More important, the tests appeared to prove that a large proportion of America's juvenile delinquents, criminals, prostitutes, tramps, and paupers were mentally deficient. Numerous studies, coming at the same time, reinforced a conviction that heredity was the major cause of feeblemindedness. Such developments seemed to confirm what a generation of asylum superintendents had preached—largely unheeded—concerning the heredity and menace of the feebleminded.

Those engaged in studies of the feebleminded felt the excitement of pioneers whose scientific investigations shed new light on the causes of many social problems and pointed the way to new solutions. If the feebleminded were more prevalent than had been realized and were a proven menace to both present and future generations, then new policies were a necessity in the care and control of the feebleminded, in the treatment of crime, and in the approach to poverty and prostitution. The feebleminded were no longer a peripheral problem but a central problem of great importance—one that demanded a eugenic solution. The urgency and intensity with which many reformers tackled the menace of the feebleminded made it the most important aspect of the early eugenics movement in America.[3]

## Testing the Feebleminded

The Vineland Training School, a private institution for the mentally retarded, was the center for developments that contributed most to the myth of the menace of the feebleminded. When Edward R. Johnstone, a man of great energy, great organizing ability, and a jovial, outgoing personality, took charge in 1898, he made the school a showplace for the best methods in caring for the feebleminded. In 1904 Vineland opened a summer school that provided the first training for teachers of the retarded; in 1906 the School chose Goddard to direct the first laboratory for the study of mental deficiency; and in 1912 it sponsored an extension department that took the lead in educating the public concerning the need for adequate care of the feebleminded. Goddard, a personable and enthusiastic worker with a flair for popularization, had studied with G. Stanley Hall at Clark University and taught at a State Normal School in Pennsylvania before coming to Vineland. At Vineland, through his work with mental testing and his study of the heredity of feeblemindedness, he soon assumed a place in the eugenics movement second only to that of Davenport himself.[4]

For some time prior to the introduction of the Binet tests, there had been a psychological testing movement in the United States. The most important early figure was J. McKeen Cattell, who had become interested in the measurement of human differences while studying in Wundt's laboratory in Germany and later had come under Galton's influence. In 1890 Cattell published an important article on "Mental Tests and Measurements," in which he described the tests that he had been giving to students at the University of Pennsylvania.[5] The tests, like those of Galton, were mostly measurements of senses, reaction time, muscular strength, and memory span. In this period, tests were scored separately: no effort was made to combine the scores to gain a measurement of a person's over-all capacity or to correlate the scores with an individual's age level. It was such tests—tests of motor control, reaction time, and memory— that Goddard first used in his researches at Vineland.

Alfred Binet, French pioneer in psychological testing during the 1890's, was the one who transformed such tests into measurements of intelligence. In 1904 the French Minister of Public Instruction appointed him a member of a commission to study the education of sub-normal children in the Paris schools. When the commission decided that the feebleminded should be placed in special classes, Binet and his student, Thomas Simon, undertook to find an objective method to distinguish them from the merely lazy, indifferent, or backward.[6]

In 1905 they published their first scale for measuring the intelligence of children, a scale considerably revised in 1908 and 1911. The 1911 revision, just before Binet's death, contained five tests for each age level from three to fifteen (omitting years eleven, thirteen, and fourteen).[7] On the scale, an idiot was not expected to pass the tests for age three, nor an imbecile those for age eight. Binet was chary about setting an exact limit for higher grades of feeblemindedness, however. Since a seven-year-old child who failed the eight-year tests obviously was not subnormal, Binet suggested that two years' retardation for children was an indication of feeblemindedness.

The Binet scales included many of the older types of psychological tests, including several measuring reaction or memory span (like the five-year test of choosing the heavier of two cubes or the eight-year test of repeating five digits). Many new tests were introduced to determine a child's judgment and grasp of the world about him (like the six-year test of defining familiar objects and the ten-year test of criticizing absurd statements). And some of the tests, as Binet admitted, measured school learning (like the eight-year test of counting backward from 20 to 0). The combination of tests at each age level, however, was designed to give a fairly close indication of a child's mental age. Because of the types of tests involved, the scale had to be administered in an individual interview with the subject.

In 1908 Goddard, with many doubts, began using Binet's early scales at Vineland.[8] The following year, at the annual meeting of the American Association for the Study of the Feebleminded, he reported that the tests "indicate the grade of the child with surprising accuracy." [9] Their great value, he went on, was that they provided a method to classify a child according to trainability almost immediately upon admission to an institution.

At the next meeting of the Association, a committee on classification of the feebleminded—consisting of Walter Fernald, Goddard, and others—submitted an influential report. In the interim, Goddard had given Binet tests to 400 children at Vineland and found that, while seven tested at the twelve-year level, none tested above twelve. He therefore recommended a threefold classification of adult feebleminded: idiots through two years mental age, imbeciles through seven years, and morons (a term he adopted from the Greek, *morōs,* sluggish or stupid) through twelve. His recommendation received the endorsement of the Association.[10]

In 1911 Goddard published a revision of the Binet scale, based on the testing of 2,000 normal children (the entire school population of a small New Jersey town). Goddard's revision, which adapted the wording and content to American experience, was for several years the standard scale used in the United States.[11] The great attraction of the tests was that they seemed to provide for the first time an objective measurement of human intelligence. While at first they were used primarily to recognize feeblemindedness, many persons immediately perceived that the tests, if they were really measures of innate intelligence, could answer some of the basic questions posed by eugenics—questions concerning the intelligence of social classes and races and questions concerning the inheritance of intelligence.

Goddard's own faith in the ability of the Binet tests to measure innate intelligence, apart from learning and experience, was almost unbounded. The questions, he affirmed, "involve the things that a child learns as he grows older without being taught at all; that is to say, he acquires them as his mind develops without needing any instruction." Because they were tests of mental development, not training, "any person who has lived in any sort of environment for the requisite number of years is able to do these tests, even though he has never been to school, even for a day, and by failing in these they [*sic*] manifest their mental defectiveness." In addition, though Goddard admitted that only trained psychologists could diagnose accurately to the year and month by means of the tests, even an untrained person could use the tests profitably.[12]

The Vineland summer school became, for a time, a major center for training in administration of the tests. Just as the Eugenics Record Office turned out eugenics field workers, so Vineland turned out Binet testers—many of them sharing Goddard's faith so that criticisms of the tests "only arouse a smile and a feeling akin to that which the physician would have for one who might launch a tirade against the value of the clinical thermometer." [13]

Despite their faith, Binet testers soon found that the measurement of intelligence by the Binet tests was a good deal more complicated than measuring temperature with a clinical thermometer. There were, for instance, problems in administering the tests. From the beginning psychologists recognized that only when the tester established rapport with the subject and only when the subject tried to do his best, free of nervousness or fear, could the results reflect his intelligence.[14] They also recognized that the scores could be meaningful only if each tester presented the questions in the same manner and scored the answers according to the same standards. An equally perplexing problem was the standard by which a person was to be judged normal or feebleminded. It soon became evident to many testers that a twelve-year mental age was too high, and soon they were using eleven, ten, or even lower. There were also differences over the number of years of mental retardation to be allowed among young children before declaring them feebleminded. Some used Binet's suggestion of two years' retardation; others used Goddard's of four. Most, recognizing that a four-year retardation had a different meaning for a child of five than for a child of twelve, used different standards for younger and older children.

The problems involved in interpreting and standardizing the Binet scale led to a number of revisions and scoring methods.[15] The most important was the Stanford revision, devised by Lewis M. Terman at Stanford University and published in 1916.[16] The Stanford revision had a total of ninety tests, fifty-four from Binet and thirty-six new, including vocabulary tests. Like the Binet scale, each test was given an age level, but the score was in terms of the now familiar Intelligence Quotient (I.Q.), in which a person's mental age was divided by his chronological age and multiplied by 100. Thus, a child of ten who tested ten would have an I.Q. of 100, while if he tested eight his I.Q. would be 80. The Stanford revision was widely used for testing in schools and colleges and soon became the standard scale for measuring intelligence. Yet even with this scale there was disagreement whether the boundary for feeblemindedness should be an I.Q. of 75, 70, or even lower.

In short, during these early years as the Binet testers went out to investigate the intelligence of the American public, there were many differences of opinion over standards, scoring, and the value of the tests themselves. Certainly there was reason enough to interpret any results conservatively and tentatively. Yet the acceptance of the evidence from Binet testing, more than any other factor, led to the crusade against the menace of the feebleminded.

## *Testing the Delinquent*

Long before the advent of Binet tests, prison and reformatory officials had been concerned with the number of defectives within their institutions. The long hereditarian emphasis, capped by criminal anthropology, had stressed a close relationship between insanity, feeblemindedness, epilepsy, and crime. Numerous prison physicians reported that among prisoners there were many who, because of imbecility, epilepsy, or insanity, were not responsible for their crimes and were not amenable to prison discipline or to reform. The need to remove such persons from the prisons and reformatories, so that these institutions could concentrate upon the physically and mentally normal criminals, was already a commonplace among criminologists.[17]

When Binet testers first entered the prisons and reformatories, therefore, they expected to unearth feeblemindedness, and their surprise was not that they found the feebleminded but that they found so many of them. The discovery bred a demand that prisons, reformatories, and courts be staffed with psychiatrists and psychologists for the detection of mental defect. Each psychologist then added another report confirming the startling presence of the feebleminded. And thus the movement fed upon itself and led, during the decade after 1910, to the widespread use of psychologists and psychiatrists in the courts, reformatories, and prisons of the more progressive cities and states.

Virtually without exception the innumerable reports from the testing of delinquents indicated that feeblemindedness was a major cause of antisocial behavior. The results seemed almost to solve the problem of the causation of crime.

Many investigators found that 90 per cent or more of the delinquents were feebleminded; those who reported results as low as 25 per cent often felt required to offer apologetic explanations.[18] A psychologist who tested two hundred juvenile delinquents before the famous court of Judge Ben Lindsay in Denver, Colorado, reported without surprise that a substantial proportion were feebleminded. "These figures add nothing new to the sum of the world's knowledge," he pointed out. "They merely corroborate and emphasize what we already know, that a large proportion of our delinquents are feeble-minded. We know further that two-thirds of these cases of feeble-mindedness are due to heredity, and that feebleminded people reproduce at twice the normal rate of the general population. But instead of sterilizing or segregating these people, we are buying them Bibles." [19]

Many of the psychological clinics, established to advise judges in the recently established juvenile courts and to aid in the rehabilitation of delinquents in reformatories, became centers for investigations and propaganda favoring eugenics. The first such clinic was the Juvenile Psychopathic Institute in Chicago, founded in 1909 at the urging of Julia Lathrop. There Dr. William Healy began the studies of juvenile criminal behavior that made him famous as a pioneer in the modern psychological and psychiatric study of delinquent motivation. One of his first concerns was the relation between mental defect and crime, for during his first year at the clinic he uncovered sixty-eight young delinquents who were decidedly subnormal, thirty-two of whom were institutional cases. He felt that among recidivists—or incorrigibles—mental defects were especially prevalent.[20] At first Healy accepted the Binet tests as a valuable means for separating the mentally normal delinquent from the feebleminded, and he devised tests of his own to determine emotional traits. Although he soon lost faith in the Binet tests and stressed many factors that might cause delinquent behavior, he still claimed in his monumental study, *Individual Delinquent,* published in 1915, that "mental defect forms the largest single cause of delinquency." [21]

While Healy was for a time a moderate eugenist, William J. Hickson, who directed the Psychopathic Clinic for the Municipal Court of Chicago that began operations in 1914, was considerably less moderate. Within two months after the Clinic's opening, his wife, a trained Binet tester, had tested 245 cases and found that 84.49 per cent "were distinctly subnormal morons" while one-half the few remaining cases were, at best, borderline. Hickson was convinced that the study was both carefully and conservatively conducted.[22] With Chief Justice Harry Olson of the Municipal Court, he was a proponent of an alarmist eugenics until well into the 1920's.

In Ohio in 1912, examination of one hundred consecutive admissions to the Girls' Industrial Home found 59 per cent feebleminded, while examination next year of a similar group at the Boys' Industrial School revealed 46 per cent feebleminded and 26 per cent borderline.[23] Such investigations led to the establishment in Ohio of a Bureau of Juvenile Research in 1914 to study juveniles before the courts and assign them to a reformatory or to an institution for the feebleminded, epileptic, or insane. Dr. Thomas H. Haines, the psychiatrist who became Clinical Director of the Bureau, undertook an intensive ten-month survey of one thousand consecutive admissions to the state reformatories and found that "fifty-seven per cent of these juveniles (570 of the thousand), are *mental defectives—* definitely feebleminded." [24] Haines worked in his own and neighboring states to extend custodial care in an effort to fight the menace of the feebleminded.

In California, the Whittier State School requested aid in the psychological study of youths under its care. Terman and a research fellow, J. Harold Williams, undertook the study in 1914 with the new Stanford revision and found 28 per cent definitely feebleminded, 25 per cent borderline, and the rest about evenly divided between dull normal and normal. They felt that the borderline cases would have been feebleminded under the usual Binet tests and that their figure of 28 per cent was therefore rock bottom.[25] Shortly afterward, the Whittier school established a Department of Research under Williams' direction, which in 1920 became the California Bureau of Juvenile Research. In his research Williams hired field workers from the Eugenics Record Office and kept in close contact with Davenport.

Much of the testing was concentrated upon juvenile delinquents, but the testing of adult criminals exposed the same sad truth: that feeblemindedness was a major cause of antisocial behavior. Especially the recidivists, who constituted the greatest problem both before the courts and in the prisons, appeared to be mentally deficient. Dr. Guy G. Fernald, resident physician at the Massachusetts Reformatory, found that 24 per cent of the inmates were feebleminded and that the feebleminded tended to be the recidivists.[26] Dr. Victor V. Anderson, psychiatrist to the Boston Municipal Court, placed the number of feebleminded among criminals at only 10 per cent. But it was "this ten per cent that form the very backbone of recidivism the treatment of which has been so unintelligent, so expensive, and so futile simply because society has failed to recognize that feeblemindedness, not crime, is being dealt with." [27] In a study of one hundred feebleminded criminals, he found that they averaged an impressive 18.25 arrests apiece. His conclusion was that the probation system, while excellent for the normal criminal, failed, when it failed, because of the low mentality of the repeater.

The Binet testing movement came at a time when reformers were battling the evils of the white slave traffic and conducting intensive studies of the forces back of prostitution. The Massachusetts Commission for the Investigation of the White Slave Traffic, in one of the most significant investigations of the vice, gave Binet tests to one hundred young prostitutes and two hundred experienced prostitutes. Not only did more than half test feebleminded, but the behavior of the prostitutes confirmed what the tests indicated:

> The general moral insensibility, the boldness, egotism and vanity, the love of notoriety, the lack of shame or remorse, the absence of even a pretense of affection or sympathy for their own children or for their parents, the desire for immediate pleasure without regard for consequences, the lack of forethought or anxiety about the future—all cardinal symptoms of feeble-mindedness—were strikingly evident in every one of the 154 women.[28]

In Albany, New York, several investigators tested fifty prostitutes in their place of occupation, administering the tests on Sunday afternoons when the girls were more rested and refreshed than at other times during the week. They found that 54 per cent of the girls were feebleminded as compared with 85 per cent of the girls in a home for wayward girls. They also tested nine streetwalkers and found only 46 per cent feebleminded, which is what they had expected because "a greater degree of resourcefulness was required to solicit on the street, evade arrest, and carry the responsibility of the more independent existence." [29] Clearly, then, prostitution, like crime, was essentially a problem of mental defect.

These were but a few of the many tests of the delinquents, criminals, and prostitutes in the decade after 1910. During the same period there were also sporadic investigations to uncover feeblemindedness among drunkards, tramps, orphans, paupers, and social failures generally.[30] Almost universally the use of mental tests revealed a large proportion of mental defect among the socially undesirable.

Another important result of the Binet testing was that, for the first time, it was possible to estimate the proportion of the general population that was feebleminded. This could be done through mental testing of school populations or through intensive surveys of a small geographical area. Estimates varied widely, from three in one thousand to over three in one hundred—a variation not at all surprising considering the wide differences in definition of feeblemindedness and the practical difficulties in accurate diagnosis.[31] Even the most conservative estimates, however, showed the feebleminded to be more prevalent than had before been realized and therefore made their care and control more important than had been recognized.

From the testing of delinquents came the discovery and labeling of a new type of social menace, variously called the moral imbecile, psychopath, constitutional inferior, or (most commonly) defective delinquent. The defective delinquent was a feebleminded person—usually a moron since lower varieties of the feebleminded lacked the necessary intelligence—who had antisocial and criminalistic tendencies. The "typical" defective delinquent acted without forethought, without remorse, driven by passions he was unable to control or understand. Such persons were the perpetrators of brutal murders and sex assaults and were incorrigible in their criminal tendencies. The great value of intelligence tests was believed to be that they spotted the defective delinquent and labeled him for what he was: a moron, probably the product of heredity, allowed to grow up in a world too complicated for him to live in effectively. The fact that the defective delinquent was usually a high-grade moron, often so close to normal that he would pass for normal if not discovered by the Binet tests, made him all the more dangerous to the community. Clearly, so it was argued, the need was to discover the feebleminded, whether at large in the community or in the courts, reformatories, and penitentiaries, and to place them in institutions for permanent custody. There they could be trained, to the extent that they were capable of being trained, and could be kept from mischief and from breeding more of their kind to burden future generations.[32]

Despite their confidence in the Binet tests, many psychologists could not help but be a little embarrassed by some of the high percentages of feeblemindedness found among delinquents. Partly the percentages were explained by the selection of the criminals tested. It was argued that, on the whole, the less intelligent delinquent was likely to be caught and, among those caught, the less intelligent was most likely to be sent to reform school or prison and the more intelligent to be put on probation. Besides, defective delinquents, because they were repeaters, were more often before the courts and in the institutions than normal delinquents. The mentally defective were more likely, therefore, to find themselves sitting across the table from a Binet tester.[33] Another rationalization for the high percentages was that they provided a kind of guarantee that feeblemindedness was a major cause of social ills; for, after all, if one cut in half the more extreme percentages and accepted only the lower percentages as reliable, still some 25 to 40 per cent of crime resulted from feeblemindedness. The high percentages made it possible, in short, to be both conservative and alarmed at the same time.[34]

What motivations lay behind the acceptance of such a one-sided interpretation of crime? One, of course, was the simple fact that there were morons and imbeciles among the criminal population. No state had adequate institutions for the feebleminded while several had none at all, and inevitably many persons with feeble minds drifted into ways of crime and poverty. Another was that the results did not run counter to what many criminologists and experts on the feebleminded had for some time predicted. In fact, the tests only confirmed their suspicion that many criminals were feebleminded—confirmed it beyond expectations. A more important reason, however, was a need to explain to themselves the frequent failure of reformatories, juvenile courts, and probation systems to perform the promised task of turning the criminal from his evil ways —a failure that brought embarrassing criticism. The fact that many youths, after leaving reform schools, returned to crime was "responsible for a large part of the adverse criticism of our institutions for juvenile offenders," one reformatory superintendent pointed out. And he argued: "The only way in which this criticism can be met properly is by producing data showing that a large majority of these failures were due to mental defect on the part of the inmates and not to faults in the system of training." [35] Feeblemindedness was an easy explanation for a perverse incorrigibility that was otherwise so difficult to understand.

### *"Menace of the Feebleminded"*

The family of Deborah Kallikak, a little moron girl brought to Vineland in 1897 at the age of eight, became almost as important to the eugenics movement as intelligence testing. When the laboratory at Vineland employed field workers to investigate the family histories of the inmates, Deborah's family (under this fictitious name) became world famous. Miss Elizabeth S. Kite, one of the most efficient of the field workers, tramped the rural areas of New Jersey, visited the slums of the cities, and examined old records to ferret out relatives and trace pedigrees.

The story, as she finally pieced it together, was as follows. Deborah's great-great-great-grandfather had been one Martin Kallikak, a young man of good family, who, at the outbreak of the American Revolution, sprang to his country's defense by joining the local militia. At one of the taverns frequented by the militia he met a feebleminded girl (name unknown), by whom he had an illegitimate son. The son, who bore his father's name, though in later years known more commonly as Old Horror, spawned a family as degenerate as the Jukes. No matter where Miss Kite traced the descendants of Old Horror, whether in the city tenements or rural hovels, the story was always the same: feeblemindedness, poverty, and immorality. Old Horror had 480 descendants, of whom 143 were feebleminded, forty-six normal, and the rest of doubtful or unknown mentality. The descendants included twenty-six illegitimate children, thirty-three sexually immoral persons (chiefly prostitutes), twenty-four alcoholics, three epileptics, three criminals, and eighty-two who died in infancy. What made the Kallikak family still more interesting was that Martin Kallikak, upon leaving the Revolutionary army, married a Quaker girl of good family, and from this marriage came a line of doctors, lawyers, judges, educators—in short, respectable and honorable citizens all. Both families lived in New Jersey, sharing the same surname but unaware that they were related.[36]

In 1912 Goddard published *The Kallikak Family,* written in a popular vein, with many lurid details concerning the degraded poverty and immorality of the degenerate branch of the family. He considered the family a perfect demonstration of the working of the laws of heredity; for "the biologist could hardly plan and carry out a more rigid experiment and one from which the conclusions would follow more inevitably." Dugdale's earlier study of the Jukes, Goddard admitted, really proved nothing concerning the hereditary nature of crime, pauperism, and prostitution. "If the Jukes family were of normal intelligence," he explained, "a change of environment would have worked wonders and would have saved society from the horrible blot. But if they were feeble-minded, then no amount of good environment could have made them anything else than feeble-minded." [37] In the Kallikak family, on the other hand, it was clearly the inherited feeblemindedness that created the degraded environments in which one branch of the family lived; it was the good blood in the members of the other branch of the family that made them respected citizens in their communities. No amount of environmental reform could have given the degenerate Kallikaks honor, intelligence, or ambition. At least, so Goddard argued. And thus the Kallikak family chronicle was hailed as another proof that feeblemindedness was hereditary and that it underlay much of the crime and pauperism in American society; the sterilization or segregation of that nameless colonial girl would have saved New Jersey great cost in human tragedy and degradation.

What was now needed to demonstrate conclusively the hereditary nature of social failure was proof that the Jukes, too, had been a family of hereditary feeblemindedness and were not therefore the tragic result of bad environment. Fortunately the opportunity came in 1911 when Dugdale's original notes of his investigation, giving the real names and other data concerning the Jukes family, were found in the cellar of the Prison Association of New York. The notes were turned over to the Eugenics Record Office, and Arthur H. Estabrook, a eugenics field worker, began the task of tracing the contemporary descendants of the family. The task was made more difficult by the dispersal of the original Jukes shortly after Dugdale's study because of the shutdown of a cement factory in 1880, so that in 1912 not a single Juke remained in the ancestral habitat in rural New York. Estabrook followed them throughout New York and into Connecticut, New Jersey, and Minnesota with such good effect that he was able to trace 2,111 Jukes in addition to the 709 that Dugdale had described. Estabrook found, in fact, that 1,258 Jukes were still living and reproducing when he published *The Jukes in 1915*. In it he reviewed the entire history of the notorious family that had sprung from a single vagabond born nearly two hundred years before.[38]

Estabrook's conclusion was that "one half of the Jukes were and are feeble-minded" and further that "all of the Juke criminals were feeble-minded" [39]—a startling conclusion, all the more startling since his own figures in the body of the report do not bear it out. In nine generations he found 366 pauperized adults, 171 criminals, 175 prostitutes, 282 alcoholics, and 131 feebleminded.[40] Certainly 131 was a great deal less than one-half of all the Jukes and was even less than the total number of criminals. Yet the study added one further link in the chain of circumstantial evidence that heredity and feeblemindedness lurked inevitably back of social failure.

In the decade after 1910, the Jukes, the Tribe of Ishmael, and the Kallikaks were joined by still other families, all with fictitious names, all accepted as proof that from heredity flowed feeblemindedness and social failure. There were the Pineys, a group of interrelated degenerate families studied by the indefatigable Miss Kite in the pine barrens of New Jersey; the Family of Sam Sixty, discovered in Ohio when Sam Sixty was arrested for sexual assaults on his young sons and daughters; the Happy Hickory Family, a five-generation family of feebleminded also unearthed in Ohio; and the Dwellers in the Vale of Siddem, otherwise known as "timber rats" or "bark eaters," descendants of New York squatters driven from their land only to find refuge in a rugged valley along a tributary of the Mississippi in Minnesota.[41] Still others, chronicled by the Eugenics Record Office itself, were the Nam Family, descended from a Dutchman and an Indian princess in western Massachusetts and intermarrying with the Naps, Nars, and Nats; the Hill Folk, a New England rural degenerate family; and the Dack family, the shiftless and immoral descendants of an Irish immigrant couple in western Pennsylvania.[42]

All of the families except the Pineys were traced by eugenics field workers, trained at the Eugenics Record Office. The methods by which the histories were collected and interpreted showed, if anything, retrogression since the days when Dugdale trudged through rural New York investigating the Jukes. While Dugdale had tried to balance heredity and environment, the later family studies, with monotonous regularity, credited all to heredity.

The information from Binet testing and family studies was buttressed by many state surveys into the problem of the feebleminded. The surveys, undertaken not only to gather knowledge but also to arouse the public to the local need and dangers, followed the same pattern in state after state. An inevitable feature was a series of visits to representative almshouses, reformatories, prisons, and other such institutions to uncover the feebleminded. Usually, too, a few typical schools were visited and the Binet tests given in order to estimate the percentage of feeblemindedness among the general population. Then it was possible to subtract the number of feeble-minded in institutions from the total number in the state to give an estimate of the number still loose in the community. The horror of the situation could then be driven home by stories of brutal crimes and abject immorality of a few "typical" morons and by printing pedigrees of a few degenerate families to highlight the hereditary nature of feeblemindedness.

The recommendations, like the findings, followed the same pat-tern: that state institutions for the feebleminded be established or expanded to house and care for the feebleminded at large in society and for those kept in the almshouses, reformatories, and prisons; that school systems have medical inspection and set up special classes to give the moral and industrial training designed to save the feeble-minded from social failure; that courts and reformatories set up clinics to diagnose the delinquents that come before them; and that the state establish a commission to register and oversee the feeble-minded throughout the state.[43]

Out of this activity—special classes in the public schools, Binet testing, family studies, and state and local surveys—came greater masses of information and misinformation concerning the feeble-minded than ever before assembled. From the evidence the feeble-minded stood indicted: they clogged the public schools; they were the root of much crime, intemperance, immorality, and poverty; they constituted up to 3 per cent of the general population; and they cost the states great sums for prisons, asylums, and almshouses. All the information indicated that they were largely the product of heredity, and some information suggested that they were far more prolific than the population in general.[44] Yet only a small percent-age were in institutions where they could be kept from spawning others like themselves.

Hence the menace of the feebleminded became the battle cry of an intensive public crusade to extend the care and control of the mentally deficient. The menace of the feebleminded was the subject of Sunday school tracts, was lectured about before women's clubs, business clubs, and colleges, and was a major topic in most periodicals devoted to social reform.[45] In virtually every state there was an organized campaign, typical of the many organized campaigns of the Progressive Era, to awaken the public and secure legislation. In this manner the results of the Binet tests, the family studies, and the state and local surveys were widely disseminated.

# Chapter VIII

# Decline of a Myth

The menace of the feebleminded was largely a myth—but a myth based on investigations of specialists and passed on to the public as a discovery of science. The myth faced increasing attack, an attack framed largely in scientific terms. But behind the attack often lay broader issues.

For most persons involved in the campaign against the menace of the feebleminded, the implications were not disturbing. They were engaged in scientific reform. And if one expert told them crime could be fought by institutionalizing the feebleminded while another advised tenement house reform, they were perfectly satisfied to institutionalize some who were feebleminded and provide better homes for others who could be reformed. Their approach was pragmatic, without either a rigid environmentalist or hereditarian philosophy.

Nevertheless, such authorities as Goddard and Davenport had specifically drawn deterministic and conservative implications: that the poor and criminal were what their genes had made them and therefore environmental reform was futile. Others recoiled from such fatalism. One psychiatrist, likening such a view to the doctrine of original sin, warned: "whether it be the theological or the eugenical dogma of predestination that is allowed to paralyze social action relative to reclaiming the criminal, the effect is the same." Similarly, in a statement read at the 1913 Race Betterment Conference at Battle Creek, Michigan, Jacob Riis, a prominent muckraker who had labored nobly in behalf of the poor of the slums, complained: "We have heard friends here talk about heredity. The word has rung in my ears until I am sick of it." He told of bad boys whose reform he had witnessed and expressed his own faith that "there are, dear friends, not any who are deliberately bad, but plenty whom we make bad." At any rate, the decline of the myth of the menace of the feebleminded was accompanied by a renewed faith in the reform of the criminal and the training of the feebleminded.[1]

## Psychological Testing

From the beginning, voices were raised in criticism of the use being made of the Binet tests, and even the most enthusiastic Binet testers at times admitted to feelings of uneasiness. For one thing, it was generally admitted that the tests were too hard at the upper mental ages, from ten to twelve—a fact especially embarrassing since this was the age level of most of the delinquents who were being labeled feebleminded. Even many of the most confirmed advocates of Binet tests, in addition, acknowledged that a mental age of twelve was too high for a boundary between feeblemindedness and normality and that the boundary should be lowered one, two, or even three years.[2]

A few critics entered more serious objections to the use of the tests. Some had already leveled the fundamental charge that the tests were a measure of education as well as intelligence and could not therefore pretend to diagnose innate mental age. "Those who think this scale measures general ability apart from schooling and other advantages should read Binet himself on this subject," was William Healy's curt comment.[3] In the 1920's psychologists became increasingly aware of the influence of education and social background on the test results.

Doubtless the most disturbing early critic of the Binet tests was J. E. Wallace Wallin, a psychologist whose broad training and readiness for controversy made him a formidable opponent. He had taken graduate training in psychology at Yale, Clark, Michigan, and Princeton, taught in 1910 at Vineland while Goddard was in Europe, and later established and directed a Psycho-Educational Clinic for the St. Louis public schools.[4] At St. Louis he became increasingly doubtful concerning the concept of the high- and middle-grade moron and concerning the simple explanation of crime and prostitution that the concept provided. He therefore gave the tests to several acquaintances of his in a rural community, all of whom had in common poor schooling in youth but modest success for themselves and families in later life—and all tested as morons. One was a farmer and businessman, with life savings of $30,000, who had served as superintendent of schools and of a local Sunday school. Of his nine children, two were professors and the other seven were equally successful. This man, by the Binet tests, had a mental age between ten and eleven and thus, in the prevailing climate of the day, should have been segregated in youth and perhaps sterilized. Since neither he nor the others could be regarded as feebleminded, Wallin declared, neither should delinquents and criminals of the same mental age.[5]

Wallin's criticisms provoked spirited defenses of the Binet tests and did little to halt their use in uncovering feeble minds among the nation's delinquents.[6] But the criticisms of Wallin and others, when capped by the results of mental testing in the Army during World War I, finally provided sobering evidence of the abuse of mental testing. The Army results were a *reductio ad absurdum* of the assumption that all persons below the mental age of twelve were under suspicion of feeblemindedness.

Development of the Army tests occurred when, with America's entrance into war, the American Psychological Association authorized its president, Robert M. Yerkes of Harvard, to appoint committees to aid in the war effort. Yerkes himself took the chairmanship of a committee on methods for psychological examining of recruits. Late in May of 1917 the members of the committee—including Yerkes, W. V. Bingham, Henry H. Goddard, Thomas H. Haines, Lewis M. Terman, F. L. Wells, and G. M. Whipple—assembled at Vineland to prepare tests that would aid the Army in weeding out mental incompetents. The major task was to devise tests that could be administered to large groups, since the Binet scales, which required an individual interview, were obviously impractical for so extensive a job. After many trials and innumerable revisions, two group tests were worked out: Scale Alpha for those literate in English and Scale Beta, with directions in pantomime, for those unable to understand English because of foreign origin or illiteracy.[7]

Soon all men entering the Army were required to take the tests, and the scores were recorded on personnel cards. Although the original purpose had been to discover the feebleminded, the scores were found valuable in choosing officer candidates and making assignments. By January 31, 1919, some 1,726,000 men had taken the tests, and psychologists were in a position to draw sweeping conclusions concerning the intelligence of the American public (so far as that intelligence could be measured by the tests).[8]

Although results of the Army testing were not published until 1921, the rumor had leaked out by early 1919 that on the Army tests 47.3 per cent of the white draft and 89 per cent of the Negro draft had a mental age of twelve or under (while 10 per cent of the white draft and 48 per cent of the Negro draft had a mental age under ten).[9] In short, nearly one-half of the American population was feebleminded or, as the official report noted, "feeblemindedness, as at present defined, is of much greater frequency of occurrence than had been originally supposed."[10] The results demonstrated clearly, most psychologists immediately realized, that millions of useful citizens, with scores on mental tests that would formerly have classed them as morons, were by no means feebleminded. Wallin easily drew the obvious lesson that "the vast majority of delinquents and criminals who have been classed as feeble-minded during the last decade (and whose intelligence ages have ranged from X to XII) are not feeble-minded at all, certainly no more feeble-minded than many millions of citizens who are law-abiding, respectable and self-supporting."[11] After 1919 the early reports of a high proportion of feeblemindedness among delinquents appeared less frightening and less convincing.

In the post-war era, in fact, a number of psychologists took a second look at the intelligence of the criminal. Several studies showed the prison population to have the same over-all intelligence as the general population, and one study, at least, found the criminal population to be superior. Probably the best modern opinion is that delinquents have a lower average intelligence, as measured by tests, than the nondelinquent population. But delinquents tend to come from lower socio-economic backgrounds and their tested intelligence is fairly representative of the background from which they spring. For this reason, it is extremely difficult to make generalizations concerning the relation of intelligence to delinquent behavior.[12]

The new investigations were not as numerous as the earlier ones and the new attitudes were not presented with the same missionary fervor. They did not, therefore, make their way so quickly into textbooks and speeches before women's clubs. Well into the 1920's the impression remained, even among many Americans directly concerned with crime, that crime and mental defect worked hand in hand.[13]

## *Criminology*

The myth of the menace of the feebleminded arose just as criminology in the United States had recovered from the impact of criminal anthropology. Many students of crime, indeed, still admitted that they had gone to school to the criminal anthropologists and praised the earlier movement for initiating the medical and psychological study of the criminal individual; a few in 1910 still clung to the belief in a hereditary criminal type; but criminal anthropology lived on chiefly in the popular superstition that the criminal heart could be read in the criminal face. Most criminologists by then either denied that criminals could be distinguished physically from noncriminals or else, convinced that crime was caused by feeblemindedness, claimed that "the physical anomalies which have been found so common among prisoners are not the stigmata of criminality, but the physical accompaniments of feeble-mindedness." In either case, criminal anthropology was regarded chiefly as an exploded myth from the simpler days of criminology.[14]

With the passing of criminal anthropology there also passed the belief, among criminologists, that criminality was directly inherited. Instead, the emphasis was placed upon the inheritance of such defects as feeblemindedness, insanity, and epilepsy that were thought to underlie criminal action.[15] In point of fact, however, the new hereditarian theory paralleled in many ways the earlier criminal anthropology, with the measurement of I.Q. replacing the earlier search for stigmata of degeneration. Both theories traced criminality to a single cause and linked crime primarily to heredity; both were a deterministic and largely pessimistic approach to prevention and reform. The defective delinquent became the new criminal type.

The relation of feeblemindedness to criminal behavior all but dominated the discussions of crime after 1910. Criminologists agreed that the standard methods of treatment failed when applied to the defective delinquent, who was not responsible for his actions. The proper institution for the defective delinquent was an asylum for the feebleminded or, preferably, a special institution from which he would be released, if ever, only when he no longer endangered himself and society.[16] This was a major topic for discussion at meetings of criminologists and prison experts.

Establishment of psychological and psychiatric clinics to study delinquents and criminals, however, led to wider and more balanced

views of the causes of criminal action. Nothing showed this more
clearly than the work of Dr. William Healy, who, more than anyone else, revolutionized the study of the criminal during the period. Early in his investigations at the Juvenile Psychopathic Institute in Chicago he sensed that, although criminology was plenti-
fully endowed with theories, the theories contained little that was
helpful to those engaged in a day-by-day effort to unravel criminal
motivation. At the clinic he used Binet tests and, when he published
*Individual Delinquent* in 1915, still felt that feeblemindedness was
the most important single cause of delinquency.[17] But the reason
for the impact of his book was that it expressed what so many psychiatrists and clinical psychologists had been moving toward: a feeling that criminal motivation was infinitely complex and that each
individual delinquent deserved to be studied as a case in himself.

Examinations at the Juvenile Psychopathic Institute turned up
many factors other than feeblemindedness. Medical examinations
uncovered bad eyesight, adenoids, syphilis, and malnutrition. Psychological testing went beyond the testing of intelligence to the testing of attentiveness, coordination, personality traits, and vocational
aptitudes. Histories of the delinquent's physical and emotional development, his home environment and associations, and his school
and occupational record revealed tensions and influences that made
a mockery of any simple theory of crime based upon heredity or
feeblemindedness.[18]

In his book Healy praised the new case study method of psychiatric investigation developed by Adolf Meyer and the psychoanalysis
of Freud. His book took issue with many of the traditional ap-
proaches to the study of crime. He passed over stigmata of degeneration in a few brief sentences, cast doubt upon the reliability of
Binet tests, and pointed out that charts showing crime in many generations of a family no more proved that crime was hereditary than
that it was environmental.[19] Two years after publication of *Individual Delinquent,* Healy published another, *Mental Conflicts and
Misconduct,* in which he reported, in a simplified Freudian way,
cases of delinquents whose conduct was rooted in sexual conflicts
and repressions. He came to such studies because he found that
many a delinquent was beset by mental conflicts and was "fairly
hungry to delve with some understanding person into the real in-
wardness of his tendencies to misconduct." [20]

Important advances in many fields made possible the new approach to criminal motivation. Medicine brought the Wassermann

test for syphilis, an expanding knowledge of endocrine disorders, and new discoveries in the field of nutrition. Psychology not only furnished a more critical use of mental tests but rapidly developed tests for personality traits and vocational aptitudes. Psychiatry contributed the newer case study method and the insights of psychoanalysis, influences that centered on early childhood and sexual drives rather than heredity in interpreting the apparently irrational behavior of delinquents. These diagnostic tools were combined with the investigative methods in social work and the large body of material on the relation of crime to economic dislocation, family insecurity, and school and environmental influences. Psychologists and psychiatrists in the court and reformatory clinics and in the numerous child guidance clinics that spread throughout the nation in the 1920's accepted Healy's *Individual Delinquent* as authoritative and rejected any one-dimensional approach to delinquent motivation.[21] Although some psychiatrists and clinical psychologists continued to show a concern for heredity and retained their memberships in eugenics organizations, no competent criminologists by the 1920's could continue to speak loosely of a "criminal type" or "the menace of the feebleminded."

## Institutional Care

For a time the myth of the menace of the feebleminded guided the policies of those charged with the institutional care of the feebleminded. From long experience they had come to believe that the feebleminded, if released from an institution, would almost invariably enter upon a life of immorality and crime and would all too often bring forth children to burden future generations. Nearly every superintendent had had painful experiences with inmates who were released only to return to the institution because they became pregnant, proved unmanageable, or committed a brutal crime—and it was easy to assume that these cases were typical. Within the institutions, therefore, superintendents adopted a policy of retaining their charges for life and resisted efforts by parents to secure release of their offspring. In those states where commitment laws were weak, they campaigned to strengthen the method of commitment so that parents and guardians could not remove the feebleminded without the approval of the institution.[22] To carry out the policy of lifetime custodial care, many institutions intensified their efforts to establish farm and work colonies where those with children's minds in adult bodies could contribute to their own support, for the super-intendents knew that the extension of custodial care could win public support only if it was shown to be practical and inexpensive.[23]

Before long, however, the assumptions that underlay the policy crumbled before the facts. Most revealing was a study, under the direction of Walter E. Fernald, of the patients who had left the Waverley School in Massachusetts between 1890 and 1914. Some of them were runaways, some were discharged because they did not seem vicious, but the majority had been released over the protest of the institution after political pressure or court order. Out of the 1,537 who had departed, the social worker was able to follow up 646 patients (470 males and 176 females). Many of the women had turned out as expected: they had shown themselves sexually promiscuous (eleven bore illegitimate children) or had been otherwise delinquent, so that over sixty were returned to Waverley or to another institution. Yet many had made partial or complete successes of their opportunity. A few of the women had proved entirely self-supporting and many more were at least able to help at housework without being a burden. Twenty-seven had married and had a total of thirty-three living children. ("The social worker saw nearly all of these children, and was not sure that any of them were defective.") [24]

Among the men there were also the expected failures: twenty-three arrested but not sentenced, thirty-two arrested and sentenced, and 111 recommitted to Waverley or some other institution. But 250 were no menace to the community and were either completely self-supporting or working under careful guidance. Of those who failed, both men and women, most had revealed immoral tendencies while at Waverley and received inadequate supervision upon their release. Thus, while the survey confirmed that many had failed, its importance lay in the proof that many had made the grade and that a program for parole and community supervision of the feeble-minded had every possibility for success.[25]

Nor was Fernald the only one to have his opinions jolted by facts. His good friend, Dr. George A. Wallace of the Wrentham State School in Massachusetts, had been faced with the problem that his higher grade boys and girls either ran away or were freed by court order. With many misgivings, he had therefore begun a parole system, so that the institution could continue supervision and not lose all control of its former inmates. So successful was the experiment that he became an enthusiastic supporter of parole.[26]

Even more impressive were the results of experiments by Dr. Charles Bernstein at the Rome State Custodial Asylum in New York. Beginning in 1906 he had established farm colonies for the brighter boys and later had set up work colonies where the boys could hire out to do odd jobs and unskilled labor, returning to the colony at night. Beginning in 1914 he also initiated colonies where the girls, similarly, could be hired for domestic service. From the colonies the boys and girls could graduate to parole and, if they made good, could be discharged from the institution. From 1912 to 1919, he paroled 240 girls and 276 boys with remarkable success. Still other follow-up studies from the special public school classes for the backward and feebleminded gave evidence that a majority of the students later made their humble contributions to society. Indeed, had it been otherwise, the schools would have failed in their purpose.[27]

By the early 1920's it was obvious that the alarmist period had resulted from a concentration upon those feebleminded (and assumed feebleminded) who had failed—who became criminals, prostitutes, and vagabonds—and from overlooking entirely the majority of the persons of similar intelligence who had somehow made out in society and therefore did not come to attention. The Army tests had established that millions who, by test scores, were of low mentality had nevertheless lived normal and blameless lives. The follow-up studies, coming at the same time, demonstrated that even individuals who were without doubt feebleminded need not inevitably lead lives of depravity and destitution.

Like new converts, many who had warned against the menace of the feebleminded recanted their old superstitutions. Dr. Fernald, who had previously spoken with authority on the menace, confessed to his fellow superintendents in 1918 that "there are both bad feeble-minded and good feeble-minded, that not all the feeble-minded are criminalists and socialists and immoral and anti-social." Then, in a statement worthy of a man who had devoted his life to the feebleminded, he declared: "I never lose an opportunity to repeat what I am saying now, that we have really slandered the feeble-minded. Some of the sweetest and most beautiful characters I have ever known have been feeble-minded people." [28] Goddard, too, humbled by the results of the Army tests and by the follow-up studies, admitted that he was glad to have learned the truth and confessed modestly: "I suppose I have been as guilty as anybody in my small way in the past in emphasizing the menace of the feeble-minded." [29]

The conversions did not come easily, however. From 1917, when the members of the American Association for the Study of the Feeble-minded first heard of the need for revision, until 1921, when nearly the entire annual meeting was devoted to follow-up studies, the members repeated again and again the new doctrine, as if they hoped by sheer repetition to re-educate themselves.[30]

In a more critical climate, earlier studies of the heredity of fee-blemindedness also seemed neither so alarming nor so convincing. Often they seemed almost to indict themselves.

Increasingly, critics posed embarrassing questions about the Kal-likaks. How, for instance, could anyone know the mentality of a nameless girl from Revolutionary days? [31] How, when the diagnosis of feeblemindedness is so difficult, could a person determine that the deceased Kallikaks were feebleminded? How, in fact, could a social worker diagnose feeblemindedness in living Kallikaks after but brief visits with them?

Miss Kite's own description of her investigations, faithfully re-corded in *The Kallikak Family*, supplied the answer: she had been so shocked by the poverty and immorality of the Kallikaks and by their appearance that she had taken these to be nearly infallible indices of mental level. In one hovel, she saw a deaf boy; "a glance sufficed to establish his mentality, which was low." The father, too, "though strong and vigorous, showed by his face that he had only a child's mentality. The mother in her filth and rags was also a child." At another farm, Miss Kite could tell from the destitution of the place that it could be inhabited only by the feebleminded; then "the door opened, revealing a sight to which, alas, the field worker was only too accustomed. She gazed aghast at what appeared to her to be a procession of imbeciles." [32] While she diagnosed the living from brief acquaintance, she diagnosed the dead primarily from hearsay. She was obviously all the more ready to label mem-bers of the family feebleminded because she was dealing with what she regarded as a family of hereditary feeblemindedness. Only that could explain her readiness to assert that an unknown colonial girl was feebleminded. So convinced was she, in short, that destitution and immorality flowed from feeblemindedness and that feeblemind-edness was inherited, that she used these assumptions in making her diagnosis. Thus her investigations assumed what they purported to prove.[33]

In *The Inheritance of Mental Disease*, published in 1925, Abra-ham Myerson provided a summary of criticisms that had been leveled at the heredity studies of Goddard and Davenport. Ironically, he declared that many of the studies showed how unnecessary a medical education was "when a woman can as a result of a dozen or two of lectures make all kinds of medical, surgical and psychiatric diagnoses in an interview or by reading through a court record." Like others, he stressed that insanity, epilepsy, and feeblemindedness were general terms covering a wide variety of often unrelated diseases. Those insanities resulting from cerebral arterio-sclerosis, brain tumor, meningitis, syphilis, pellagra and the use of alcohol and drugs made up a substantial proportion of institutional cases and, he claimed, were not inherited. Feeblemindedness often derived from birth trauma, infectious childhood diseases, parental syphilis, cretinism, or injury. Thus, he stressed that many common mental diseases were chiefly environmental in origin and that, most certainly, the Mendelian inheritance of mental disease had not been proved.[34]

Myerson's own verdict concerning the heredity of mental diseases was rather tentative. From his own researches, he concluded that there was a genetic basis to paranoia, schizophrenia, and manic-depressive psychosis, but beyond that he would not go. He admitted that feebleminded persons, showing no evidence of organic disease, tended to re-occur in certain families, and he therefore supported eugenical sterilization of familial types of feeblemindedness. Otherwise his program leaned heavily upon environmental reforms: to end unhealthy living conditions and malnutrition, control the use of alcohol and drugs, and conquer the diseases that led to mental illness.[35] For those awed by the authority of Davenport and his fellow workers, Myerson provided in convenient form the refutation of their investigations.

### Hope

Out of the myth of the menace of the feebleminded and the decline of that myth developed the modern attitude toward the feebleminded. The introduction of the Binet tests and the results of many surveys created an awareness that the feebleminded were more numerous than had been realized. The campaign to secure custodial care for the feebleminded demonstrated that such a goal, even if desirable, was beyond reach and that the overwhelming majority of the feebleminded would continue to live outside institutions. The follow-up studies then revealed that this was not only inevitable, but often advisable. Of course, those feebleminded who showed immoral tendencies or lived in depraved or impoverished families were still most likely to become institutional cases. But it was now realized that there were among the feebleminded, like the normal-minded, both good and bad and that their character and the environment into which they were placed were the key factors in their success or failure.

The 1920's marked, in many ways, a new era in attitude and policy, an era in which despair was replaced by qualified hope. No longer did research center on the collection of appalling family histories or uncovering the morons among the criminal and destitute; instead, the emphasis fell more on the study of endocrinology, blood chemistry, and other efforts to understand and distinguish the various types of feeblemindedness. Earnest pleas for lifelong custodial care to halt the burden of mental defect gave way to discussions of parole, public school classes, and other efforts for community guidance and supervision of those with retarded minds. The new policy included early diagnosis through medical examinations in the public schools, expansion of special classes in the public schools, and increased education of parents in care and supervision. In the better institutions, the emphasis shifted to the preparation of those with sufficient intelligence so that they could have an opportunity to take their place in the world outside—a program that gave hope to inmates who before had had to abandon hope.[36] Such a program displaced eugenics as the principal concern, but as Goddard pointed out: "I am willing to say that if we educate properly the moron we may very safely neglect this question of eugenics and marriage for a large proportion of them." [37]

The new attitude involved a major change within the eugenics movement. No longer did specialists in feeblemindedness and delinquency maintain that eugenics might wipe out feeblemindedness or solve the nation's problems of crime and poverty. Hence they retired from the movement or became more moderate in their approach. The new attitude, of course, did not banish a legitimate concern to prevent those types of feeblemindedness for which abundant evidence of a genetic basis existed. Even the legitimate concern, however, was more tentative and less urgent than before, for most experts increasingly recognized the complexity of heredity and the limitations of existing knowledge. Only persons who were unaware of the new evidence or who, through conservatism or a hereditarian bias, ignored it could continue through the 1920's to raise the cry of the menace of the feebleminded.

Through ignorance and bias, however, the myth survived for a decade or more. It had been the basis for numerous books, articles, pamphlets, and speeches. For over a decade the menace of the feebleminded had inspired a nationwide campaign to awaken the public and to secure clinics, custodial care, and sterilization laws. The newer studies remained largely buried in technical journals and did not drive out the older attitudes. Goddard's books, long after he had abandoned the views expressed in them, continued throughout the 1920's to be a standard source for many who sought information on mental defects.[38]

Even among many of those acquainted with the problem, the earlier myth and its simple solution of crime and poverty remained attractive. When Mrs. Nellie Stermer-Koulik was indicted in Chicago in 1922 for mass poisoning, for instance, Chief Justice Harry Olson of the Municipal Court, himself a confirmed eugenist and friend of Davenport, was suitably shocked by the psychiatric report that Dr. William J. Hickson submitted. The report stated that Mrs. Stermer-Koulik's mental age was eleven, that one of her sons, a delinquent, had been diagnosed as feebleminded in 1918, and that two other sons were behind bars. "If we had had a field worker, a eugenics expert, to check up on the history of this whole family at the time one moron was discovered," the Judge lamented, "then the police might have been warned to watch this woman. . . ." And he threatened, "We are going to apply soon to the Eugenics Record Office of the Carnegie Institution for such a worker, then, when we find one case, we can seek out and locate the next." [39]

In fact, an obsession with feeblemindedness and low mentality pervaded the eugenics movement of the 1920's. Many a book and article continued to use the Jukes and Kallikaks to scare the American public. The early concern with the menace of the feebleminded merged with a larger concern of eugenists with what they believed to be the nation's faltering intelligence. Orthodox eugenics of the 1920's held that a large proportion of the nation's population was of low intelligence, although not actually feebleminded, and that such persons—tramps, poor farmers, slum dwellers, unskilled laborers, Negroes, and immigrants—were breeding and swamping those relatively few families that still carried the light of intelligence and initiative in their genes. Thus the earlier myth of the menace of the feebleminded was transformed into a larger myth: the menace of the mass man.[40]

# Chapter IX
# Legislative Battle

Although eugenists launched campaigns for permanent custodial care, sexual sterilization, and marriage restriction to halt the increasing burden of mental disease and delinquency, they were far from united on the value and urgency of such programs. Most eugenists enthusiastically backed custodial care to halt the menace of the feebleminded, both because the menace seemed so great and because institutional care appeared to be best for the feebleminded themselves. But the enthusiasm of some eugenists for sterilization was matched by the fear of others that neither existing knowledge, common decency, nor public opinion justified such laws. Finally, even the most optimistic eugenists regarded legal restriction on marriage to be little more than a harmless gesture that was largely futile in the battle against the breeding of the unfit.

Through the appeal for legislation, the American public doubtless received its major education in the eugenics creed. In carrying its program to the public, eugenics took its place among a multitude of reform projects competing for attention in the Progressive Era and its proponents followed much the same methods as the other groups that battled to aid the unfortunate and alleviate social ills. Despite appeals to voters, however, the legislative victories of eugenics arose more from expert testimony before legislative committees than from public demands. Support came chiefly from state boards of charity, institutional superintendents, professors, and others whose readings and interests kept them abreast of the latest findings in psychiatry, criminology, and the study of the feebleminded. Eugenics remained primarily a movement of specialists rather than a popular crusade.

## Custodial Care

The campaign for permanent custodial care of the feebleminded took precedence, for it did not raise the legal and moral objections of sterilization and was more effective than regulation of marriage. The Training School at Vineland, which had pioneered the investigations that created the myth of the menace of the feebleminded, also provided the organization to lead the fight for custodial care. In 1910 Edward R. Johnstone, superintendent of the School, organized a committee to win better care for feebleminded and epileptic children in New Jersey. The committee was successful not only in securing greatly increased appropriations for state institutions but also in establishing compulsory medical examinations in the public schools for early diagnosis of mental retardation. Soon Johnstone found that other states needed similar campaigns but that he and Goddard could not handle the many requests for lectures and advice. Consequently, in 1912 his brother-in-law, Alexander Johnson, began direction of an extension department at Vineland to conduct a nationwide educational campaign.[1]

Two years later, at a meeting in Mrs. Harriman's home, the extension department was expanded into a national Committee on Provision for the Feebleminded, with headquarters in Philadelphia. Those present and forming the Committee included most of the prominent superintendents of institutions for the feebleminded, members of several state boards of charity, Thomas W. Salmon of the National Committee for Mental Hygiene, plus Davenport, Goddard, David Starr Jordan, and others. Indeed, Davenport and his friends had for some time impressed upon Mrs. Harriman the menace of the feebleminded and the need for greatly expanded custodial care. Although Mrs. Harriman provided the chief financial support, General Coleman DuPont, Henry Clay Frick, R. Bayard Cutting, and Bleecker van Wagenen all contributed substantially to the project. To direct the campaign for expanded care, Joseph P. Byers became executive secretary and Alexander Johnson field secretary, while field workers like Miss Kite of Kallikak fame were employed as investigators to provide the needed facts and figures.[2]

Because of their long experience in charitable and institutional work, Byers and Johnson were excellent choices to lead the campaign. Johnson, an accomplished public speaker, was intimately acquainted with the care of the feebleminded and widely liked in re-

form circles. He had begun his career working for the Associated
Charities of Cincinnati in 1882 and in quick succession became
secretary of the Charity Organization Society of Chicago, secretary
of the Indiana Board of State Charities (through the support of
Oscar McCulloch), and superintendent of the Indiana School for the
Feebleminded. (While superintendent, he appointed Johnstone to
be principal of the school department and thus started him on his
career that led to the superintendency of Vineland.) From 1904 to
1913 Johnson was secretary of the National Conference of Charities
and Corrections. In that capacity he gave the problem of the feebleminded a prominent place in the yearly deliberations and trav-
eled from state to state to promote interest in their care. Thus he
was well prepared for his work with the Committee on Provision,
which eventually included more than 1,100 lectures in 350 cities in
thirty-three states and Canada, given before legislatures, reform
groups, universities, churches, business organizations, women's clubs
and anyone else who would listen.[3]

The Committee attempted always to work with local civic and
charitable groups with two aims in view: first, to secure appointment of a state commission to investigate the feebleminded residents of the state and, second, to conduct an intensive educational
campaign based on the findings of the commission. The National
Committee for Mental Hygiene, which received grants from the
Rockefeller Foundation to conduct state surveys, worked closely
with state commissions and with the Committee for Provision.

The educational campaign appealed to both the fear and the
compassion of the public. On the one hand, the campaign stressed
the menace of the feebleminded and warned that, of the more than
275,000 feebleminded persons in the United States, only 20,000 were
in institutions. On the other hand, as Johnson explained to a group
of social workers, the feebleminded deserved pity. "It is the thing
to do for the feeble-minded—get them out of the big world where
they have such a hard time because they are not like other folks."
He likened the feebleminded, young and old, to children, "concerning whom the Master said it was better for us to have a mill-stone
around our necks and to be cast into the depths of the sea, than that
we should cause one of these little ones to offend, or that we should
offend one of these little ones." [4]

Although the Committee on Provision was active in most states,
its most valuable work was in the South, where almost no institutional care existed and where a relative lack of organized reform

groups made outside aid most important. Fortunately the campaign occurred in a period of prosperity and at a time when many southern states were making initial efforts to bring their institutions into line with those of the rest of the nation.

Arkansas, where no institution for the feebleminded existed, was one of the first targets of the Committee. While still secretary of the National Conference of Charities and Correction, Johnson had already aroused an interest among social reformers in Little Rock. For two months in 1914 he returned and lectured throughout the state, with the result that the legislature in early 1915 provided for the appointment of a state Commission on the Feebleminded. Because the legislature failed to appropriate funds, the state commission appealed to the Committee on Provision for help, which in turn persuaded the National Committee for Mental Hygiene, the U. S. Public Health Service, and the Eugenics Record Office each to send a field worker to aid in a survey. Meanwhile, Johnson took another swing through the state in the summer of 1915, later helped to draft the commission's report on the extent of the feebleminded problem in Arkansas, assisted in preparing a bill, and then in the week that the bill was introduced gave an illustrated lecture before the state legislature. In early 1917 a bill passed to appropriate $50,000 for an institution. Unfortunately, the legislature later annulled the appropriation, and in 1925 Arkansas was one of four states that still had no special provision for the feebleminded.[5]

Another of many campaigns in the South began in July of 1915 when Byers took Albert S. Johnstone, secretary of the newly created South Carolina Board of State Charities, on a guided tour of the Eugenics Record Office and the Vineland Training School and thereby impressed on him the need to care for the feebleminded. In the fall Johnson went South with his stereopticon slides and took with him a field worker to gather data. He lectured before the state Conference of Charities and Public Welfare and, as usual, won converts—among them the governor. At the governor's request, Johnson lectured the legislature in January, but a bill for an institution failed in the closing rush. The Committee on Provision allowed the field worker to continue her investigations of the almshouses, jails, and orphanages to gather material for a new attempt. In addition, Byers invited the governor to visit Vineland and then sent him home with a draft of a bill and an exhibition to show the legislature. Later Johnson returned again to South Carolina and in January, 1918, once more addressed a joint session of the legislature. This time a bill passed establishing South Carolina's first training school for the feebleminded.[6]

In states outside the South, the Committee on Provision offered lectures and exhibitions, but seldom needed to take a direct hand in organizing campaigns. In Pennsylvania the Public Charities Association ran a campaign after the legislature had in 1913 appropriated funds to find a site for a new institution and then taken no further action. To collect information, the Association had Wilhelmine E. Key, a psychologist and graduate of the field workers course at the Eugenics Record Office, make a detailed survey of an appropriate district. In an orthodox and widely publicized report, she declared that the feebleminded were intemperate and immoral, that feebleminded mothers averaged seven children to one-half that for normal mothers, and that the feebleminded comprised 3.2 per cent of the population but occurred in concentrated areas of interrelated families.

With such information as the basis of the campaign, the Association organized a large exhibition in Philadelphia, viewed there by 100,000 persons, and then took the exhibition to twenty-five other communities, accompanied by slides and by a one-act play entitled *The Woman Unawake.* From a speakers' bureau in Philadelphia, lecturers were channeled to P-T.A.'s, medical societies, women's clubs, and churches—all of which were asked to pass resolutions. In each legislative district prominent persons were requested to approach local legislators. The result was to secure a new institution. In all these activities, however, the role of the Committee on Provision had been limited to giving advice, lending Johnson and Kite as speakers, and aiding in the preparation of exhibitions.[7]

With America's entrance into World War I, the Committee on Provision turned its attention to the war effort. It provided financial support that enabled psychologists to travel to Vineland and prepare the group tests for the Army. In addition, it employed Miss Kite to keep a watch over the feebleminded women of New Jersey and thus protect young soldiers from their corrupting influence. Because many of its members and financial supporters shifted their support to National Committee for Mental Hygiene with its greater prestige, the Committee on Provision failed to survive the war. Before the treasurer joined the YMCA and died in Paris, he left enough money to last until the end of 1917. In the spring of 1918, therefore, the Committee on Provision shrank and once more became the extension department of the training School at Vineland.[8]

In the postwar period, the National Committee for Mental Hygiene continued its state surveys of the feebleminded and for a time continued the urgent demand for custodial care.[9] But gradually the alarmist period drew to an end, and with it there ended the extensive campaign for permanent custodial care of the feebleminded. Those studies and surveys that continued to be made increasingly emphasized the need for special classes in the public schools and extra-institutional supervision of the mentally defective. No longer were the surveys primarily vehicles for eugenics propaganda, and they therefore ceased to play a major role in the eugenics movement.

In the decade after 1910, the campaign to extend the care of the feebleminded spread to nearly every state and produced significant results. Many states, especially in the South, established their first institutions, and other states constructed additional institutions or expanded existing ones. As a result, the numbers cared for in institutions nearly tripled from 1904 to 1923: [10]

| Year | No. of States with Institutions | Resident Inmates |
|------|---------------------------------|------------------|
| 1904 | 24 | 14,347 |
| 1910 | 30 | 20,731 |
| 1923 | 43 | 42,954 |

Yet measured in other terms, the accomplishment was not so impressive as it appeared. The number of feebleminded in institutions more than doubled from 1890 to 1904, for instance, so that the growth thereafter was only a quickening of a process already under way. Furthermore, the number in institutions in 1923 represented only about four per ten thousand of the general population and thus an insignificant proportion of the total feebleminded.[11] Considering that many of those in institutions were of low grade and incapable of procreation, eugenists were far from their goal of preventing or even appreciably lessening reproduction by the feebleminded.

More important than the tripling of the number in institutions was the vast growth in extra-institutional care for the feebleminded. From almost nothing at the turn of the century, there began to develop, at least in the more progressive states, a comprehensive system of medical inspection, clinics, public school classes, institutional parole systems, and community supervision. If the alarmist period did relatively little for eugenics, it accomplished a great deal for the feebleminded.

## Sterilization

Half grudgingly, half willingly, the eugenics movement in America became associated in the public mind with sexual sterilization. The sterilization movement so caught the public eye that to many people eugenics and sterilization seemed one and the same. Especially for critics of eugenics, sterilization provided one of the few concrete manifestations of the movement and therefore one of the few concrete targets, often a very vulnerable target. The morality and scientific validity of sterilization, as a result, have often stood at the center of discussions of the morality and validity of eugenics itself.

Yet in all probability over half of those sympathetic with eugenics in the 1910's and 1920's opposed the campaign for sterilization laws or hung back because they felt such laws were premature—ahead of both public sympathy and scientific knowledge. Even those who supported sterilization admitted many of the complaints of their foes: that the laws were often unscientifically, carelessly, and even cruelly drawn, that they applied usually to persons already in institutions and therefore unlikely to have children, and that they were futile since enactment was rarely followed by vigorous enforcement.[12] For reasons such as these, neither the Committee on Provision for the Feebleminded nor the National Committee for Mental Hygiene supported sterilization.[13] Some of the most effective criticism of sterilization, in fact, came from persons whose sympathies were with eugenics.

The argument that sterilization would lead to fornication and debauchery was never put more strongly than by Walter E. Fernald, who even in his most alarmist period still opposed sterilization of the feebleminded. He told of his experience in a small town where a feebleminded girl had had an ovarectomy and where the men and boys stood in line before the house to have intercourse with her while her mother was at work. The result was an epidemic of gonorrhea. He also told of a young carpenter who fell from a house roof and injured himself so that he was sterile. When the word spread about town, "the number of women with whom he had sexual relations, the fact that he had young girls who made dates with him days and weeks ahead, knowing he was sterile and that the danger of pregnancy was absent, made a most profound impression on my mind," Fernald related. "Now if one sterile man had that experience in one community I fail to see why a dozen sterile men would not constitute a very formidable moral risk." [14]

The moral objections aroused by sterilization were brought into relief in 1909 when the American Prison Association debated a plea by Dr. Harry Sharp, who had pioneered sterilization in Indiana, for the sterilization of criminals. Several members backed a prison warden who asked: "Who may you be, ladies and gentlemen, that set yourselves up to be greater in your judgment than the Almighty powers that brought us all into existence? When you say that I, or you, or this man or that man shall be deprived of offspring I say you are flying in the face of the Almighty." [15]

In reply a woman member of the Pennsylvania Prison Association countered with a Biblical reference that "we must have eunuchs for the kingdom of heaven's sake." Another lady, secretary of the King County Humane Society in Seattle, warned that sympathy should not be reserved only for the criminal, "but for the helpless, unfortunate children of the degenerate and criminally depraved who are brought into the world handicapped at their birth, cursed before they see the light of day, stunted mentally, morally and physically. They are the ones that are punished—they are the ones that pay the price, yea, even unto the third and fourth generation." [16] Nevertheless, in the long run the proponents of sterilization were unable to shake an underlying feeling with many people that sterilization was immoral.

The Catholic Church in particular took a firm stand against sterilization, as it did against birth control, on the grounds that sterilization was a "very grave mutilation" and a mortal sin against nature because it frustrated reproduction. The Papal Encyclical *Casti Connubii* in 1930 confirmed the opposition of the Church. From the beginning the Church constituted a major political force both against enactment of sterilization laws and against their enforcement once enacted.[17]

A committee on sterilization of the Institute of Criminal Law and Criminology—although a majority of its members were advocates of sterilization like Harry H. Laughlin, Harry C. Sharp, Bleecker van Wagenen, and Thomas D. Crothers—summarized the scientific arguments for and against sterilization. Even those abnormalities caused by a dominant gene, the Committee pointed out, are passed on to but one-half the offspring. Although sterilization would be effective against a dominant gene, it would be as likely to prevent the birth of a normal as an abnormal child. In the case of recessive abnormalities, on the other hand, most of the genes are transmitted by carriers who are themselves normal and generally unrecognizable. Hence sterilization would be relatively powerless to reduce the incidence of the gene. (This objection was especially important, of course, since eugenists of the Davenport school held that most mental aberrations were recessive.) Despite the objections, however, the Committee backed sterilization, a decision not too hard to understand considering its membership.[18]

Not all advocates of sterilization stressed only the eugenic arguments. Some declared that the sterilization of defectives, even if not always justified on the grounds of heredity, would at least prevent procreation by those unfitted for the responsibilities of parenthood. Others maintained that sterilization might cure a person of evil propensities or provide a fitting punishment for rapists and perverts. Yet to most eugenists such an argument complicated and endangered the campaign. A punitive motive meant that the laws were almost certain to be declared unconstitutional as cruel and unusual punishment. A therapeutic argument for sterilization or asexualization undercut the contention that vasectomy and salpingectomy were simple operations that rendered a patient sterile without affecting his physical, mental, or sexual development. Nevertheless, therapeutic and punitive motives found their way into many of the laws.[19]

Unlike the campaign for custodial care, the drive for sterilization had little central organization. In one state a physician might organize sentiment for a law, in another an asylum superintendent, in still another the members of the state board of charities. What unity the movement had came mostly from the Eugenics Record Office— but not from Davenport himself. Although Davenport could be found on both sides of the sterilization issue, he was in his better moments primarily a research man who complained, "nowadays, when people get an idea about a thing, they become enthusiastic and rush to pass laws before they know what they are doing." [20]

Harry H. Laughlin, assistant director of the Records Office, was the one who became a zealot for passing laws. A man little liked by others; with no sense of humor, more than his share of dogmatism, and no tolerance of criticism from others, he allowed his prejudices so to dominate his conclusions that his fellow scientists could not take him seriously. Himself an epileptic, happily married but childless, he was a man for whom every activity assumed grandiose proportions. For him, eugenics was a solemn and noble crusade, and upon every document and report in that crusade he lavished meticulous care.

Laughlin operated through the Committee to Study and Report

on the Best Practical Means of Cutting off the Defective Germ-Plasm in the American Population, organized under the Eugenics Section of the American Breeders' Association. (The length of the name suggests that Laughlin chose it.) Bleecker van Wagenen, who financed its work, served as chairman and Laughlin as secretary. In its report for 1914, the Committee took the high ground that "society must look upon germ-plasm as belonging to society and not solely to the individual who carries it." The report estimated the socially inadequate varieties of the American people at 10 per cent of the total population and advocated segregation, sterilization, and education in the facts of heredity as the chief means of reducing defective germ-plasm. Such a program, the Committee promised, would in two generations largely purge the United States of its burden of undesirable germ-plasm.[21]

Along with the report, Laughlin submitted a detailed history of sterilization in the United States. Typical of Laughlin's reports, it was a compendium that included complete texts of all laws passed, an analysis of administration state by state, and a history of litigation with the texts of briefs and court decisions. To it, he added the draft of a model sterilization law that would both satisfy the courts and fulfill his own concept of what a scientific eugenical sterilization law should accomplish.[22]

Laughlin's model law called for the sterilization of all those who were potential parents of socially inadequate offspring. The socially inadequate, by his definition, consisted of the feebleminded, insane, criminalistic ("including the delinquent and wayward"), epileptic, inebriate, diseased, blind, deaf, deformed, and dependent ("including orphans, ne'er-do-wells, the homeless, tramps and paupers").[23] The potential parents of such offspring would be subject to sterilization whether inside or outside an institution, so that the law would not be discriminatory class legislation and so that the greatest eugenic good would result. In order to assure due process of law, the state eugenicist, whose duty it would be to study the heredity of the state's socially inadequate, would be required to secure a court order for sterilization. While administrative features of his model law were unexceptionable, the choice of candidates for sterilization went far beyond what anyone except the most extreme hereditarian (like Laughlin) would consider justified.

After the first sterilization law in Indiana in 1907,[24] fifteen other states—all in the North and West—followed suit by the time of America's entrance into the First World War: Connecticut, Washington, and California in 1909, New Jersey and Iowa in 1911, Nevada and New York in 1912, North Dakota, Michigan, Kansas, and Wisconsin in 1913, Nebraska in 1915, and Oregon, South Dakota, and New Hampshire in 1917.

The campaign in Wisconsin indicated some of the typical forces involved in enacting and enforcing the laws. By the 1890's those charged with the care of the poor, delinquent, and defective were increasingly concerned with heredity and were already hinting at the need for castration of the feebleminded and criminal. When the state opened a Home for the Feebleminded in 1895, Dr. A. W. Wilmarth was brought from Pennsylvania as superintendent and soon became the central figure in a campaign for sterilization. By 1907, the year that Indiana passed the first such law, Wisconsin's first law was introduced into the legislature by the Legislative Visiting Committee, which had the duty of inspecting the state mental and penal institutions. Elmore T. Elver, the young Madison attorney who spoke for the Committee, assured the legislators that most doctors and superintendents were united in its support. In 1907 the bill passed, but without appropriations to put it into effect; in 1909 a second attempt failed completely; not until 1913 did a bill finally pass and receive the signature of the Progressive governor, Francis E. McGovern.[25]

By then the lines for and against sterilization had been drawn. The State Board of Control backed the bill, as did most of the state's superintendents, led by Dr. Wilmarth. So too did many of the leaders of the state medical society. At the University of Wisconsin a number of professors, especially in biology and sociology, favored the bill—chief among them the liberal and controversial sociologist, Edward A. Ross. Charles R. Van Hise, president of the University and a leader in the conservation movement, praised sterilization as a means for the conserving of man. Opposition came from the Archbishop of Milwaukee and other religious leaders and from many persons whose sentiments would not allow them to back the bill. On the whole, then, the bill had the backing of reform forces in the state.[26]

The bill, as passed, was typical of many of the early sterilization laws. The State Board of Control was authorized to appoint a surgeon and a psychiatrist who, together with the superintendents of the state and county institutions for the criminal, insane, feebleminded, and epileptic, could examine cases and, if they unanimously found that procreation was inadvisable, could order the safest and most effective operation. Five years after passage of the law, only sixty operations had been performed—all at the Home for the Feebleminded, sometimes at the request of a parent and never when a parent or relative objected.[27]

American laws preceded by twenty years the sterilization laws of other countries and were pioneering ventures watched by eugenists of other lands. But the pioneering nature of the laws can hardly explain their early crudities. Two of the laws, by Washington and Nevada, were not eugenic at all but purely punitive. They permitted a judge, at the time of sentencing, to impose sterilization "whenever any person shall be adjudged guilty of carnal abuse of a female person under the age of ten years, or of rape, or shall be adjudged a habitual criminal." All laws passed by 1921 and many passed thereafter applied to rapists or sexual perverts and were therefore at least partly punitive or therapeutic in purpose. Even those that were primarily eugenic in purpose applied sterilization to a bewildering variety of persons with little attention to scientific classification. All applied to the feebleminded and most to epileptics and the insane, but also included in various laws were confirmed criminals, drunkards, drug addicts, syphilitics, moral degenerates, and prostitutes.[28] Doubtless the oddest bill was that introduced by a Missouri legislator for sterilization of those "convicted of murder (not in the heat of passion), rape, highway robbery, chicken stealing, bombing or theft of automobiles." [29] Even Laughlin might have been amused.

The administrative machinery of the early laws assumed that sterilization was solely a medical decision to be left to the determination of a board of experts. Most of these statutes did not provide for notice to parents or near kin, nor for defense counsel and cross-examination of witnesses, nor for appeal to the courts. In addition, they applied only to persons in institutions and not to the same classes, eugenically more dangerous, who dwelt outside institutions. A few of the early laws, however, pointed the way toward better things to come. The New Jersey law, signed by Governor Woodrow Wilson in 1911, provided that the inmate be represented by counsel and that a decision for sterilization could be appealed to the courts. Also the law signed by Governor Hiram Johnson of California in 1913 (repealing the earlier law of 1909) made some sense eugenically since it provided for sterilization of the hereditary insane upon release from an asylum—a provision extended to the feebleminded in 1917.[30] Aside from the machinery, the real objection to the laws was that the experts claimed considerable knowledge about the heredity of mental aberrations but were in fact misled; the laws, had they been enforced, would have been not only grossly unfair but scientifically absurd.

The fate of the laws varied from state to state, but in general a combination of lax enforcement and court decrees left them relatively innocuous. The punitive law of Nevada received its first test when a state judge sentenced a young rapist to prison and ordered him sterilized because he was epileptic and, the judge reasoned, ought not to have children. A United States District Court in 1918 promptly declared this unconstitutional as cruel and unusual punishment. In Indiana, Dr. Sharp performed 176 operations on volunteers in the Indiana Reformatory prior to the 1907 statute and 125 compulsory sterilizations afterwards, but in 1909 a new governor, who opposed the law, requested that the practice cease. By the time a subsequent governor encouraged enforcement once more, reformatory officials believed the law unconstitutional and initiated a test case of a teen-ager arrested for incest with his twelve-year-old half sister. Since the law did not provide for notice or appeal, it was found unconstitutional in 1921 for denying due process of law.[31]

In other states, too, officials cautiously instituted test cases to protect themselves. New Jersey officials selected an epileptic girl whose mother was also epileptic and whose father was allegedly feebleminded. The state Supreme Court in 1913 held the law unconstitutional as discriminatory class legislation because it applied only to those epileptics who were in state institutions, and thus deprived those in institutions of equal protection of the laws. New York officials chose an unusually strong case in Frank Osborn, a feebleminded son of a feebleminded father and mother. He was one of sixteen children, of whom eight had died in infancy, five others (like Frank) were in state institutions for the feebleminded, and a sister was a prostitute. Despite this, the state Supreme Court in 1915 perpetually enjoined enforcement of the law, and further litigation came to an end when Governor Alfred E. Smith, in 1920, signed a repeal measure which had passed the legislature unanimously.[32] Thus no sterilizations were performed under the laws in either New Jersey or New York.

After World War I, the sterilization campaign continued, but in a relatively more reasonable form. By this time it was clear that the laws, in order to pass muster in the courts, would have to provide due process of law, would have to avoid punitive motives, and should probably be applied to defectives both in and out of institutions so that they would not be class legislation.[33] Most of the states that had passed laws earlier added amendments or new laws during the 1920's, while fourteen states, including many southern states, enacted their first laws. First laws came in North Carolina and Alabama in 1919, Montana and Delaware in 1923, Virginia in 1924, Idaho, Utah, Minnesota, and Maine in 1925, Mississippi in 1928, West Virginia and Arizona in 1929, and Vermont and Oklahoma in 1931. On the whole, the statutes of this period were better drawn. They were less likely to number rapists and perverts among those subject to sterilization, were more likely to provide for notice, counsel at hearings, and appeal to the courts, and often applied to defectives in and out of institutions or to persons about to be released from an institution. By 1931, thirty states had passed a sterilization law at one time or another, and in twenty-seven states the laws were still on the books, if not always enforced.[34]

During the 1920's several developments removed some of the medical and legal doubts that had earlier beclouded the subject of sterilization.

Since the California law called for sterilization of the insane and feebleminded upon their release from institutions and since over half of the sterilizations of the country were in California, this state provided an ideal laboratory to investigate the effects of the operation. There E. S. Gosney, a businessman with an enthusiasm for eugenics, supplied funds for such a study. To undertake the investigation, he secured the services of Paul Popenoe, a native Californian whose varied career had included journalism, exploration, editorship of the *Journal of Heredity* after 1913, service during World War I as a captain charged with enforcing laws prohibiting prostitution and sale of intoxicants near army camps, and active work in the American Social Hygiene Association to encourage sex education.[35] Gosney also obtained the cooperation of prominent lawyers and physicians to assess the legal and medical aspects of sterilization. In 1928, he founded and endowed the Human Betterment Foundation (with Gosney as president, Popenoe as secretary, and David Starr Jordan on the Board of Directors) to continue investigations. Out of the investigations came twenty-five influential papers that demonstrated, on the whole, the success of sterilization in California.[36]

In 1930, in *Sterilization for Human Betterment,* Gosney and Popenoe presented in popular form the results of the California experience. By following up persons who had been sterilized and released, they answered many of the questions that had been raised by the arguments over sterilization. From 1909 to 1929 there were 6,255 sterilizations in California (601 more males than females), with the insane outnumbering the feebleminded by more than two to one. In that time there occurred three known failures of vasectomy and four known failures of salpingectomy (that is, pregnancy had occurred after the operation), and there were four deaths from the operation. Other than this, sterilization had proved a success. "Our investigations show," they reported, "that it has no effect upon sex desire, sex performance, or sex feeling of the subject, except a favorable psychological effect in some cases particularly where the fear of pregnancy is removed." [37] Of the insane patients, six out of seven of those queried were satisfied with the operation. Nor did it have the bad moral effect that had been predicted. Among the feebleminded, three-fourths were sex delinquents on admission to the institution, yet only one in twelve became sex delinquents on release under supervision. Social workers were therefore nearly unanimous in support of the program. So successful had it become, in fact, that all persons released from the Sonoma State Home for the Feebleminded and one out of six of the new inmates admitted to the hospitals for the insane were being sterilized. Indeed, many mentally retarded or unstable persons were being admitted to the institutions merely to be sterilized and then released.[38]

At the same time, the legal doubts that enshrouded sterilization were dispelled by the case of feebleminded Carrie Buck. Born to a feebleminded and immoral mother, Carrie had been adopted at the age of four by a family in Charlottesville, Virginia. There she attended school until the sixth grade and then, unable to continue further, did housework under strict supervision. But she proved unmanageable and was soon pregnant. In January, 1924, as a result, she, like her mother before her, was committed to the State Colony for Epileptics and Feebleminded, where her child was born. In the fall she was chosen for the first sterilization under the Virginia law passed that same year, and her case began its course toward the Supreme Court of the United States.[39]

Arthur H. Estabrook, the eugenics field worker who had earlier collected the material on *The Jukes in 1915,* investigated Carrie's family background. Laughlin, as the eugenics expert, then journeyed to Virginia to interpret the information for the Circuit Court of Amherst County. He explained that Carrie's mother had a mental age of seven years, eight months; that Carrie's mental age was nine; and that her six-months-old baby was "supposed to be mental defective." Carrie's ancestors were difficult to trace because they belonged "to the shiftless, ignorant, and worthless class of anti-social whites of the South," but enough was known, Laughlin claimed, to assure the court that Carrie's feeblemindedness and immorality were inherited. Estabrook, too, took the stand and declared (this in 1925) that feeblemindedness was a simple Mendelian recessive. Finally, the superintendent of the State Colony testified that a great saving would result if girls like Carrie could be sterilized and released rather than held in the institution for the twenty-five years of their child-bearing period.[40]

The order for sterilization was upheld by both the Circuit Court and the Virginia Supreme Court. Finally, in the spring of 1927, the United States Supreme Court, in the famous decision of Justice Oliver Wendell Holmes in *Buck* vs. *Bell,* held that sterilization fell within the police power of the state. "We have seen more than once that the public welfare may call upon the best citizens for their lives," Justice Holmes, himself a sympathizer with eugenics, wrote in a much-quoted passage.

> It would be strange if it could not call upon those who already sap the strength of the State for these lesser sacrifices, often not felt to be such by those concerned, in order to prevent our being swamped with incompetence. It is better for all the world, if instead of waiting for their imbecility, society can prevent those who are manifestly unfit from continuing their kind. The principle that sustains compulsory vaccination is broad enough to cover cutting the Fallopian tubes. . . . [And in a famous aphorism he concluded] Three generations of imbeciles are enough.[41]

Thus, with but one dissent, the Supreme Court put its seal of approval upon the Virginia sterilization law, and brought renewed vigor to the sterilization campaign.

Another hopeful sign for advocates of sterilization was that the United States in the late 1920's no longer stood alone in the adoption of sterilization laws. The Canadian province of Alberta enacted a sterilization law in 1928, followed five years later by British Columbia. In the Scandinavian countries, a determined campaign for sterilization during the 1920's finally achieved success with passage of a law in Denmark in 1929, the first such in Europe. Within a few years Finland, Sweden, Norway, and Iceland followed suit. In 1933 Germany under the Nazis put its notorious sterilization program into effect. And across the channel in England the Eugenics Society conducted a valiant but losing battle for sterilization.[42]

The reported success of sterilization in California, the approval of the Supreme Court, and the support from other nations brought a brief revival to the movement. Within four years of the court decision, five more states (Mississippi, West Virginia, Arizona, Vermont, and Oklahoma) enacted their first sterilization laws, while ten states amended or replaced their earlier laws to bring them into line with the Virginia statute. Equally important, states that had not enforced or had only timidly enforced their laws began a more consistent enforcement. In North Carolina, for instance, the law of 1919 had never been used, but new laws in 1929 and 1933 made sterilization a state policy.[43]

Oddly enough, in actual administration the laws have been used chiefly for their social rather than their eugenic consequences. In North Carolina, for instance, a major motive has been to control breeding in the so-called social problem group—those with lives characterized by poverty, loose marriage liaisons, illegitimacy, and dependence on relief. The cases recommended for sterilization (in North Carolina persons both in and out of institutions may be sterilized) reveal this clearly: a single girl of twenty-five, unmarried, epileptic, parents dead, who was subjected to repeated seductions; a seventeen-year-old girl (I.Q. 58), committed to reform school for prostitution, whose mother was dead and whose father was a drunkard suspected of incest; or an unmarried Negro woman of thirty-one (I.Q. 70), with eight illegitimate children by as many fathers, whose family had been on and off relief for sixteen years. In such cases no attention was paid to heredity, for the chief aim was to relieve the suffering and the drain on charity that childbirth entailed.[44]

By the 1920's those institutions using sterilization were also concerned with social, as well as eugenic, consequences. A few institutions for the feebleminded have included sterilization as part of a program to prepare their charges for life in the outside world, on grounds that the feebleminded stood a better chance for success if they avoided pregnancy out of wedlock and avoided the financial and social responsibilities of children in wedlock. In the case of the insane, too, an important aim has been to prevent pregnancy in those emotionally unfitted for childbirth or the responsibilities of child raising. Litigation has usually been avoided since, even when a law authorizes compulsory sterilization, officials have generally sought the consent of the patient or a relative. At any rate, in administration of the laws, little effort has been made to trace pedigrees or to limit sterilization to those whose defect was known to be hereditary.[45]

Indeed, it is doubtful if present knowledge provides justification, on eugenic grounds, for a state policy of sterilization. The indignity and (in the case of women) danger of the operation can hardly justify the negligible and largely unknown eugenic results. Whether sterilization can, on occasion, be justified on social grounds is another question. Certainly, in states where sterilization is used, a number of superintendents and social workers have praised the results. Yet, without safeguards, a policy of sterilization is fraught with danger to the rights of the individual—danger that persons will be pressured into an operation against their wills or that, in the southern states, it will be employed primarily against members of the Negro race.

By the end of 1931, twenty-four years after the first law, somewhat more than 12,145 operations had been performed under the laws, 7,548 of these in California alone. At that time sterilization of the insane outnumbered sterilization of the feebleminded about two to one, while sterilization of epileptics, criminals and others was negligible.[46] By the end of 1958, the total sterilizations under the laws had risen to only 60,926. Although California still led with 20,011, such southern states as North Carolina, Georgia, and Virginia were performing more sterilizations relative to population. By then the number of persons sterilized for feeblemindedness had slightly topped the number sterilized for insanity, and about three out of five of those sterilized had been women.[47] How many sterilizations have been performed for eugenic, contraceptive, or other reasons outside the law cannot of course be estimated. In any event, in comparison with the total number of insane and feebleminded in the United States since 1907, relatively few have been sterilized.

## Marriage Regulation

All eugenists acknowledged that the regulation of marriage was desirable in theory but most agreed too that it was futile in practice—futile because the socially inadequate would never be bound by mere laws in their breeding habits and because the laws would never be properly enforced.[48] Doubtless there were good reasons for the skepticism. Toward the end of World War I, for example, J. E. Wallace Wallin prepared a series of bills on mental defect for the Missouri legislature. A bill barring marriage of the feebleminded was not among them because Wallin, like most eugenists, was convinced that such a law would not be enforced and could not control reproduction of unmarried feebleminded girls. But a delegation from the women's clubs of the state insisted, as a price for supporting his other bills, that a law be included fining any clergyman or clerk of court who permitted a feebleminded, insane, or epileptic person to marry. In 1947, over a quarter of a century later, Wallin checked and found that no fine had ever been imposed under the law.[49]

The leaders of the eugenics movement, because of their skepticism, did little to promote laws to restrict the marriage of defectives.[50] They left the promotion, instead, to local women's clubs, churches, physicians, and charity groups. Since the states had a long tradition of regulating marriage and since, in addition, such laws cost nothing, they rarely became involved in controversy.

Often the effort to pass eugenic marriage laws worked hand in hand with the campaign, set in motion by a growing concern over venereal disease, to pass laws that made blood tests and doctor's certificates mandatory in order to receive a marriage license. As long as marriage was forbidden to those with venereal disease, it appeared reasonable to extend the prohibition to the feebleminded, insane, and epileptic. One example, and a controversial one, was the Oregon Hygienic Marriage Examination and License Bill, which required both applicants to pass a medical examination for venereal disease, contagious diseases, and mental illness. If either partner failed the test, the marriage would be prohibited unless one partner underwent sterilization. When submitted to a referendum in 1921, the law lost by a vote of 65,793 to 56,858.[51] Because laws controlling the marriage of those with venereal disease were partly to prevent the birth of diseased infants, they were often called eugenical marriage laws, despite the fact that, as every good eugenist knew, eugenics was concerned with genes, not germs. After 1909, when Washington passed the first such law, eugenics on occasion received a little free publicity from their passage.[52]

By the middle 1930's, forty-one states had laws to prohibit marriage of the insane and feebleminded, seventeen to prohibit marriage of epileptics, and four to prohibit marriage of confirmed drunkards.[53] As in the case of the sterilization laws, a variety of motives led to their passage. Some of the laws denied the right of marriage because such persons could not make contracts, others because they would probably make poor parents, and still others because their offspring were believed likely to inherit the defect of the parent. Whether such laws have prevented some insane, feeble-minded, or epileptic persons from applying for marriage licenses is difficult to judge, but the laws have seldom stood in the way of any who have applied.

The legislative battle of the eugenics movement consisted, then, of a long list of partial victories that added up to over-all defeat. The campaign for custodial care of the feebleminded demonstrated primarily that the goal lay beyond reach and that most of the feeble-minded would have to be cared for and supervised outside of in-stitutions. In twenty-seven states sterilization laws remain in force. But they have seldom been enforced and, where they have been, their eugenic significance has been negligible. Finally, in the case of marriage laws, few eugenists would claim, either before the laws were passed or afterwards, that they were an effective means to stamp out undesirable genes. Probably a major accomplishment of the legislative campaign lay in the opportunity to educate the pub-lic in eugenics doctrines, to make the public eugenics-conscious. Certainly the course of the campaigns left little chance that an edu-cated American would not read or hear of the dangers from heredi-tary defectives. Certainly, too, the general public did not become eugenics-conscious, and a continued complaint of eugenists remained the difficulty of arousing the public to the importance of heredity.

# Chapter X

# Eugenics and Race

The extreme racism associated with eugenics did more to bring eugenics to public notice and to cause eventual scientific repudiation of the early eugenics movement than any other single factor. A mutual attraction brought on the marriage of racism with eugenics. Many eugenists, already predisposed to nativism, found in the powerful and popular movement to restrict immigration a forum for placing eugenic attitudes before the public as well as an opportunity to strike a blow against what they believed to be degeneration of American stock. "Eugenics can never amount to anything practically," Irving Fisher wrote Davenport in 1912, "until it has begun, as Galton wanted it, to be a popular movement with a certain amount of religious flavor in it, and as . . . there is already a sentiment in favor of restricting immigration, . . . this is a golden opportunity to get people in general to talk eugenics." [1]

Racists and restrictionists, at the same time, found in eugenics the scientific reassurances they needed that heredity shaped man's personality and that their assumptions rested on biological facts. [2] In 1911 Prescott Hall of the Immigration Restriction League re-established contact with Davenport, his old Harvard classmate, and the two shortly agreed that the Eugenics Section of the American Breeders' Association needed a committee on immigration. Hall and Robert DeC. Ward became the leading members of the committee. Despite Davenport's cautious suggestion that "I do not at the present time think the committee wants to commit itself to the matter of liberalization versus restriction or to any propaganda excepting that of bringing about a more careful study of the whole situation," the committee immediately became a center for restriction propaganda.[3] Soon thereafter, with the formation of the American Genetic Association, Hall and Ward also became the leading members of its committee on immigration.[4] When they advocated immigration restriction on racial grounds, then, they spoke as representatives of America's eugenists and geneticists. Both the *Journal of Heredity,* official organ of the American Genetic Association, and *Eugenical News,* edited by Laughlin at Cold Spring Harbor, were avidly racist and restrictionist.

### Race and Anti-Race

The growth of racial attitudes based on scientific premises provoked impressive scientific criticism. Franz Boas, who combined a critical mind with a sympathy for other peoples and cultures, was both the leading American anthropologist and the leading opponent of the assumptions of racial inequality. As early as 1894 he attacked these dogmas and, in his book, *The Mind of Primitive Man* (1911), provided the most important statement of the anti-racist case.[5]

Boas acknowledged the essential logic of a racist outlook: that peoples and races differ in character and achievement and that the differences could well represent inherent abilities. He pointed out, however, that in an earlier period the Chinese or Egyptians could have argued that the Anglo-Saxons were barbarians incapable of civilization; yet given an opportunity, the Teutonic tribes demonstrated a certain capability. Civilization, in fact, was the sum of the contributions of many races; the achievements of a race were often the result of chance that brought its members into favorable contact with civilization; and the diverse achievements of various races could represent varying opportunities rather than varying innate abilities.[6] Even the many anatomical differences among races that had been cataloged by physical anthropology proved nothing concerning racial inequality, for little was known about the relationship between physical and mental traits.[7]

Boas' attitude was one of skepticism: he did not deny inequality of mental traits among races—indeed, he thought inequality rather likely—but he denied that differences had yet been proved or that they were very great. Among American anthropologists generally, Boas' influence and the understanding that came through sympathetic study of diverse cultures were decisive in creating a climate unfavorable to racist dogmas.[8] As a result, Americans who subscribed to these theories were seldom anthropologists and were forced to look to Europe for anthropological findings to buttress their case.

Racist doctrines not only lacked scientific support among anthropologists but met insistent attack in the public arena. With the growth of a movement for the restriction of the immigration, the National Liberal Immigration League and other groups organized to combat restrictionist propaganda. Jews, whose history of persecution gave them a special sensitivity to racial discrimination and whose business and professional success gave them special strength among the new immigrants, did much to finance the counterattack. As a result, every Congressional committee that heard pleas for exclusion on racial grounds also heard statements in rebuttal; every important restrictionist publication brought forth articles and books in reply. The mounting strength of racism, therefore, did not result from lack of opposition but from the confidence of its adherents that science sided with them, sentimentality with their opponents.

Racist writings followed a fairly set pattern. Almost invariably they opened with a general explanation that modern science held heredity to be the key in shaping man's personality. Eugenics, it was claimed, provided the proof, for the works of Galton, Pearson, and many American eugenists were never-failing sources for evidence that nature dominated nurture in the life of man. With the disproof of the inheritance of acquired characters, racists denied that American institutions could mold the immigrant or his children to the American pattern. Hence the exclusion of "inferior" races had the same justification as other eugenics programs. "The same arguments which induce us to segregate criminals and feebleminded and thus prevent their breeding," Prescott Hall explained in 1910, "apply to excluding from our borders individuals whose multiplying here is likely to lower the average of our people." [9]

Having established the importance of heredity in general, racists could then proceed to describe, in impressionistic fashion, the major characteristics of particular races without the formality of demonstrating that any specific trait was hereditary. (At least the Kallikaks were accorded the courtesy of a pedigree study before condemnation, but entire races were condemned without a similar consideration.) Even the word race, as some acknowledged, was often used to refer to national, language, or religious instead of biological groups. Although most racists claimed to be describing some particular mixture of Nordic, Alpine, and Mediterranean stock, the stereotypes of national and linguistic groups had become so widespread that few could be consistent. Their writings were, in fact, largely literary exercises, in which the writer carefully chose his terms so that what in one race might be described as "intelligence" would in another be "craftiness."

One of the most successful such writings was by Edward A. Ross, the popular, eloquent, and liberal sociologist at the University of Wisconsin. An avid eugenist, he set out in 1912 on a sixteen-month study, *The Old World in the New,* and provided a vivid portrayal of the threat to American stock.

He found that the Celtic Irish were gifted with imagination and oratorical ability to aid them in politics but that their lack of industry and love of alcohol often placed them on charity. Italians— especially short, dark, long-headed Mediterraneans from southern Italy and Sicily—were given to crimes of sex and violence. They had a high proportion of "low foreheads, open mouths, weak chins, poor features, skew faces, small or knobby crania, and backless heads. Such people lack the power to take rational care of themselves." Slavs, Ross reported, were a yielding and servile people, whose ignorance and subjection to priestcraft held them in the bottom rungs of unskilled labor. They were not especially criminal, though wife beaters and alcoholics. In discussing eastern European Jews, he admitted the power of "subtle Hebrew brains," but regretted that their intelligence served for tricky, underhanded business practices. "None can beat the Jew at a bargain, for through all the intricacies of commerce he can scent his profit." He berated Jews for clannishness, for preferring city life over farming, for sensuality ("The fact that pleasure-loving Jewish businessmen spare Jewesses but pursue Gentile girls excites bitter comment"), and for financing the campaign against immigration restriction.[10]

In contrast, the native American type—American racists agreed— was predominately of fine Nordic stock, fused from the English, German, Dutch, and Scotch-Irish who had settled the colonies and stamped the national character. "It is not vain glory," the president of the National Institute of Immigration averred, "when we say that we have bred more than sixty millions of the finest people the world has ever seen. Today there is to surpass us, none. Therefore any race that we admit to our body social is certain to be more or less inferior." [11]

Not only did these propagandists consult biology to support their views on heredity but also to confirm their conviction that races should preserve their purity and avoid race mixture. In the nineteenth century the phenomenon of hybrid vigor, in which the cross-

ing of two varieties often produced a hybrid superior in some respects to either parent, was well known. Such a concept underlay
the hope of many Americans that the amalgamation of immigrants
in America might produce a people superior to the races from which
they sprang. In the twentieth century, however, the earlier faith
gave way to more exclusive doctrines.

One such doctrine was based on analogy with what nineteenth-
century agricultural breeders had called reversions—in which a hybrid from two domestic strains appeared to have traits characteristic of a wild variety. Most such cases soon received a simple Mendelian explanation.[12] With no support from biologists, a few racists
argued after 1908 that closely related races (like the Nordic strains
that produced the American type) could safely interbreed but that
widely varying races (like Nordics and Mediterraneans, or whites
and Negroes) should not be crossed, since the result would be a reversion to the lowest type. "The greater the divergence between
crossed varieties," one writer explained, "the more powerful does
the reversionary tendency become." As late as the mid-1920's, Henry
Pratt Fairchild, a eugenist and sociologist, still justified exclusion
of southern Europeans on the thoroughly discredited grounds that
mixture with Nordics produced reversions, or, as he put it, "the
result to be looked for in the offspring is . . . a primitive, gen-
eralized type—often spoken of as a 'reversion,' 'atavism,' or 'throw-
back.' "[13]

A more important attitude, again one built on analogy with agricultural breeding, was that the crossing of closely related stocks
might produce hybrid vigor but that crossing of distant stocks often
created highly variable hybrids that would, especially in later generations, prove disharmonious and inferior. Such a view had wide
scientific support. Edward M. East took time out from his important work in corn breeding at Harvard to write on corn and man
and to condemn race crossing. Davenport added his authority to the
view that "miscegenation commonly spells disharmony—disharmony
of physical, mental and temperamental qualities. . . . A hybridized
people are a badly put together people and a dissatisfied, restless,
ineffective people."[14] Some racists argued that the Nordic could
safely amalgamate only with Nordics and not with other white races;
others that the white races could safely intermarry but should avoid
the colored races. There was, in short, general agreement on the
principle but much disagreement on its application.[15]

In fact, however, the agricultural analogy begged the question:

for the question that really needed answering was not what happened in the crossing of plants and animals but what happened in the crossing of human stocks. "There is an extensive literature on race mixtures," Samuel J. Holmes, a zoologist and moderate eugenist at the University of California, pointed out, "but from the scientific standpoint most of it is exceedingly superficial and disappointing. It is frequently marred by prejudice, and rarely is any attempt made to separate the social and biological factors that conspire to determine the status and characteristics of mixed breeds." [16] Thus the analogy with agricultural breeding gave scientific support to an exaltation of racial purity that in fact had no scientific foundation.

The culmination of the racist argument—its haughty conservatism and exclusiveness—came in the writings of Madison Grant and Lothrop Stoddard. Grant's obsession was with the new immigration and, in his 1916 book on *The Passing of the Great Race,* he lamented the decline of Nordic influence in his own nation and Europe. Although Stoddard too detested the new immigration and worshipped the Nordic, his book, published in 1920, was directed instead at *The Rising Tide of Color against White Supremacy.* A Harvard Ph.D., lawyer, journalist, eugenist, and disciple of Grant, he feared that the awakening of the peoples in Asia, Africa, and South America foreshadowed eventual colored domination, mongrelization, and the destruction of civilization.[17]

Grant's writings revealed the insecurity that molded his defensive attitudes. He told how "in the city of New York, and elsewhere in the United States, there is a native American aristocracy resting upon layer after layer of immigrants of lower races." With alarm he described how New York "is becoming a *cloaca gentium* which will produce many amazing racial hybrids and some ethnic horrors that will be beyond the powers of future anthropologists to unravel." The old stock American, "too proud to mix socially with them," was retiring from the scene; "he is to-day being literally driven off the streets of New York City by the swarms of Polish Jews. These immigrants adopt the language of the native American; they wear his clothes; they steal his name; and they are beginning to take his women, but they seldom adopt his religion or understand his ideas." [18] From the complaints, one can almost see Grant: a conservative and distinguished looking New York bachelor lawyer of an old and aristocratic lineage. A man of wealth, he had been a sportsman hunter and served as chairman of the New York Zoological Society. The ideas that he picked up from his biologist friends like Davenport or from his readings in European anthropologists he converted into pleas for aristocracy and racial exclusion.

His book was an incredible hymn to the tall, blond, blue-eyed, long-headed Nordic, that race of pioneers, adventurers, organizers, and aristocrats. He found Nordics wherever civilization had flourished—they had carried Sanskrit to India, created the civilizations of ancient Greece and Rome until overwhelmed by lesser races, accounted for the greatness of David and, in all probability, of Christ, and settled America to give the infant nation its character. The class divisions in Europe, he believed, still reflected the ascendancy of the conquering Nordics, with Nordic aristocrats on top and Alpine peasants at the bottom. The great race was passing, however, for in nearly every nation of Europe the extension of democracy transferred political power from Nordic to other hands. In America, too, through immigration, the old stock Nordics were giving way to inferior races; already amalgamation and ruin were in progress:

> Whether we like to admit it or not, the result of the mixture of two races, in the long run, gives us a race reverting to the more ancient, generalized and lower type. . . . The cross between a white man and a negro is a negro; . . . and the cross between any of the three European races and a Jew is a Jew.

Much as he feared the colored races, his special concern was for the new immigration, a concern he justified on the grounds that "race feeling may be called prejudice by those whose careers are cramped by it, but it is a natural antipathy which serves to maintain the purity of type." [19]

Grant's book completed the transformation of race into an explicit and eloquent expression of elitist attitudes. In the nineteenth century the developing racism had already justified exclusion of the Negro from social or political rights. Now, within the white community, race was identified with class and class with biological fitness. Among the coterie of extremists who set the tone of biological racism, there was contempt for the sentimental doctrine of human equality and a longing for government by the well born—by those great men and great races that everywhere had been the carriers of civilization. Thus eugenics and racism united in a scientific doctrine of an elite about to be swamped by the incompetence of those whose inheritance placed them among the enemies of civilization. [20]

The works of Grant and Stoddard, despite their inconsistencies and absurdities, won not only wide popular interest but also a good measure of scientific approval. *Science* adjudged Grant's book a "work of solid merit," while the *Journal of Heredity* declared, "the book contains little with which specialists are not familiar, but it supplies a readable account of recent work" and added: "in the field of anthropology he has followed the latest authorities." [21] (The *American Anthropologist,* significantly, did not review the book at all.) Grant's Nordic doctrines, in the 1920's, were repeated before Congressional committees and in popular magazines until they became an important facet of American thought. The works of Grant and Stoddard became standard sources, and remain so today, for white supremacy advocates of the South.

With the introduction of intelligence tests, psychologists hoped for the first time to measure objectively the mental differences between races and thus settle the vexing qustion of racial inequality. The findings, at first, were most gratifying to the restrictionists and became a major weapon in their arsenal for attacking those who claimed that racism was a product of prejudice.

The Army testing in World War I, a major factor in moderating the use of tests in diagnosing feeblemindedness, provided the first important data on the relative intelligence of racial groups. Carl C. Brigham, a psychologist who had helped direct the Army testing, analyzed the results by race and by nationality. They could not have better supported the white supremists' case had they been planned that way. Brigham found that the average of every white group exceeded the average of the Negroes and that within the white population the old immigration clearly bested the new. The average mental ages for the various foreign born were: England 14.87, Scotland 14.34, Holland 14.32, Germany 13.88, Denmark 13.69, Canada 13.66, Sweden 13.30, Norway 12.98, Belgium 12.79, Ireland 12.32, Austria 12.27, Turkey 12.02, Greece 11.90, Russia 11.34, Italy 11.01, and Poland 10.74. The only disquieting factor was that scores increased according to the number of years that an immigrant had dwelt in the United States. Brigham assumed, however, that the quality of immigrants had declined in recent years rather than that adaptation to American life and language affected test scores.[22]

Testing of immigrant groups in the 1920's generally confirmed that, with the exception of Jews, new immigrants did not score as well as old immigrants or the native born. Although some investigators noted the social and economic handicaps under which the

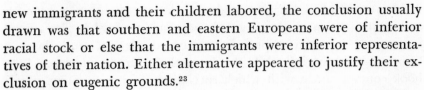

new immigrants and their children labored, the conclusion usually drawn was that southern and eastern Europeans were of inferior racial stock or else that the immigrants were inferior representatives of their nation. Either alternative appeared to justify their exclusion on eugenic grounds.[23]

Intelligence testing of Negroes, begun by 1913, has continued relentlessly to the present and has furnished masses of statistics for debating the level of Negro intelligence. Through the 1920's, the average Negro scores, despite much overlapping, were consistently below the scores of whites from similar age groups, even when investigators attempted to choose representatives from the two races with equivalent social and educational backgrounds. Despite reasons for caution, a moderate conclusion at the end of the decade was that the lower score of the Negro

> is present among infants, elementary school children, high school pupils, university students and adult men. It occurs on Binet tests, on verbal tests, on non-verbal group tests and on performance tests. These results are sufficiently numerous and consistent to point to a racial difference in intelligence.[29]

Some found further evidence of innate Negro inferiority in the fact that mulattoes, strengthened by their white heredity, performed better in the tests than Negroes although they shared in the discrimination and deprivations of Negroes.[24] As a result of such findings, those whose sympathies were with a racist point of view stressed the consistently poorer showing of Negroes; those with sympathy for the Negro's plight emphasized the wide overlap in scores and the possible improvement that could result from greater equality of opportunity.

As late as 1930, then, perhaps the preponderance of opinion among those working with intelligence tests was that the results of the tests lent considerable credence to racist assumptions. Only during the 1930's—as a consequence of new studies and the general trend of academic thought away from racism—did investigators decide that the evidence was not sufficient to draw any conclusion.

## Victory

The chief goal of restrictionists, as the century opened, was enactment of a literacy test for adult immigrants in order to reduce drastically the flow of immigration, especially the so-called new immigration from southern and eastern Europe. The restriction movement enjoyed broad support. By this time, the American Federation of Labor, disturbed by the impact of immigration upon wages and working conditions, provided the most powerful backing. A number of social workers and settlement workers added their voices out of a conviction that they could best assist those immigrants already here if the continued flow of immigration was reduced. Many Americans, too, believed that immigrants were a major contributor to the nation's burden of crime, mental disease, and poverty—a danger of special interest to eugenists.[25] Finally, business leaders, although their support wavered depending upon their need for unskilled labor, distrusted the contagious radicalism that immigrant groups allegedly imported with them.[26]

While organized opposition to restriction stemmed chiefly from immigrant organizations and from certain business interests, restrictionists privately acknowledged that their greatest hurdle was the pride that many an American took in his nation as an asylum for the oppressed. "This sentimental humanitarian attitude is the chief obstacle," Robert DeC. Ward confessed to Edward A. Ross, "although, of course, the steamship and railroad interests are very powerful. Still, if the Anglo-Saxon Americans were not so much imbued with this sentimental spirit, which is working havoc for the future race, the task in Congress would be far easier." [27]

A major step in reviving the campaign for restriction, after declining interest in the early twentieth century, was establishment by Congress in 1907 of an Immigration Commission to investigate the impact of immigrants upon American society. The Commission consisted of nine members, three from the House of Representatives, three from the Senate (including Henry Cabot Lodge), and three appointed by President Theodore Roosevelt. The key appointee was Jeremiah W. Jenks, an economist and restrictionist with considerable experience in directing legislative investigations. That the Commission required a staff of three hundred and an appropriation of a million dollars for its two years of field work and year of compilation gave immense authority to the forty-two volumes that resulted.[28]

The Commission, which investigated chiefly the social and economic effects of immigration, filled most of its volumes with impressive and detailed figures showing the impact of new immigrants upon wages, working conditions, sanitation, housing, crime, and mental illness. Often by ignoring the factor of recent arrival in the economic and social status of new immigrants and comparing them with a somewhat idealized picture of previous immigrants, the Commission demonstrated what most of its members had assumed: that the new immigration exerted a generally unsatisfactory influence upon American society. As a result of its investigations, the Commission, with but one dissent, duly recommended a literacy test for adult immigrants, but on economic rather than racial grounds: to alleviate an oversupply of unskilled labor. The principal result of the Commission's report, however, was to fix the stereotyped distinction between the desirable, easily assimilated old immigrants and an undesirable, unassimilable new.[29]

After the Commission's report, the campaign to enact a literacy test gathered renewed force. A bill was passed by Congress in 1913, only to meet a veto from William Howard Taft, and again in 1915, to meet Woodrow Wilson's veto. Finally, in 1917, during the tensions of a World War, Congress enacted a bill over Wilson's veto. In addition to the long-hoped-for literacy test, the law established an Asiatic zone from which all immigration was excluded. (This kept out Indians and East Indians and, along with the Chinese exclusion act and the 1907 Gentlemen's Agreement with Japan, went a long way toward effectively barring all orientals.) Restrictionists were exultant. "The new law is, in its essentials, a eugenic measure," Robert DeC. Ward declared, "perhaps the most comprehensive and satisfactory ever passed by Congress." [30]

The exultation turned to anguish, however, when proponents found that the literacy test sifted out relatively few immigrants and thus failed to accomplish the drastic restriction that its supporters anticipated. The law became, therefore, merely a first step and not the culmination of the restriction drive.

The culmination came in a postwar atmosphere of intense emotional reaction. The war period had created a dedication to 100 per cent Americanism, a distrust of the loyalty of hyphenated Americans, and a hatred of radicals and pacifists, often with foreign names, who opposed the nation's entrance into war. The postwar period brought labor unrest and a Red scare, involving frantic attacks on suspected radicals and highly publicized arrest and deportation of alien radicals. Into the atmosphere of fear and distrust came reports from abroad that the nation faced a deluge—exceeding the average of over one million yearly in the prewar period—of immigrants from war-racked Europe, beaten peoples, Jews fleeing persecution, peasants from poorer races. At the same time, organized labor's opposition to uncontrolled immigration was sharpened by a brief postwar depression. In the changed climate of opinion, representatives of the new immigrants stood almost alone in continued defense of the melting pot.[31]

While many factors contributed to a more restrictive policy, eugenists had an important role in shaping the form of that policy.

The center for eugenics influence was the House Committee on Immigration and Naturalization under Albert Johnson, the Republican Congressman from Washington who became its chairman in 1919. Johnson, originally a small-town newspaper editor, was elected to Congress in 1912 as a conservative with a record of strong action against foreign radicals and strikers and a crude hatred for oriental immigrants. Before the war he was already in contact with Hall, and by 1920 was a correspondent and acquaintance of Madison Grant. In June, 1920, Laughlin, whose attitude was warped by deep-seated prejudices and an extreme hereditarian outlook, gave the Committee his opinion on the biological aspects of immigration. Johnson, impressed by Laughlin's testimony, appointed him "Expert Eugenics Agent" of the Committee, so that he would continue his investigations. Off and on for nearly a decade, Laughlin appeared before the Committee with masses of statistics and charts to prove the threat from "inferior" races.[32]

Johnson was greatly impressed by the eugenists, who could assure him that his untutored prejudices were the best of science. Eugenists, in turn, liked the stocky Congressman with the good sense to be guided by their science, made him a member of several eugenics committees, and in 1923 elected him president of the Eugenics Research Association, the highest honor at their disposal.

In 1921, after an unsuccessful effort by Johnson to suspend immigration altogether, Congress finally passed and Warren G. Harding signed a bill limiting immigration to 3 per cent of the foreign born of each nationality in the United States according to the census of 1910. The law allowed a maximum of 355,000 entrants yearly, about 55 per cent old immigration and 45 per cent new immigration. This meant retaining the prewar rate for northern Europe but slicing that from southern and eastern Europe to about one-fifth. In 1922 the temporary act of 1921 was extended for two more years.[33]

During passage of the act of 1921 and in the years following, as the nation debated a permanent policy, American racism reached its climax. Testimony before Congress, political speeches, and numerous books and articles carried the concepts of Nordic superiority and race purity to the public. Most publicists affirmed that democracy demanded a people who were vigorous, intelligent, patriotic, and united in common ideals. They explained, almost nostalgically, that America had once been such a nation. The longing for the old and agony over the new was expressed in a racial mystique: that fine Nordic traits had created American institutions and the ineradicable traits of lower races were bringing their destruction. "The teachings of science, the records of history, the warnings of common sense, our own bitter present experience, cry out unto us," the nation was warned. "There is no ground on which utterly alien people, alien in race, in language, in customs, . . . should be admitted to our citizenship. . . . It is monstrous." [34]

Such ideas found expression among scientists and in popular form. At the well-publicized Second International Congress of Eugenics, held in New York in 1921, Henry Fairfield Osborn as president and Madison Grant as treasurer guided the emphasis. (In planning the Congress, Davenport warned Osborn on the necessity of keeping out crackpots—only scientific men like Grant and Stoddard should be permitted to speak on race!) Osborn, in his opening presidential address, asked the world's eugenists to grieve with him that the fine Nordic Americans were being engulfed by races of different traits and ideals. A public exhibition, prepared by Laughlin, depicted the danger to America from immigration. Later the exhibition was taken to Washington for a three-month showing to Congressmen.[35]

At a more popular level, Hiram W. Evans, in a widely reprinted address, spoke about the menace of modern immigration to persons assembled on Klan Day at the State Fair of Texas in October, 1923. He spoke with authority, for he was Imperial Wizard of a revived and powerful Ku-Klux Klan that in many rural towns across the nation battled for a superior white Protestant America against insidious Catholics, Jews, and Negroes. He explained how, "humbly and without bias of any kind," he had undertaken a statistical, anthropological, and eugenical study of race, using the works of Stoddard, Grant, Davenport, and Laughlin. While the South labored beneath a Negro problem, he reported, the North and West faced an equal threat from inundation and intermarriage with Jews and other inferior races from southern and eastern Europe. ("Would you have your daughter marry a Jew?" he asked.) The Imperial Wizard demanded a virtual halt to immigration and a quota system based upon the 1880 census when the nation was still Nordic.[36]

When Congress framed a permanent policy in 1924 racial considerations were foremost, and every Congressman became his own eugenist. The major debate was whether to base quotas on the number of foreign born of each nationality according to the census of 1910 or to reduce the proportion of new immigrants still further by using the census of 1890. The proponents of the 1890 census argued that, since the total population of the United States was overwhelmingly of northern European origin, the census of 1910 actually discriminated against old-stock Americans while that of 1890 gave a fairer distribution of races. Implicit in such an argument, of course, was the conviction that the racial composition of immigration was the important consideration. Out of the debate, almost by accident, arose the notion that to base immigration upon the national origins of the entire white population rather than on the foreign born in a particular census year would assure primarily Nordic immigration and avoid the charge of discrimination. As finally passed, therefore, the law of 1924 temporarily based immigration from each nation upon 2 per cent of the foreign born from each country according to the census of 1890 and required a cabinet committee to determine the national origins of the entire population. After 1927 immigration would be limited to a yearly total of 150,000, apportioned according to national origins. (The act of 1924, in addition, barred immigration of all persons ineligible for citizenship, a provision that excluded all orientals and thus unilaterally undid the Gentlemen's Agreement with Japan.) Delays resulted from difficulties in estimating the national origins of the American people after three centuries of intermarriage and from securing Congressional acceptance of the quotas. Not until July 1, 1929, did the national origin quotas go into effect and become the basic American immigration policy.[37]

The immigration laws of the 1920's, as everyone realized at the time, closed an era in American history and largely ended the eugenists' participation in attacks on "inferior" races. Madison Grant might continue to lament that "we have lost our national homogeneity of race, tradition and religion." But most nativists believed the laws had rescued the nation from the brink and that Americans, having made the decision to keep America for Nordic stock, could begin to re-forge the bonds of social and racial unity. In immigration policy, at any rate, they believed the nation had chosen the road that eugenics had pointed out.[38]

## Miscegenation

Those campaigning for restriction of immigration often drew a parallel between the earlier importation of Negro slaves and the current influx of immigrants: in one case, planters desired cheap labor for farming; in the other, capitalists desired cheap labor for their mines, mills, and railroad building—but in both cases, so ran the argument, the lust for profit had irremediably weakened the quality of the nation.[39] The old stereotypes of the Negro were revived and given an aura of scientific respectability. Davenport, for instance, lauded Negroes for what he regarded as their fine traits: good nature, sense of humor, native love of music, and "dog-like fidelity." Madison Grant, praising them for subserviency to whites, declared: "Negroes are never socialists and labor unionists" and therefore not as dangerous as the immigrant. Most racists, at the same time, agreed that the Negro had an overdeveloped sex instinct, premature cessation of intellectual growth, and a tendency to revert to savagery.[40]

Since twenty-eight states already banned intermarriage of whites and Negroes and only negligible miscegenation occurred in other states, eugenists never launched a formal campaign for laws against miscegenation.[41] On the whole, however, they recognized such laws as being eugenic in their effect and, in a number of writings, lent them scientific support. Some, like Madison Grant, declared: "The laws against miscegenation must be greatly extended if the higher races are to be maintained." Others, more cautiously, stated that, because the effects of race mixture were largely unknown, a people would be foolhardy to permit a policy of race mixture that could never be reversed once it had started.[42]

The laws against miscegenation were bewildering in their variety. Some applied to a vaguely defined group called Negroes or mulattoes; others specified that a person with one-fourth, or one-eighth, or one-sixteenth, or any Negro parentage whatsoever was forbidden marriage with a Caucasian. Many of the laws, especially in the West, included various orientals and American Indians among those forbidden to marry Caucasians. Naturally the emphasis upon Nordic greatness and racial purity in the 1920's contributed to an effort to extend and strengthen laws barring miscegenation. In Virginia in 1924 (the year of the state's sterilization law), the legislature, with the advice of Madison Grant, forbade marriage of a white person to another person with any trace "of any blood other than Caucasian." And in 1926 Georgia, too, greatly strengthened her laws to preserve racial purity.[43] But in most states where sentiment demanded such laws, they already existed, and in other states the National Association for the Advancement of Colored People led the fight against their passage.[44]

In its racist side, eugenics perhaps touched most closely the thoughts and emotions of large groups of the American public. Eugenic concepts reached into the halls of Congress and state legislatures, sounded on the political hustings, and filled numerous popular books and articles. In the end, however, eugenics paid a high price for its temporary but entangling alliances. When racism lost its scientific standing in the 1930's and the Nazis showed what use could be made of race prejudice, then a recoil against the racism of the 1920's became the major factor in bringing a repudiation of eugenics and destroying the emphasis on heredity that had characterized much of American thought in the previous two decades. Since the 1930's, educated Americans have generally looked with deep suspicion upon efforts to frame a hereditarian interpretation of human nature.

*Chapter XI*

# Divided Stream

In the 1920's eugenics faced a dividing of the ways. On the one hand, the harsh hereditarian and racist elements reached a nadir of pessimism. A number of eugenists so frightened themselves with their own assumptions that they saw little hope for a society, threatened by inferior classes and races, that still clung to democracy and placed its faith in education and reform. On the other hand, an important feature of eugenics was a search for further knowledge concerning man's heredity, and the search brought growing humility before the complexity of man and his genes. In the 1920's began the studies that, in the 1930's, produced a scientific reconstruction of eugenics.

## Climax of Woe

Many eugenists had, from the beginning, been conscious that the stand a person took on heredity and environment often reflected his social philosophy. The attack against the menace of the feeble-minded had been the major aspect of a general feeling among many eugenics leaders that social failure—from crime and intemperance to poverty and unemployment—stemmed from low intelligence of hereditary origin. Goddard, among others, was specific in drawing the conclusion that social reform was largely futile since crime and slums reflected the inborn traits of those who produced them.[1] Very early, too, many eugenists equated biological fitness with social class and concluded that college-educated, native, white Protestants (like themselves) were the bearers of the valuable genes of society. Hence they longed, as one eugenist put it, for "that eugenic ideal, when the best shall survive, and the best shall govern." [2]

Such eugenists were convinced that their social views had not colored their science but that science led them with infallible objectivity to their social doctrines. They stood upon science and asked others to abandon sentimentality. "The faith of the social worker, the legislator, the physician, the sanitarian in his method of improving the race is very literally the kind of faith that St. Paul described as the substance of things hoped for, the evidence of things not seen," Paul Popenoe claimed. "We eugenists have a stronger faith, because it is based on things that are seen, and that can even be measured. We think we can prove that it is, on the whole, man who makes the environment, not the environment which makes man." [3]

Earlier eugenists had interspersed political and economic comments in books ostensibly scientific in content; in the 1920's the works of many eugenists became pessimistic tracts on economics and politics with an ever thinner underpinning of science.

In the results of the Army testing during World War I lay a record of the nation's intelligence that many eugenists found alarming. Although democracy depended upon the mental capacity of its citizens, Edwin G. Conklin declared, "forty-five millions, or nearly one-half of the whole population, will never develop mentally beyond the stage represented by a normal twelve year old child." Worse yet, the high birth rate of the lower classes foreshadowed an even greater intellectual incompetence in future generations. "Suffrage is exercised by every individual above the grade of imbecile who has accomplished 21 years of mundane existence," Edward M. East of Harvard lamented. "Thus our whole governmental system is out of harmony with genetic common sense." [4] He attacked all schemes for governmental paternalism since they would permit, sometimes even encourage, the unintelligent to reproduce their kind.

Goddard agreed with these conclusions and called for an extensive testing program so that each person could be fitted into the niche in society that suited his mental level. Philanthropists, he argued, in their longing to aid the downtrodden, failed to realize that the downtrodden were where their mental age placed them and would be unhappy if given the responsibilities of greater wealth or ease. An ideal democracy was a government in which the competent understood and guided the incompetent; "the truest democracy is found in an institution for the feebleminded and it is an aristocracy —a rule by the best." [5]

Probably the most influential exponent of a eugenics of pessimism was William McDougall, the eminent Briton who in 1920 came to America to direct the Harvard department of psychology. McDougall was greatly influenced by Galton, and his *Introduction to Social Psychology,* published in 1908, which had an astonishing vogue, was thoroughly hereditarian. Combining several currents in psychology, he declared that "the human mind has certain innate or inherited tendencies which are the essential spring or motive powers of all thought and action, whether individual or social." Some of the tendencies were special instincts that operated by emotional excitement leading to action (like the instinct of curiosity and emotion of wonder, or the instinct of pugnacity and emotion of anger). Others were more general innate tendencies such as imitativeness or sympathy. Individuals and races differed in the relative strengths of the instincts and tendencies and thus differed in their inherited personalities. The impact of such a psychology was what underlay much of the eugenists' faith that man's personality was rooted in the genes and might therefore be improved by breeding.[6]

McDougall intended his psychology to have social applications and, immediately after arrival in his adopted land, began to write on the theme, *Is America Safe for Democracy?* History, he held, was strewn with dead civilizations because the inherited capacities of the citizens could no longer cope with the complexities of civilization. Since the poorer stocks in a democracy were likely to have freedom to reproduce, democracy was incompatible with the maintenance of a stable civilization, and he foresaw America's impending degeneration. He suggested that democracy be replaced by a caste system based on biological worth, in which political rights would depend on caste and in which laws would prevent marriage between castes and restrict breeding by inferior castes.[7]

Such doctrines were carried to a wider public by publicists such as Albert E. Wiggam and Lothrop Stoddard. In such popular books as *The Fruit of the Family Tree* and *The New Decalogue of Science,* Wiggam explained the overpowering and unalterable workings of heredity, announced that mankind was rapidly deteriorating, but hoped the nation, abandoning "radicalism, socialism, bolshevism, democracy, autocracy, anarchy and every other nostrum," would adopt a strenuous program of eugenics. Stoddard's *The Revolt against Civilization: The Menace of the Under Man* reached the low point of pessimism, however. The wreck of civilizations, he said, came from the multiplication of the "under men," biologically unfit

and nursing an implacable hatred for civilization out of a consciousness of their own inferiority. In the victory of Bolshevism in Russia
and in the fading intelligence, degraded immigrants, crime waves,
and modern poetry in America he perceived the march of the under
man that could be met only by creating a eugenic aristocracy to rule
society.[8]

In such doctrines, early eugenics reached its logical culmination
as the scientific foundation for a reactionary social philosophy. By
the 1920's, those who purveyed these doctrines appeared to speak
for the movement itself. They did much to reinforce the conservative influences that dominated much of the decade.

### Population and Intelligence

While the public image of eugenics was overcast by harsh and
pessimistic propaganda, the 1920's were at the same time a period
of significant research in human heredity. Some of it confirmed
eugenists in their fears but much of it indicated a need for considerable caution. To determine what research was needed, Davenport, as a key figure in the Eugenics Research Association, compiled
suggestions from most of the nation's eugenists. Time and again he
prepared new programs for research, each more detailed than the
previous one, each acknowledging wider areas in which little reliable
information existed. Eventually the programs constituted an admission that very little was yet known about human heredity.[9]

A major area for research, eugenists agreed, was population
changes and their effects upon national intelligence. The basic need
was for reliable information on how various classes differed in average intelligence, on the birth rates of classes, and on the way these
factors altered the nation's intelligence from generation to generation. In addition, eugenists privately admitted that no scientific data
existed on race crossing in man; yet the pressing problems of immigration and the Negro demanded the guidance of science. Still
another group of problems involved the role of heredity not only in
transmitting specific diseases and defects but in shaping man's total
personality and achievement. Eugenists hoped, by intensifying the
study of pedigrees, to learn about the heredity of specific traits and,
by initiating studies of twins, to learn something of the comparable
effects of nature and nurture upon intelligence, personality, and
physical development.

Above all else eugenists valued intelligence; yet the study of intelligence and its heredity was surrounded with complexities. Galton's initial research had involved inheritance of what he vaguely called genius, but he had had to use a person's prominence and reputation as a measure of genius. While this was perhaps the best standard available at the time, it had an obvious disadvantage in that many people of genius do not become prominent and many prominent people lack genius. In the early twentieth century, with the development of educational psychology, a few psychologists studied the learning capacity of students in school subjects and equated this with innate intelligence. Shortly thereafter, with the introduction of intelligence tests, some psychologists believed they had finally found an objective measure of intelligence. By means of the tests, they hoped to determine the relative intelligence of classes or races and to trace the inheritance of intelligence from parents to children. While the tests were doubtless a considerable improvement over previous methods, psychologists became increasingly aware that cultural and social background significantly affected test scores. As a result, study of the heredity of intelligence has been haunted by the question: What in fact do intelligence tests measure?

Edward Lee Thorndike, who at the turn of the century began his long, distinguished, and influential reign at Teachers College, Columbia University, was the most important early figure in turning American psychologists to a study of intelligence. Thorndike acknowledged William James, under whom he studied at Harvard, and Francis Galton, whose researches fascinated him, as the two men who most shaped his interests. At Columbia he put his graduate students to work on problems involving inherited differences in learning capacity while he himself pursued researches that confirmed him in his hereditarian and conservative leanings. His mathematical, coldly analytical mind was such that his conclusions seemed to follow inevitably from his marshaled evidence.[10]

Early in the century he tested the ability of fifty pairs of twins in learning skill—the first important American study of twins—and concluded that heredity chiefly shaped man's capacities. Later he chose two groups of adults from different social classes and found one group clearly superior in an ability to do simple arithmetic. He then gave both groups the same special course and afterward tested them once again. While both groups had improved, the superior group was further ahead than before. Equal opportunity, he concluded, did not create equal ability but magnified the inborn differences that already existed. Heredity, in fact, largely determined environment, for a person with special inborn capacities would seek out an environment in which to realize them. Such views made Thorndike a convinced eugenist, with little faith in environmental reform.[11]

In his educational psychology, Thorndike, like McDougall, placed great emphasis upon inborn reflexes, instincts, and capacities, including learning capacity. A weakness of the American public school system, he believed, was that it rested "on a total disregard of hereditary differences between the classes and the masses." His influence was important in making educators aware of a need to discover talented students and devote special attention to their education.[12]

The major American contribution to the study of intelligence was Lewis M. Terman's monumental study of genius. Born in rural Indiana and educated at a normal school and the state university, Terman, like many other psychologists of his day, went to Clark University for his doctorate. There his interest centered on mentally defective and on gifted children. After taking a position at Stanford University in 1910, he worked on his Stanford revision of the Binet tests and, during the war, assisted in the Army testing program. While standardizing his Stanford revision, he began the study of gifted children and in 1921 received a foundation grant that permitted him to undertake an extensive research program. In his study, he felt that he was continuing investigations that first began with Galton's *Hereditary Genius*. Indeed, Terman once wrote that "of the founders of modern psychology, my greatest admiration is for Galton." [13]

From the major cities of California, Terman and his staff studied a main group of 643 gifted children, plus other groups that brought the total number of gifted children studied to well over one thousand. The main group ranged in age from eight to twelve and in I.Q. from 140 to 190. The gifted children exceeded control groups in general health, in sociability, and in emotional and moral traits. Their fathers were concentrated in those occupations requiring above average intellectual ability: 31.4 per cent were professional, 50 per cent semi-professional or business, 11.8 per cent skilled labor, and 6.6 per cent semi-skilled labor. Unskilled labor was represented in but one case, a farmer who took a laboring job at a university so his child would be able to attend college. Compared with the general population, the large percentage from business and professions was remarkable. There were other signs of intellectual achievement in the families of the gifted children: fourteen of the children had relatives who were memorialized in the Hall of Fame, and twelve had parents or grandparents in *Who's Who*. In follow-up studies of 1927-28, six years after the original investigation, and again in 1936, 1940, 1945 and 1959, Terman and his associates found that, on the whole, the gifted children retained their mental superiority and their over-all excellence in health and emotional stability.[14]

His studies, Terman felt, disproved the common belief that precocious children tended to be maladjusted or puny and gave "considerable support to Galton's theory as to the hereditary nature of genius." [15] Convinced of the importance of superior intellects for the success of the nation, he regretted the declining birth rate of the families from which the gifted children sprang.

The writings of Terman and Thorndike were part of a growing interest among educators in the 1920's in finding the gifted children and providing special instruction that would develop their capacities. A few of the more advanced educational systems inaugurated special classes and programs on the theory, as Goddard expressed it, that "gifted children are literally the greatest of natural resources." The emphasis was often explicitly eugenic. Leta Hollingworth, whose book, *Gifted Children,* was the standard text on their characteristics and education, stressed how right the eugenists were in urging the gifted to breed early and often.[16]

Much additional evidence at the time indicated that, despite considerable overlapping, social classes differed in innate intelligence. The Army tests, which provided evidence on so many issues, assisted here. They showed a steady increase in median intelligence from unskilled laborers through skilled laborers, clerks, technicians, businessmen, and members of the professions. Psychologists in the 1920's found, too, that the intelligence of school children, as measured by tests, tended to vary according to the occupation of the parents.[17]

By the late 1920's eugenists received confirmation of their earlier fears that the birth rate rose as social class fell. An important study in 1930, dividing urban dwellers into professional, business, skilled labor, and unskilled labor classes and the rural dwellers into farm owners, farm renters, and farm laborers, furnished evidence that the birth rate bore an inverse relation to assumed eugenic worth. The number of children per one hundred wives was: [18]

| *Urban* | | *Rural* | |
|---|---|---|---|
| Professional | 129 | Owners | 247 |
| Business | 140 | Renters | 275 |
| Skilled | 179 | Laborers | 299 |
| Unskilled | 223 | | |

There were of course grounds to doubt that intelligence tests really mirrored innate intelligence of classes and to question whether reliable information existed on the inheritance of so complex a trait as human intelligence. Nevertheless eugenists were not unreasonable in contending that, if intelligence was lowest in the classes that bred fastest, then the nation's intelligence was suffering a gradual erosion.

In the 1920's, as a result, eugenists came increasingly to feel that the control of population growth and changes was at the center of a successful eugenics program. In books like Edward M. East's *Mankind at the Crossroads* (1923), the eugenic concern over the quality of population merged with the neo-Malthusian fear of overpopulation. As a biologist, East painted a grim picture of mankind soon to face war and starvation by outrunning the supply of food and rapidly degenerating because of reproduction by the incompetent. At the crossroads, mankind had a choice between the road to ruin or a road to continued progress. That progress could come only by lowering the birth rate, and lowering it in all classes, not just among those of greatest eugenic worth.[19] During the 1920's most of those concerned with population wrestled with the problem of quality—some, like Edward A. Ross, agreeing with East; others, like Warren Thompson, finding much to criticize in the eugenists' assumptions.[20]

## *Genetics*

Although developments in the study of intelligence and population trends tended, often, to confirm eugenists in their convictions, developments in genetics undercut much of the ground upon which the earlier movement was built. While Davenport and other eugenists studied man, the more thoughtful and competent geneticists investigated humbler forms of life that were subject to laboratory control. About the time of the founding of the Eugenics Record Office, Thomas Hunt Morgan and his colleagues at Columbia University initiated their famous studies of the fruit fly. Their work, which won a Nobel Prize, showed that the interaction of the genes and the relation of genes to environment were far more complicated than most eugenists admitted or understood.[21]

Nevertheless, because balanced geneticists rarely wrote on man, the new developments remained largely hidden from the educated public, and eugenists continued their domination of human genetics. In 1929, in his book, *Heredity and Human Affairs,* even so competent a geneticist as East cited the studies of the Jukes and Kallikaks with favor and accepted the conclusions of Davenport and Goddard as proof that insanity, feeblemindedness, and epilepsy were simple recessive traits.[22] The *Journal of Heredity,* official organ of the American Genetic Association, was edited by prominent eugenists and continued into the 1920's to publish uncritical and naïve studies of human heredity.[23]

In a slender volume entitled *Prometheus,* H. S. Jennings made one of the few efforts to bring the new findings to public attention. Director of the zoological laboratory at Johns Hopkins University and a moderate eugenist, he was disturbed by the deterministic and pessimistic doctrines that passed for scientific eugenics. He explained that the genes, "a great number of discrete packets of diverse chemicals" arranged in definite order as chromosomes, constituted a chemical laboratory within a cell.[24] The development of an individual was the final product of the interaction of the chemicals with one another and with materials from outside the cell. At times, of course, the specific action of a single gene might alter a trait and thus yield Mendelian ratios. But one could no longer speak of the identity of gene and trait, for each trait required the interaction of many genes and the environment, while each gene might take part in the formation of many traits.

Jennings stressed that heredity was not an iron determinism, since environment could do much to shape the development that the genes controlled. In the embryo of an animal, for example, a cell that would have formed the eyes could be transplanted and would form skin or brain; its relation to other cells determined what it would become. He also told of a Mexican salamander, living in water, that had a heavy body, flattened tail for swimming, and external gills; but the same salamander, if raised in a dry environment in a zoo, would lose its external gills and breathe air and would grow small and slender. In man, the genes controlled the endocrine system and thus diabetes could result from inherited inability to produce insulin; yet artificial administering of insulin could overcome the defect. Men and animals did not inherit their characteristics; "what their parents leave them are certain packets of chemicals which under one set of conditions produce one set of characters, under other conditions produce other sets." [25]

Jennings also stressed that, except for a few characteristics, there was a wide unpredictability from human matings. Each person carried many genes and "any pair of parents may thus produce, not merely thousands, but millions of different combinations, each yielding a child of different characteristics." Hence he argued, in a bit of purple prose,

> But whatever eugenic measures are attempted, so long as biparental inheritance is kept up, the variety, the surprises, the perplexities, the melodrama, that now present themselves among the fruits of the human vine will continue. Capitalists will continue to produce artists, poets, socialists, and labourers; labouring men will give birth to capitalists, to philosophers, to men of science; fools will produce wise men and wise men will produce fools; who mounts will fall, who falls will mount; and all the kinds of problems presented to society by the turns of the invisible wheel will remain.[26]

Young geneticists, attracted by exciting developments in experimental genetics and skeptical of the scientific standing of human genetics, mostly remained in experimental work. The possibilities for experimental genetics became even greater after 1927, when Hermann J. Muller announced his Nobel-prize-winning discovery that radiation greatly increased the mutation rates of genes and thus provided more mutant strains with which to experiment. As a result, eugenics fell increasingly into disrepute among geneticists and, in the United States, little work was done in human genetics. For many scientists, especially the younger men, eugenics ceased to be regarded as a science by the 1930's and was not so much opposed as ignored.

Naturally such developments modified Davenport's views, for, as director of the Department of Genetics, he was in close contact with experimental genetics. While his outlook remained extremely conservative and hereditarian and he did not retract his earlier work, he recognized that the relation between gene and trait was more complicated than he had assumed. After the First World War his interest turned to the study of human growth. He published on the inheritance of body build and began extensive measuring of growing children to plot their development. Increasingly he stressed the genes as factors controlling growth and recognized that environmental influences might intervene to affect the result.[27]

Davenport frequently reverted to his former ways, most notably in 1926 when he supervised a study of race crossing in Jamaica. To do the field work, he selected Morris Steggerda, a humorless and unimaginative zoology Ph.D., so typical of Davenport's choice of helpers. Steggerda subjected Negroes, whites, and browns to sixty-three physical measurements and to numerous psychological tests. The result was a mass of graphs and charts showing differences in physical and mental traits between whites and Negroes (including a superiority of Negroes over whites in musical ability and a superiority of whites over Negroes in intellect). Davenport concluded that the study showed a tendency for hybrids to be both physically and psychologically disharmonious. Negroes had relatively longer arms and legs than whites, for example, and he feared that the crosses might inherit the long legs of the Negro and short arms of the whites and would have "to stoop more to pick up a thing on the ground." William E. Castle's criticism of Davenport's conclusions is still worth reading.[28]

Despite such occasional reversions to an earlier attitude, Davenport's instinct for scientific caution grew and he became, especially in private, quite critical of much of the eugenics propaganda that at other times he continued to sponsor. "Perhaps it is only the beginnings of 'old fogyism,' " he wrote Leonard Darwin, the British eugenics leader, "but I can't help but feel that propaganda may outstrip knowledge and bring disrepute upon the subject of the propaganda." Patience often replaced his earlier demand for immediate acceptance of eugenics. "As facts are fully known they are bound to get into the textbooks and become a part of the education of the young," he counseled. "Then we may depend on the young generation applying them. . . . I feel with Galton that the plant 'eugenics' rooted in the good soil of well ascertained fact; well fertilized by education, will develop into a vigorous and fruitful growth." [29]

## Psychology and Personality

Such general interpretations of personality as Freudian psychology and behaviorism had a major, if somewhat indirect, role in weakening the eugenics movement. The behaviorism of John B. Watson, enunciated before the War, reached the status of a fad by the 1920's. Influenced by animal psychology, he hoped to turn the study of human motivation into an objective science by dealing not with the intangibles of thought but the tangibles of observed behavior: to study how an infant is conditioned through stimulus and response. He emphasized the limitless plasticity of the infant and the power of training to mold the infant's personality. His special goal was to banish hereditarian emphasis, especially as based on the innate instincts of McDougall's psychology. "Everything we have been in the habit of calling an 'instinct' today," he declared,

"is a result largely of training—belongs to man's *learned behavior.*"
For the many psychologists who followed in his wake, the study of
the way the family and culture built habits and attitudes became
the major emphasis—and thus they turned from heredity to environment.[30]

Although Freudian psychology was quite different in its assumptions, it had the same effect of focusing upon infancy and youth in
the formation of personality. When Sigmund Freud's views reached
America before World War I, many psychiatrists rejected them, not
only from moral revulsion over the emphasis upon sex but from a
long-held conviction that mental disease was rooted in physical
causes. "Those of us who are inclined to the view that there is always a physical cause for a mental act, and perversion of physical
function whenever there is a perversion of mental acts," one psychiatrist declared, "want proof before we will accept his opinions."
Such psychiatrists warned that the new movement would draw psychiatry away from fruitful physiological and biochemical investigations of insanity into the realm of myth.[31] A hereditarian interpretation had won acceptance partly because it explained the irrational
and often incorrigible behavior patterns of the psychotic or delinquent by ascribing them to inborn and largely uncontrollable tendencies; Freudian psychology instead located such behavior in unconscious drives and childhood repressions. Acceptance of Freudian psychology minimized heredity; for the relation of genes to physical
malfunction was clearer than their relation to an Oedipus complex.

For anthropologists, too, Freud provided explanations for those
seemingly ineradicable traits that had formerly been ascribed to
race heredity. Their roots lay instead in childhood experience. "If
S. Freud is right in assuming that these forgotten incidents remain a
living force throughout life,—the more potent, the more thoroughly
they are forgotten," Franz Boas noted quite early, "we should have
to conclude that many of the small traits of individuals which we
ordinarily believe to be inherited are acquired by the influence of
the individuals among whom the child spends the first five years
of its life." With the new insights for understanding behavior, cultural anthropologists undertook intensive studies of the way in
which cultural patterns shaped the growing child to fit the culture.[32]

While Freudians and behaviorists altered the understanding of
personality, a number of students hoped that a careful study of
twins and foster children would answer major questions concerning

the role of heredity and environment in shaping man. By now more perceptive students no longer asked the old and hackneyed question: Which is more important, heredity or environment? They realized that both were absolutely essential. Instead, the question was: Given a similar heredity, how much variation can differing environments produce? Or, given a similar environment, to what extent are individual differences the result of heredity? For this purpose, twins provided natural subjects for experiment. Identical twins had the same heredity but, if raised apart, might have differing environments. Fraternal twins, while varying in heredity, were often raised together and thus shared a reasonably similar environment.

Although Galton had pioneered the study of twins in the 1870's and Thorndike had tested a few pairs of twins at the turn of the century, most studies before the late 1920's had been relatively superficial.[33] By then, however, Horatio H. Newman, a geneticist, Frank N. Freeman, a psychologist, and Karl J. Holzinger, a statistician—all at the University of Chicago—formed a team to conduct the most important study of twins. In 1937 they reported on nineteen identical twins raised apart, plus fifty identical and fifty fraternal twins raised together. For identical twins, the mean difference between traits were: [34]

|  | Identicals Reared Apart | Identicals Reared Together |
|---|---|---|
| Height | 1.8 cm. | 1.7 cm. |
| Weight | 9.9 lbs. | 4.1 lbs. |
| Binet I.Q. | 8.2 | 5.9 |

Such results, on the surface, suggest that environment exercised only a limited influence in differentiating twins even when separated as babies. The mean figures do not tell the entire story, however, since most of the separated twins were raised under relatively similar environments. Those few who were raised in widely differing environments showed considerable variation in test results. Two identical girl twins, separated at eighteen months, with one completing college and becoming a school teacher while the other grew up in a backwoods environment, had an I.Q. difference of twenty-four points. Although personality traits were difficult to test, twins in general, while often strikingly similar in personality, appeared to vary more in this than in other traits when raised apart.[35]

Foster children have, on the whole, proved less satisfactory subjects than twins. From a study of whether their intelligence and personality resembled more closely that of their real parents or their adopted parents, one would expect to learn something of the ability of environment to shape heredity. Often, however, the father of foster children is unknown and the mental level of the mother difficult to determine. Besides, it is likely that children with more promising heredity would be placed in more promising homes, in which case it could not be determined if success was due to heredity or environment. In general, the studies demonstrated that foster children placed in the best homes had the highest I.Q.'s, as measured by tests, and that the scores of foster children lay between those expected on the basis of their true parentage and those expected in their foster environment.[36]

While the studies have by no means ended the nature-nurture controversy or settled the bounds of heredity and environment, they have done much to define the issues and narrow the range of informed disagreement. In general, the studies indicate that heredity sets limits to mental and physical development but that environmental factors can play an important part within those limits. Personality appears to be especially shaped by environment. Hence it still remains possible to stress the limits set by heredity or the shaping influence of environment.

### Organization

In the 1920's eugenics received its guidance from the Eugenics Research Association, founded at Cold Spring Harbor in 1913 to encourage research, and the American Eugenics Society, organized by Irving Fisher in the early 1920's for propaganda. While both organizations had numerous committees and most of the committees wrote numerous reports, they accomplished, in fact, very little.

By late 1924 Fisher had secured Leon F. Whitney as full-time field secretary of the American Eugenics Society to direct its fund raising and propaganda. A public relations man, Whitney exhibited such a notable lack of scientific training combined with an enthusiasm for extreme eugenics doctrines that even Davenport was greatly disturbed. While the Society hoped to convert the nation to eugenics, its major activity was to sponsor the work of Mrs. Mary T. Watts, who for over a decade had been conducting Fitter Family Contests at agricultural fairs in the Midwest. The "fitter families" were judged on the basis of pedigrees, submitted before the fair, and on the basis of a physical and mental examination at the fair. Thereby the public would learn that human breeding could be guided like animal breeding and was a good deal more important. Certainly such contests were a piddling accomplishment for an organization whose expectations had once been so high.[37]

The Eugenics Research Association, composed in 1928 of three hundred persons interested in human heredity, continued to draw up programs for research and to hold annual meetings; but it did little else. With its limited funds, the Association subsidized some minor research projects and judged a few essay contests in eugenics. Again, its goals exceeded its grasp.[38]

In 1928 Frederick Osborn, soon to assume leadership of the American eugenics movement, made his sudden entrance into the movement. Earlier he had been a business man, active as a railroad president, director of several corporations, and partner in a banking firm, but had developed an interest in evolution and man. (Indeed, his uncle was Henry Fairfield Osborn, the eminent paleontologist and a respected and conservative leader within the eugenics movement.) In 1928 Osborn carried out a long-standing plan to retire from business at the age of forty, and immediately approached Davenport with an offer to finance a research program for the Eugenics Research Association. Soon he became treasurer and a leading member of the Association. He also supported the American Eugenics Society, became its secretary, and has been its moving force ever since.[39]

Upon retirement, Osborn secured a small office in the Museum of Natural History near the office of Margaret Mead. There, under the guidance of Clark Wissler and Harry L. Shapiro, curator and assistant curator in anthropology, he began a two-year reading course in genetics, psychology, and sociology. Soon he employed a small staff to assist him in assembling and interpreting the known facts on heredity and environment. Through his studies, he found increasing reason for dissatisfaction with the prejudices and generalizations that characterized much of the eugenics movement.[40]

In 1933 Gladys C. Schwesinger, a member of his staff, published a substantial volume, *Heredity and Environment,* in which she summarized previous investigations on the nature-nurture issue. She found little evidence to support either extreme hereditarians or extreme environmentalists in their positions. The next year Osborn, with Frank Lorimer, interpreted much of the statistical evidence on population in *Dynamics of Population.* He admitted that various

races and immigrant groups differed in average intelligence according to tests. But since those groups with lower average scores were
also the ones whose lack of economic and cultural opportunities
would place them at a disadvantage in taking the tests, the tests
provided no valid grounds for branding some races innately inferior to others. He therefore firmly rejected the racism that eugenists like his uncle had made a major tenet of the eugenics creed.[41]

With regard to social classes, Osborn stressed the overlapping of
abilities between classes and regretted the class appeals of so much
eugenics literature. He concluded that there existed little evidence
of significant genetic differences within the broad middle classes in
America. Some evidence, however, indicated that the frequency of
genes for superior mental ability was greater in professional and
business classes and lower in underprivileged classes of some rural
and slum areas. The differential birth rate, then, was doubly unfortunate: not only because it was dysgenic but because it meant
highest reproduction among those groups least able to provide cultural and educational opportunities for their children.[42]

Osborn's conclusion was that eugenics and reform worked hand
in hand, since those policies that raised the cultural and economic
opportunities of depressed groups would tend also to lower their
birth rates. He hoped for recognition of a need for a national policy
to control population. Such a policy would include the spread of
birth control information. It would also involve substantial fellow-
ships for promising scholars, maternity benefits, and higher pay for
young people—all to provide young couples with the economic freedom to plan their families as they saw fit.[43]

Because of his dissatisfaction with the earlier eugenics movement,
Osborn gradually disassociated himself from the Cold Spring Harbor group. As a leading member of the American Eugenics Society
he used his influence, when vacancies occurred on the board of directors, to replace such men as Laughlin and Madison Grant with
persons of scientific reputation and more balanced views.[44] Osborn's
eugenics creed was a natural outcome of events of the previous
decade. His rejection of racism lay in the skeptical attitude with
which American anthropologists had long regarded racist assumptions. His tentative and moderate conclusions on heredity of mental
traits derived from developments in genetics and psychology of the
1920's. His emphasis upon population control was part of an increasing emphasis of eugenists upon demography.

To the public, eugenics in the 1920's showed a side that was class-conscious, and reactionary. During the decade the campaign for immigration restriction on racial grounds reached its victorious climax. From the press came books that, on a biological basis, rejected democracy and much of the American tradition upon which democracy was based. Increasingly it became clear, however, that the scientific basis for such doctrines was at best dubious, at worst contradicted by the evidence. Eugenics thereby earned a reputation that a responsible leadership would, in the future, find difficult to overcome.

# Chapter XII

# Eugenics Today

Even at high tide, the eugenics movement in America never became a popular one in the sense that, say, abolition or temperance had been popular movements. While widespread racism certainly existed, it more often led to legal, social, and economic discrimination than to measures that were specifically eugenic. Even eugenists with a racist outlook could not regard such activities as evidence for popular acceptance of eugenics, while other eugenists viewed the association of their movement with racism to be its great tragedy. In other fields, eugenics fell far short of the popular acceptance that its supporters desired. For many eugenists, the lack of public acceptance was a major disappointment. It meant that their foremost goal—that young couples be guided by eugenics in choosing a mate and planning their families—was never realized. It meant, too, that eugenists could not muster the support they desired for the institutional care, educational policies, and research programs that they deemed necessary.

Eugenics, in fact, remained a movement of the experts; therein lay its importance and strength. Its origin in the nineteenth century stemmed from the growing ranks of those concerned with care and treatment of the poor, delinquent, mentally ill, and feebleminded. As part of a world movement in the twentieth century, eugenics gained influential support and leadership from biologists, psychologists, criminologists, sociologists, physicians, social workers, liberal clergymen, and many others who prided themselves upon keeping abreast of the latest developments in the study of man and the solution of social problems. These were, of course, the same sort of people involved in the progressive reforms in the early part of the century. In understanding the development of American social thought, it is important to realize that many who taught in the nation's universities or worked directly with the dependent and delinquent were convinced eugenists and that hereditarian attitudes exerted a pervasive influence upon the educated mind in the Progressive Era.

Both eugenics and progressivism appealed primarily to the "best people"—to upper middle class native Americans. Because of their backgrounds and because many shared a generally nativist attitude, they did not find the race and class consciousness of eugenics necessarily uncongenial. Eugenics had, in fact, much to recommend it. In a period that prided itself upon realism in reform, eugenics appealed to science over sentimentality. Eugenics seemed to follow logically from the assumptions of Darwinian evolution and, in a era much captivated by Darwin, a reform movement appearing in such a guise was hard to resist.

While such early leaders as Davenport and Goddard had drawn conclusions from eugenics that were opposed to environmental reform and perceptive sociologists like Lester Ward had attacked eugenics because of such implications, eugenics at first generally had the image of a scientific reform movement. Many who were reformers and eugenists did not feel a contradiction between the two. They were willing to accept the proposition that some persons were hereditarily defective and should be institutionalized; then greater care could be lavished on others whose failures were amenable to reform. On a more sophisticated level, some saw nothing inconsistent in working for environmental reforms while, at the same time, trying to assure that future generations would be so endowed that such reforms might become less necessary.

If the strength of eugenics lay in the support of the experts, its decline came as experts abandoned it. By the 1920's the elitist and racist side of eugenics dominated the movement and thus gave added reason to examine the assumptions upon which the movement rested. American anthropologists, in fact, had never been racist, and racism fell increasingly into disrepute. Most of the experts on the feebleminded, having once warned the nation concerning the menace of the feebleminded, reversed themselves and confessed their exaggerations. Geneticists, as they learned more about heredity, became increasingly cautious and scientific until the work of Davenport and other eugenists seemed hardly to be science at all. Psychologists, too, entertained a growing doubt that mental tests could measure innate intelligence, and they therefore questioned the earlier conclusions about class and race differences. For many "experts," in short, the scientific basis of eugenics seemed increasingly untenable at a time when the eugenics creed became increasingly harsh and repugnant.

Eugenics could then move in one of two directions. It could become a narrow fad dominated by extremists like Laughlin and Grant, or else it could repudiate its own early history and become a fairly modest but valid branch of the science of genetics.

## *Decline*

The most significant development in eugenics after 1930 was its rapid decline in popularity and prestige. During the 1930's the Eugenics Research Association simply faded away. The American Eugenics Society, with Frederick Osborn as secretary, continued in operation until 1940. Then Osborn left for ten years of government service, first as the officer in charge of Troop Information and Education and then as U. S. Deputy Representative to the United Nations Atomic Energy Commission. For a decade the Society was inactive.[1]

The leaders of the old eugenics movement gradually retired from the field or passed away. In 1934 Davenport retired but continued on at Cold Spring Harbor to complete his studies of human growth. During the 1930's, social developments so disturbed him that he spent much of his time organizing taxpayers associations to fight the encroachments of the welfare state. His death in 1944 came from pneumonia caught while boiling a whale's skull for a Whaling Museum of which he was curator and director. After Davenport's retirement, Laughlin remained at the Eugenics Record Office, but he felt increasingly unwanted, and rightly so. In 1939 the Carnegie Institution changed the Eugenics Record Office to the Genetic Record Office and largely ended its activities; the following year the Institution hastened Laughlin's retirement and thus severed its connection with eugenics. Paul Popenoe and Roswell Johnson diverted their attention from eugenics in 1930 when as a result of their interest in sex education and birth control, they opened an Institute of Family Relations in Los Angeles. The Institute, the first of its kind in the country, provided premarital examinations and marriage counseling.[2] Numbered among the eugenics leaders who died during the decade were David Starr Jordan in 1931, Mrs. E. H. Harriman in 1932, Henry F. Osborn in 1935, Madison Grant in 1937, and William McDougall in 1938.

As members of the older generation passed, they were not replaced and their brand of eugenics was little honored. Indeed, when, with the demise of the Eugenics Record Office, Osborn was offered back issues of *Eugenical News* for the files of the American Eugenics Society, he firmly rejected them. "During the years in which Mr. Laughlin was in charge of the Eugenics Record Office, and when Mr. Madison Grant and others with similar views were on the board of the Eugenics Research Association," he wrote, "the News contained a good deal of material on race as well as a good deal of material on social-class differences which today would be considered thoroughly unscientific. It is my belief," he added, "that this material injured the scientific standing of the Record Office, and I have very direct evidence to show that it set back the scientific acceptance of eugenics in this country." [3]

World events did much to undermine an already weakened movement. In Germany the Nazis espoused a creed of Aryan purity and superiority and displayed a morbid fascination with health, biological fitness, and human breeding. In 1935 alone, 71,960 sterilizations were performed (more than in the United States from 1907 to the present), and a total of well over 200,000 persons were eventually sterilized under Nazi administration. Rumors were rife that sterilization was performed for political as well as medical reasons. [4] In the fall of 1939 Hitler supplemented sterilization with euthanasia and in two years disposed of some 50,000 incurably insane, feebleminded, and deformed patients in gas chambers. The experience with the euthanasia program proved helpful when, in 1941, the Nazis capped their growing campaign of evacuations, torture, plunder, and murder of Jews with a systematic effort to exterminate the Jews of Europe. The result was death for four to six million Jews in an almost successful policy for the "final solution" of the "Jewish problem." [5] Such programs and such creeds brought a recoil in America against race doctrines and naturally placed the eugenics movement under suspicion.

A decade of economic depression also had an important, but less obvious, impact upon eugenics. During a period of widespread unemployment and severe social dislocations, the earlier eugenics argument that social failure lay in the genes was clearly irrelevant, and even a moderate eugenics program appeared less crucial than before. The problems of depression and an approaching Second World War overshadowed eugenics.

While eugenics declined, it also continued to moderate its attitudes, eventually bringing them into line with the scientific trends of the day. In a period less receptive to race doctrines, new studies destroyed most of the remaining scientific support for racism—especially the evidence drawn from mental testing. In his 1934 *Dynamics of Population,* Frederick Osborn was the first to point out that, while Negroes did less well than whites on the Army tests of World War I, Negroes from five northern states scored slightly higher than whites from eight southern states. Either the results were strongly influenced by environment, therefore, or northern Negroes from these states were superior to southern whites. At about the same time, an important study by Otto Klineberg at Columbia University added substantial evidence that the generally poorer performance of Negroes stemmed from lack of opportunity. By examining southern school records of Negroes who migrated north and by testing recent arrivals in the North, he concluded that northern Negroes were not a select group but fairly represented their race. More significantly, average intelligence, as measured by tests, rose according to the number of years a southern-born Negro child dwelt in the North, so that improved opportunities brought Negro test scores close to white test scores. While this did not prove equality of Negroes and whites, it did suggest that the creation of equal opportunity would bring equal scores.[6]

In the same period geneticists and anthropologists came increasingly to define race in Mendelian terms. All mankind shared a large pool of genes, and a race was a group that, through geographical isolation, developed frequencies of genes differing from those of other peoples. Such a concept minimized the differences between races and banished the notion that there exists, or ever has existed, a pure race. After all, while a race as a whole exhibits certain unique frequencies of genes, the individuals who make up a race differ greatly. From northern Europe, the abode of the Nordics, to southern Europe, the land of the Mediterraneans, the frequencies of genes for dark hair and eyes increase, yet there is no place where a line may be drawn to separate one "race" from another. The Mendelian definition recognized that race was not fixed, but that new races were continually being created by the migrations, intermarriages, and mutations that had created races in the past. Most scientists came therefore to believe that, whatever the social consequences of race mixture, there was no adequate evidence of adverse biological effects.[7]

Gradually between the mid-1920's and 1940 racism ceased to have scientific respectability,[8] and, as a result, American eugenics and racism faced a parting of the ways. Among innumerable right-wing antisemitic groups and among white supremists, race concepts and the ghost of Madison Grant lived on. The thoroughly exploded myth that one need merely stand a Negro beside an ape to see that the Negro occupies a low stage of evolution continues to have adherents, and the current segregation crisis has brought renewed attacks on the supposed evils of miscegenation.[9] Among those scientists now active in the eugenics movement, however, the racist tradition of eugenics has been largely discarded. C. M. Goethe, a Sacramento businessman who had a leading role in the eugenics movement in California, continues to purvey a racist point of view in numerous books, pamphlets, and letters written in his own inimitable style, but he is an anachronism in a movement that is eager to forget some aspects of its past.[10]

With regard to class differences in inherent ability, eugenists have generally adopted a more tentative position. They acknowledge that the genetic differences between classes and the genetic effects of a differential birth rate are far from clear. Hence, they no longer fear that a birth rate favoring the lower classes necessarily presents an immediate crisis and, by the same token, are not certain that reversing the birth rate would promise significant genetic gains. The irony has not escaped them, in addition, that in recent years, when few people would even recognize the word eugenics, the birth rate between social classes—as well as between native born and immigrant and between Negroes and whites—is approaching equality. With the dissemination of birth control information among the poor and the tendency of college-educated persons to have larger families, the class differences in child-bearing are disappearing.[11] If the result is eugenic, it was not brought about by the pleadings of eugenists.

Frederick Osborn continues to advocate the spread of birth control information and extension of those policies that, by reducing the cost of raising children, allow parents to plan their families with greater economic freedom. These include income tax deductions, free schools and recreation centers, and more scholarships. He hopes that, through such means, an economic and psychological climate can be created in which potential parents will be encouraged to consider eugenic factors in family planning. Such a program, he feels, is not controversial since its objectives are socially desirable apart from any eugenic effect.[12]

As interest in eugenics declined, so also did interest in human heredity—making the 1930's a low point for research in human genetics. By then the Eugenics Record Office had largely ceased its activities. Genetics was rarely taught in medical schools, and only a handful of physicians and psychologists carried on sporadic studies in the heredity of man. Most geneticists were active in experimental work or in agricultural breeding.

During the decade a few geneticists wrote brilliantly on human genetics, but the writings tended now to derive from the political left and to constitute a bitter attack on the class and race assumptions that underlay, or had underlain, the movement in America, England, and Germany. In America in 1935 Hermann J. Muller published *Out of the Night* and in England three years later J. B. S. Haldane, ironically enough the brilliant successor to Karl Pearson at University College, London, brought out his *Heredity and Politics*. Both men were sympathetic with Marxian socialism. (Muller, in fact, was then assisting the genetic research program of the Soviet Union until political interference and the elevation of Trofim Lysenko exasperated him.) Such books, especially that by Haldane, had tremendous influence in exposing the fallacies of a conservative interpretation of genetic knowledge.[13]

The criticism by Muller and Haldane, while generally valid, did not take into account the new direction that Osborn and others were attempting to give the eugenics movement in America. Osborn's *Preface to Eugenics,* first published in 1940 and revised in 1951, has become the standard text for the American movement and is in many respects closer to critics like Muller and Haldane than to the eugenics of the 1920's. A sign of the increasing scientific orientation of eugenics is that Muller, who never doubted the importance of improving man's genetic future, has since become a major spokesman for the movement.

## Rebirth

In recent years, especially since the Second World War, there has developed a renewed interest in eugenic problems, although the word eugenics has seldom been used. The explosion of an atomic bomb over Hiroshima precipitated widespread public interest and debate concerning the danger of increased mutations from radioactive fallout. Since Hiroshima, Congressional committees have listened with respect to the views of geneticists on the hereditary threat to mankind from natural and artificial radioactivity, popular magazines have featured articles on the subject, and the Democratic presidential candidate in 1956 cited the genetic danger to buttress his plea that the United States agree to a suspension of nuclear tests. For some scientists, like Linus Pauling, the brilliant biochemist at the California Institute of Technology, the campaign to ban bomb testing has assumed much the same emotional overtones that eugenics once had for many scientists.[14]

While debate over mutations and fallout has brought popular discussion of human genetics, a major development in eugenics has been an increasing interest in medical genetics. Gradually, though all too gradually from the point of view of eugenists, medical researchers are investigating the hereditary basis of disease and many medical schools have introduced courses in genetics. A sign of increasing activity in the study of human heredity was the inevitable formation of an American Society for Human Genetics in 1948 and the initiation of an *American Journal of Human Genetics.* The founders were determined that their organization, unlike the old Eugenics Research Association, would remain strictly scientific.[15]

Impressive evidence of the importance of heredity in many mental and physical diseases has come from recent twin studies. Like previous studies, they are based on the fact that although fraternal twins and identical twins share approximately the same prenatal and postnatal environment, only identical twins share precisely the same heredity. Hence the problem is to find a twin with a disease and then to determine whether the other twin has also developed the disease. A significant tendency for pairs of identical twins to have an abnormality more often than pairs of fraternal twins indicates that the similar heredity of the identical twins is a major factor.

Franz J. Kallmann, using such a method, has assembled impressive evidence for a genetic basis of major psychoses. In a study of 953 twin pairs in which at least one had schizophrenia and seventy-five pairs in which at least one had manic-depressive psychosis, he found the following percentages of concordance: [16]

|  | *Concordance for Schizophrenics* | *Concordance for Manic-Depressives* |
|---|---|---|
| Identical Twins | 86.2 | 95.7 |
| Fraternal Twins | 14.5 | 26.3 |
| Siblings of Twins | 14.2 | 23.0 |

Thus, if one identical twin has the psychosis, the other is very likely also to have it, but fraternal twins, who are no more closely related genetically than regular brothers and sisters, are not much more likely than siblings to be concordant. For other common diseases, the percentage of concordance has been found as follows: [17]

| | Epilepsy | Pyloric Stenosis | Diabetes | Clubfoot | Harelip |
|---|---|---|---|---|---|
| Identical | 66.6 | 66.7 | 65 | 33 | 33 |
| Fraternal | 3.1 | 3.4 | 18 | 3 | 5 |

In each of these diseases both a genetic basis and environmental influences appear to play an important role.

A practical manifestation of interest in medical genetics has been the slow development, since 1940, of heredity counseling centers in the United States. In the case of the Dight Institute for Human Genetics at the University of Minnesota, there were direct links with the old eugenics movement. Dr. Charles F. Dight, whose money founded the Institute, had been organizer and first president of an early Minnesota Eugenics Society. He had also been an eccentric Minneapolis physician, examiner for a small insurance company, and a leader in the fight for legally enforced pasteurization of milk and better garbage removal. As a result of great frugality (for a time he lived in a house in a tree) and careful investment, he accumulated a small fortune and in the 1920's wrote a will leaving his money to found a center for genetic research and counseling. Because of his long life, the Dight Institute was not established until 1941—a year after the first such clinic was established at the University of Michigan. In 1948 the research data of the old Eugenics Record Office were transferred to the Dight Institute, thus making it a lineal descendant of the Eugenics Record Office, which also in its early years had offered genetic counseling. By 1957 the number of heredity counseling clinics in the United States had grown to thirteen.[18]

Although the clinics are consulted by adoption agencies to determine whether a child is a good risk for adoption and by courts in disputed paternity cases, most consultations are with couples who, before marriage or after the birth of a defective child, want to know what the chances are that a future child of theirs will be defective. Because heredity clinics explain the odds but usually refrain from direct advice, their influence may in some cases tend to be dysgenic. Often a couple finds that the risk of a defective child is less than anticipated and will therefore chance a subsequent pregnancy. The geneticists who operate the heredity clinics recognize this, but expect that the educational work and research of the clinics will in the long run show eugenic results.[19]

In the case of a few conditions known to be generally recessive, such as albinism, infantile and juvenile amaurotic idiocy, phenylketonuria, microcephaly (pinheads), gargoylism, and some types of deafness, the geneticist can predict that the Mendelian odds of one in four will hold for subsequent children when the parents already have one such child. Other diseases, such as glaucoma, cataract, piebaldness, lobster claw, brachydactyly, polydactyly, chondrodystrophic dwarfism, and Huntington's chorea are often dominant and thus, if a parent is affected, roughly one-half the children will also be affected. The inheritance of most diseases with a genetic basis is more complex, however, so that simple Mendelian ratios do not apply. Nevertheless, from a study of the results of many marriages, geneticists can often suggest the odds—that is, they can give empiric risk figures. A counselor can predict, for instance, that, if a couple's child has pyloric stenosis, there is about one chance in ten for a subsequent boy to have the defect and about one in fifty for a subsequent girl.[20]

In the case of most types of feeblemindedness, risk figures are still very difficult to determine, especially since a diagnosis of the higher grades of feeblemindedness is partly social as well as biological. Some types of mental deficiency have been traced to recessive or dominant genes. In general it has been found that feebleminded persons of low grade, because they result from recessive genes or from disease or injury, tend to have siblings and parents representative of the population as a whole. Morons, on the other hand, are more likely to represent the lower range of the normal curve of intelligence (just as geniuses represent the upper range). Hence they tend to have parents and siblings who are themselves feebleminded or borderline cases. In an important survey in England, only 2.7 per cent of the idiots had mentally defective parents while 12.1 per cent of the morons had mentally defective parents and many others had backward or borderline parents.[21]

In recent years, geneticists have emphasized that a genetic basis for a disease is not necessarily reason for fatalism. Since genes operate by controlling the production of enzymes by cells, a number of hereditary ills can be controlled by correcting the inborn defect of metabolism. Diabetes often results from an inherited inability of the body to manufacture insulin, but artificial administration of insulin can normally control the disease. A form of mental deficiency (phenylketonuria) is caused by the body's failure to produce an enzyme that aids in the breakdown of protein, but, if caught early enough, mental deficiency can sometimes be avoided or lessened by an adjusted diet. In addition, a number of defects with a genetic basis, like harelip, pyloric stenosis, or certain types of congenital heart ailments, can often be corrected by surgery.

Thus, at a time when radioactivity increases the rate of mutations, the remarkable victories of medical science permit more persons with genetic defects to lead a normal life and have children. This, at least for some eugenists, raises the specter that each succeeding generation will bear an increasing burden of inherited ills. The example of diabetes led H. S. Jennings in the 1920's to predict that someday "each must carry with him an arsenal of hypodermic syringes, of vials, of capsules, of tablets. Each must remain within the radius of transportation of the synthetic chemical laboratory on which he must depend." In more recent years, Hermann J. Muller, among others, has added his considerable prestige to similar warnings of eventual danger from the accumulation of deleterious genes. He has called on the medical profession to make patients aware of the hereditary nature of their illnesses so that some, at least, will exercise restraint in reproduction.[22]

Already new discoveries in genetics are creating increased ability to prevent specific hereditary ills. Geneticists have, for instance, begun to find methods for spotting normal carriers of certain dangerous recessive genes. Someday therefore it may be possible to warn most such persons of the risk involved in the marriage of two persons with the same deleterious genes.[23] A few eugenists, too, have seen the possibilities in artificial insemination for both positive and negative eugenics: if men with defective genes can be persuaded to accept it, their defective genes will not be passed on; if the sperm of great geniuses is stored and used, children of high intelligence and occasional genius might possibly result. By 1959 there were already some 50,000 persons in the United States born by artificial insemination. So far it has been used mostly when the husband is sterile or when Rh incompatibility threatens a couple's child, but its use has sometimes been for eugenic reasons. Not too far in the future lies the possibility that both sperm and egg may be artificially inseminated in humans as in animals.[24]

More important for the future of eugenics is the remarkable progress now being made in unraveling the chemical processes by which heredity functions. Recently biochemists have made rapid strides in solving the complex formula of the DNA (deoxyribonucleic acid) molecules that form the genes in the cell nucleus and control the cell process. These advances mean that man will eventually understand the chemical code by which heredity is governed, that scientists may soon create life in a laboratory, and that ways of curing or controlling cancer may shortly be at hand. Beyond this lies the possibility that man may soon be able, by chemical means, to alter his own heredity: perhaps to offset hereditary defects, perhaps even to create new characteristics for man. Such possibilities lend a science-fiction-like quality to the future of eugenics and raise moral issues of considerable complexity. Certainly the programs that may be feasible in the future dwarf anything that can now be done, on the basis of present knowledge, to mold the genetic future of man.[25] Even at that, scientists are more likely to win victories against specific hereditary ailments than to bring about any over-all improvement in human intelligence and health.

The rapid advances presently being made in human genetics give promise, at any rate, that man will increasingly gain the knowledge to control his genetic future. The present debate over radioactive fallout and the expanding frontiers of science doubtless mean that both the medical profession and the public will grow in consciousness of heredity in the life and health of man. The growing interest in man's heredity is reflected in a revival of interest in eugenics. After leaving government service in 1950, Frederick Osborn reactivated the American Eugenics Society, soon turned *Eugenical News* into the *Eugenics Quarterly,* and increased its subscribers from 250 to a still modest 1,000. Among the members are anthropologists, including Harry L. Shapiro, chairman of the department of anthropology at the American Museum of Natural History and president of the American Eugenics Society since 1956; geneticists active in heredity counseling such as Franz J. Kallmann of the New York State Psychiatric Institute and Sheldon C. Reed of the Dight Institute; and persons from such varied fields as medicine, psychology, and demography.[26]

On the whole, the members acknowledge the limitations of present knowledge and recognize that they operate in a society that is oriented toward environment. Their faith is that both the limitations of knowledge and public apathy will change. "I think those who are interested in eugenics would be wise to be patient until both those things come to pass," Osborn has observed. "Otherwise we would again do as eugenics did thirty or forty years ago, espouse things which were not justified, and would turn public opinion back against eugenics." [27] Thus, while eugenists generally recognize that their movement currently has only minor influence and importance, they look forward to the day when man can, by bringing his genetic future under control, do much to make human life healthier and happier.

# Bibliographical Essay

The footnotes constitute a selected and annotated guide to the sources used in writing each section. There would be little purpose in listing those sources again in a bibliography. Instead, the aim here is to indicate the types of sources consulted, to emphasize those works that proved to be of special value, and to assess their adequacy.

A number of writers have treated some phase of the American eugenics movement. Richard Hofstadter in *Social Darwinism in American Thought* (rev. ed.; Boston: Beacon Press, 1955) briefly considers eugenics as a minor part of the total impact of Darwinian ideas. His treatment, while perceptive, tends to dismiss the movement as an odd fad. The relation of racists to eugenics is ably presented by Barbara Solomon in *Ancestors and Immigrants: A Changing New England Tradition* (Cambridge: Harvard University Press, 1956) and by John Higham in *Strangers in the Land: Patterns of American Nativism, 1860-1925* (New Brunswick: Rutgers University Press, 1955). Higham's discussion is especially good. Others have described the relation of eugenics to a special field of dependency or delinquency. Arthur E. Fink in *Causes of Crime: Biological Theories in the United States, 1800-1915* (Philadelphia: University of Pennsylvania Press, 1938) devotes much of his space to a detailed but uninterpretative description of hereditarian theories of crime. At the same time, Stanley P. Davies, *Social Control of the Mentally Deficient* (New York: Thomas Y. Crowell & Co., 1930), provides an excellent study of the rise and decline of the myth of the menace of the feebleminded. Finally, Nicholas Pastore in *The Nature-Nurture Controversy* (New York: King's Crown Press, 1949), in an effort to determine the relation of scientists' political views to their stand on heredity and environment, presents uneven biographical sketches of prominent American and British opponents and proponents of eugenics. None of these works attempts a complete picture of eugenics; none explores its roots, describes its organizational growth, traces the many scientific aspects, or evaluates its total development and impact.

The indispensable source for Francis Galton's life and the founding of the eugenics movement in England is Karl Pearson's four-volume *The Life, Letters and Labours of Francis Galton* (Cambridge: Cambridge University Press, 1914-1930). The Darwin centennial has resulted in a number of works analyzing the scientific ferment out of which eugenics arose; one of the best is Loren Eiseley, *Darwin's Century: Evolution and the Men Who Discovered It* (New York: Doubleday & Company, Inc., 1958). The attitudes of the various British eugenists are recorded in the numerous works of Galton, Pearson, Havelock Ellis, Caleb Williams Saleeby, Montague Crackanthorpe, and others. The eugenic work of Pearson and the biometricians can be followed in the Drapers' Company Research Memoirs, especially *Studies in National Deterioration* (beginning in 1906) and *Questions of the Day and of the Fray* (beginning in 1911); also important are the *Lecture Series* (1904 on) and the *Eugenic Laboratory Memoirs* (1907 on) published by the Francis Galton Laboratory of Eugenics. The *Eugenics Review,* first published in 1909, records the propaganda and development of the Eugenics Education Society. Although C. P. Blacker in *Eugenics, Galton and After* (London: Gerald Duckworth & Co., Ltd., 1952) sketches the development of eugenics ideas in England, there is no adequate critical history of the organization and impact of English eugenics by which the English movement could be compared with the American movement.

For the development of hereditarian attitudes among American students of the dependent and delinquent in the nineteenth century, the proceedings and journals of their various associations are the most revealing. These include the *Proceedings* of the National Conference of Charities and Correction (begun in 1874 and becoming the National Conference of Social Work in 1917); the *Transactions* (1874-76) and *Proceedings* (1884 on) of the National Prison Association, which became the American Prison Association in 1908; the *Proceedings* (1876-1895) of the Association of Medical Officers of American Institutions for Idiotic and Feeble-Minded Persons (after 1896 published as the *Journal of Psycho-Asthenics*); and the *Journal of Insanity,* established in 1844. The files of *Popular Science Monthly* from 1872 to 1915 and of the *Arena* from 1889 to 1909 also contained important articles. In addition, the works, autobiographies, and biographies of influential figures like Richard L. Dugdale, Josephine Shaw Lowell, Charles Loring Brace, Frederick H. Wines, Alexander Graham Bell, and Martin W. Barr were an important supplement for understanding the rising hereditarian emphasis.

The general development of racism in America during the late nineteenth century, especially with respect to immigrants, has been thoroughly described and interpreted in Higham, *Strangers in the Land,* Solomon, *Ancestors and Immigrants,* chapter nine of Hofstadter's *Social Darwinism,* Edward N. Saveth, *American Historians and European Immigrants, 1875-1925* (New York: Columbia University Press, 1948), and in numerous other books and articles on American thought and culture. Still needed, however, is a study of biological and anthropological attitudes toward the Negro following the Civil War and, if possible, of the transfer of European racism to American soil. The secondary works were supplemented by the abundant books and articles on race that flowed from the press as the century drew to a close and by the *Publications* of the Immigration Restriction League beginning in 1894.

By about 1910, when the eugenics movement was well under way in the United States, the sources became so numerous as to be unmanageable. The Charles B. Davenport papers at the Department of Genetics, Cold Spring Harbor, Long Island, New York, were invaluable. Davenport was in correspondence with nearly every major American eugenist and with many of the European leaders. The correspondence gave me a view of the private opinions, internal disagreements, and personal goals of the eugenists that would not otherwise have been possible. The relation of eugenics to research in genetics can be followed in the American Breeders' Association *Proceedings* and *Reports* after 1903 and in the *American Breeders' Magazine,* which in 1914 became the *Journal of Heredity,* official organ of the American Genetic Association. The research at Cold Spring Harbor and the founding and development of the Eugenics Record Office are recorded in Davenport's annual reports in the Carnegie Institution of Washington *Year Books,* from 1904 on. After 1910 the Eugenics Record Office published numerous *Bulletins* and occasional *Memoirs,* in which the major research was presented.

From 1916 on, the *Eugenical News,* edited by Harry H. Laughlin at the Eugenics Record Office, provided a summary of current events in eugenics and became the organ for eugenics extremists like its editor.

The popular presentation and interpretation of eugenics was full and complete, as a reference to the *Readers' Guide to Periodical Literature* under such headings as eugenics, heredity, feebleminded, or immigrants will make clear. The *New York Times,* which was mildly favorable to eugenics, ran many news stories and human interest articles on eugenics. The broad outlines of the eugenics creed were expounded in numerous books ranging from Davenport's *Heredity in Relation to Eugenics* (New York: Henry Holt & Co., Inc., 1911) to Michael F. Guyer's *Being Well-Born: An Introduction to Eugenics* (Indianapolis: The Bobbs-Merrill Company, Inc., 1916) and Paul Popenoe and Roswell H. Johnson's *Applied Eugenics* (New York: The Macmillan Co., 1918). Through the printed word and through speeches before college classes, women's clubs, businessmen's clubs, and reform groups eugenics went before the public. As important as the general indoctrination, however, were the pleas for particular eugenics reforms.

The research that underlay the astonishing rise and fall of the myth of the menace of the feebleminded is chronicled in Davies' *Social Control of the Mentally Deficient.* Histories of mental testing, which, however, omit reference to the social impact and implications of the tests, are Joseph Peterson, *Early Conceptions and Tests of Intelligence* (Yonkers-on-Hudson: World Book Company, 1925) and Frank N. Freeman, *Mental Tests, Their History, Principles and Applications* (rev. ed.; Boston: Houghton Mifflin Company, 1939). The key contemporary works were Henry H. Goddard, *The Kallikak Family* (New York: The Macmillan Co., 1912) and *Feeblemindedness, Its Causes and Consequences* (New York: The Macmillan Co., 1914). The reports of mental testing and the warnings of dangers from the feebleminded appeared in such established periodicals as the *Journal of Psycho-Asthenics;* in new ones like the *Training School Bulletin,* published after 1904 at Vineland, New Jersey, the *Journal of Criminal Law and Criminology,* begun in 1910 by the American Institute of Criminal Law and Criminology, and *Mental Hygiene,* established in 1917 by the National Committee for Mental Hygiene; in general reform journals like *Survey;* and in several psychological journals. In many ways the most revealing documents, though, were the reports of the numerous state and local surveys into the extent and danger of the feebleminded, for they often showed most clearly the motivations and unconscious exaggerations that created the myth.

A turning point in the acceptance of the myth, and a major document in the eugenics movement, was the report on the nation's intelligence in Robert M. Yerkes, ed., *Psychological Examining in the United States Army,* National Academy of Sciences, *Memoirs,* XV (Washington: Government Printing Office, 1921). Important criticisms of the myth, among many, were William Healy, *The Individual Delinquent* (Boston: Little, Brown, and Co., 1915), and J. E. Wallace Wallin, *Problems of Subnormality* (Yonkers-on-Hudson: World Book Co., 1917). Most of the same journals that published articles on the menace of the feebleminded also published criticisms.

The course of the legislative campaign to secure more extensive care of the feebleminded was fairly difficult to unravel. The best single source was the few remaining files of the Committee on Provision for the Feebleminded at the Training School, Vineland, New Jersey. The files were supplemented by Alexander Johnson's autobiography, *Adventures in Social Welfare* (Fort Wayne: by author, 1923), and by numerous speeches and articles by those active in the campaign. Sterilization, on the other hand, has aroused such interest that its history has been extensively recorded. Still indispensable, despite the biases of the author, are Laughlin's compilations of documents in *The Legal, Legislative and Administrative Aspects of Sterilization,* Eugenics Record Office, Bulletin No. 10B (Cold Spring Harbor, 1914); *Eugenical Sterilization in the United States* (Chicago: Psychopathic Laboratory of the Municipal Court of Chicago, 1922); *Eugenical Sterilization: 1926* (New Haven: American Eugenics Society, 1926); and *The Legal Status of Eugenical Sterilization,* Supplement to the Annual Report of the Municipal Court of Chicago [Chicago, 1930]. Additional historical summaries, combined with favorable or critical evaluations of sterilization, are in E. S. Gosney and Paul Popenoe, *Sterilization for Human Betterment* (New York: The Macmillan Co., 1930); J. H. Landman, *Human Sterilization* (New York: The Macmillan Co., 1932); and Abraham Myerson, *et al., Eugenical Sterilization, A Reorientation of the Problem* (New York: The Macmillan Co., 1936). An excellent study of a single state is Rudolph Vecoli, "Sterilization: A Progressive Measure?" *Wisconsin Magazine of History,* XLIII (Spring, 1960), 190-202. At the present time, the Human Betterment Association of America in New York City (formerly Birthright, Inc.) compiles facts and figures on sterilization in the United States and distributes reprints and pamphlets to encourage its wider use for eugenical and social purposes.

The successful campaign for immigration restriction and the racism that underlay it have often been described. By far the best study is Higham's *Strangers in the Land,* but others include Solomon, *Ancestors and Immigrants,* parts of Oscar Handlin, *Race and Nationality in American Life* (Garden City: Doubleday & Company, Inc., 1957), and, for the period after 1920, Robert A. Divine, *American Immigration Policy, 1924-1952* (New Haven: Yale University Press, 1957). The Edward A. Ross papers at the Wisconsin Historical Society, Madison, Wisconsin, were helpful not only in revealing Ross's views on race but also in revealing the attitudes and plans of the racists with whom he corresponded. Many government documents record the arguments of restrictionists; among the more important are the reports, in forty-two volumes, of the Immigration Commission (1911) and the many hearings of the House Committee on Immigration and Naturalization during the 1920's. Racism was a consistent theme of *Eugenical News* and the *Journal of Heredity.* The major source for race doctrines, naturally enough, was the works of such eugenic racists as Prescott F. Hall, Edward A. Ross, Madison Grant, Lothrop Stoddard, Charles W. Gould, Ellsworth Huntington, and William McDougall. The major attack on the racist case was by Franz Boas in his *The Mind of Primitive Man* (New York: The Macmillan Co., 1911) and in numerous articles. The attitude of American anthropologists is revealed in the articles and reviews found in the *Journal of Race Development* (1910 to 1919) and the *American Anthropologist.*

For understanding the eugenics currents of the 1920's, the Davenport papers provide an invaluable insight into the attitudes, the research, and the plans of the leading eugenists. But again the writings of the eugenists are the most important source. During the decade biologists like Samuel J. Holmes and Edwin G. Conklin, geneticists like Edward M. East and Horatio H. Newman, sociologists like Edward A. Ross, psychologists like William McDougall, Edward Lee Thorndike, and Henry H. Goddard, and publicists like Lothrop Stoddard and Albert E. Wiggam wrote books in which they interpreted eugenics in terms of economic and political policies. Largely their recommendations were pessimistic and reactionary. In the same period, a scientific reconstruction had begun, reflected in genetics in H. S. Jennings' *Prometheus, Or Biology and the Ad-*

*vancement of Man* (New York: E. P. Dutton & Co., Inc., 1925); in psychology in the research and attitudes summarized by Gladys C. Schwesinger's *Heredity and Environment* (New York: The Macmillan Co., 1933); and in demography in the impressive statistics assembled by Frank Lorimer and Frederick Osborn in *Dynamics of Population* (New York: The Macmillan Co., 1934).

An understanding of modern eugenics involves an understanding of modern trends in genetics, demography, psychology, and anthropology. The development of eugenics can be followed in the *Eugenics Quarterly*, which replaced *Eugenical News* in 1954. Frederick Osborn's *Preface to Eugenics* (rev. ed.; New York: The Macmillan Co., 1951), the standard summary of the modern eugenics creed, contains little with which a geneticist would quarrel. The most thorough popular presentation of reasons why anthropologists generally reject racism is M. F. Ashley Montagu's *Man's Most Dangerous Myth: The Fallacy of Race* (3d ed.; New York: Columbia University Press, 1952). Also helpful is Otto Klineberg, ed., *Characteristics of the American Negro* (New York: Harper & Brothers, 1944). A recent and authoritative treatment of the heredity of behavior is John L. Fuller and W. Robert Thompson, *Behavior Genetics* (New York: John Wiley, 1960). A more technical introduction to human genetics can be found in a good college text like Curt Stern's *Principles of Human Genetics* (San Francisco: W. H. Freeman and Company, 1949), or in one of the good paperback introductions such as L. C. Dunn and Th. Dobzhansky, *Heredity, Race and Society* (rev. ed.; New York: Mentor Book, 1946). A brilliant and influential, though now somewhat dated, discussion is in J. B. S. Haldane, *Heredity and Politics* (New York: W. W. Norton & Co., 1938). In *Heredity in Health and Mental Disorder* (New York: W. W. Norton & Co., 1953), Franz J. Kallmann presents a summary of his own and others' studies of twins, and in *The Biology of Mental Defect* (London: Sidgwick and Jackson, Ltd., 1949), Lionel S. Penrose provides an excellent analysis of knowledge about the causes of feeblemindedness. Although some geneticists feel he sometimes draws conclusions from inadequate data, Sheldon C. Reed's *Counseling in Medical Genetics* (Philadelphia: W. B. Saunders Co., 1955) is doubtless the most readable guide to heredity counseling.

# Footnotes

In the footnotes, I have used the following abbreviations:

| | |
|---|---|
| *AJMD* | *American Journal of Mental Deficiency* |
| *AmJI* | *American Journal of Insanity* |
| *APA* | *Proceedings of the American Prison Association* |
| C.S.H. | Charles B. Davenport papers, Department of Genetics, Cold Spring Harbor, Long Island, New York |
| E.R.O. | Eugenics Record Office |
| G.P.O. | Government Printing Office |
| *JCL&C* | *Journal of Criminal Law and Criminology* |
| *JH* | *Journal of Heredity* |
| *JPA* | *Journal of Psycho-Asthenics* |
| *NCCC* | *Proceedings of the National Conference of Charities and Correction* |
| *NPA* | *Proceedings of the National Prison Association* |
| *Pop. Sci. Mon.* | *Popular Science Monthly* |
| *Tng. Sch. Bull.* | *Training School Bulletin* |
| V.T.S. | Files of the Committee on Provision for the Feeble-minded, Vineland Training School, Vineland, New Jersey |
| W.H.S. | Wisconsin Historical Society, Madison, Wisconsin |

## CHAPTER I

[1] Charles B. Davenport, *Heredity in Relation to Eugenics* (New York: Henry Holt & Co., 1911), 1.

[2] Allen G. Roper in *Ancient Eugenics* (Oxford: B. H. Blackwell, 1913), provides a brief but rambling account of eugenics in ancient Greece and Rome.

[3] *The Descent of Man and Selection in Relation to Sex* (2d ed. rev.; New York: D. Appleton and Co., 1922), 136.

Darwin hoped that the poverty, drunkenness, and profligacy of the weak would decrease their fertility. He warned that "both sexes ought to refrain from marriage if they are in any marked degree inferior in body or mind; but such hopes are Utopian and will never be even partially realised until the laws of inheritance are thoroughly known." *Ibid.*, p. 632.

⁴ The best discussion of the American social Darwinists is Richard Hofstadter's *Social Darwinism in American Thought* (rev. ed.; Boston: Beacon Press, 1955). The classic statement of conservative social Darwinism is William Graham Sumner's *What Social Classes Owe to Each Other* (New York: Harper & Bros., 1883).

⁵ Nicholas Pastore in *The Nature-Nurture Controversy* (New York: King's Crown Press, 1949) showed clearly, by a biographical study of numerous scientists, that an emphasis upon heredity was normally accompanied by conservatism in social outlook.

## CHAPTER II

¹ Galton, *Natural Inheritance* (London: Macmillan and Co., 1889), p. 62.

² The main source for Galton's life is Karl Pearson's four-volume labor of love, *The Life, Letters and Labours of Francis Galton* (Cambridge: Cambridge University Press, 1914, 1924 & 1930). A shorter secondary account is in the first six chapters of C. P. Blacker, *Eugenics, Galton and After* (London: Gerald Duckworth & Co., 1952). In addition, Galton wrote a somewhat impressionistic and not very useful autobiography, *Memories of My Life* (London: Methuen & Co., 1908).

³ His genealogy is discussed in full in his autobiography, chap. I, and in the *Life, Letters and Labours,* I, chap. II.

⁴ *"The Origin of Species" and "The Descent of Man"* (New York: Modern Library Giant, n.d.), p. 373.

In 1869 Galton wrote Darwin: "Consequently the appearance of your Origin of Species formed a real crisis in my life; your book drove away the constraint of my old superstition as if it had been a nightmare and was the first to give me freedom of thought." *Life, Letters and Labours,* I, between pp. 6 & 7.

⁵ *Hereditary Genius: An Inquiry into its Laws and Consequences* (2d ed.; London: Macmillan and Co., Ltd., 1914), p. 35.

⁶ For instance, in speaking of judges, Galton wrote: "In other countries it may be different . . . , but we all know that in England the Bench is never spoken of without reverence for the intellectual powers of its occupiers." Hence, "a judgeship is a guarantee of its possessor being gifted with exceptional ability." *Ibid.,* p. 49. When Galton found that many judges stemmed from the same families, therefore, he concluded judicial qualities were hereditary.

⁷ *Ibid.,* pp. 12-32.

⁸ In *Hereditary Genius* Galton devoted a chapter to pedigrees of men eminent in each of these callings. *English Men of Science: Their Nature and Nurture* (London: Macmillan & Co., 1874) was devoted entirely to scientists.

⁹ In "Hereditary Talent and Character," *Macmillan's Magazine,* **XII**

(June, 1865), 165, Galton wrote: "If a twentieth part of the cost and pains were spent in measures for the improvement of the human race that is spent on the improvement of the breed of horses and cattle, what a galaxy of genius might we not create." See also *Hereditary Genius,* especially pp. 1 and 338-48.

[10] Galton, "The History of Twins as a Criterion of the Relative Powers of Nature and Nurture," *Journal of the Anthropological Institute,* V (1875), 391-406; reprinted in *Inquiries into Human Faculty and its Development* (2d ed.; New York: E. P. Dutton & Co., n.d.), pp. 155-73.

[11] For Galton's place in the development of psychology, see Edwin G. Boring, *A History of Experimental Psychology* (2d ed.; New York: Appleton-Century-Crofts, 1950), pp. 482ff; Gardner Murphy, *An Historical Introduction to Modern Psychology* (4th ed.; New York: Harcourt, Brace & Co., 1938), pp. 123ff.

[12] *Inquiries into Human Faculty,* footnote p. 17.

[13] *Hereditary Genius,* pp. 325-37.

[14] *Inquiries into Human Faculty,* p. 200.

[15] At the time, his view of heredity was: "We shall . . . take an approximately correct view of the origin of our life if we consider our own embryos to have sprung immediately from those embryos whence our parents were developed, and those from the embryos of *their* parents, and so on for ever." See "Hereditary Talent and Character," *op. cit.,* p. 322.

[16] For a brief historical sketch of the belief in inheritance of acquired characters, see Conway Zirkle, "The Early History of the Idea of the Inheritance of Acquired Characters and of Pangenesis," *Trans. of the American Philosophical Society,* XXXV, n.s. (1945), esp. 93-119. Loren Eiseley in *Darwin's Century: Evolution and the Men Who Discovered It* (Garden City: Doubleday & Company, 1958), chap. viii, discusses the reasons for Darwin's increasing belief in heredity of acquired characters. Galton, in cooperation with Darwin, conducted a rabbit breeding experiment to test the theory. The result confirmed Galton in his rejection of the theory but did not alter Darwin's belief. See *Life, Letters and Labours,* II, 156ff.

[17] See *Natural Inheritance,* esp. pp. 83-137. Galton first discovered the law of regression in breeding sweet peas and later applied it to human heredity.

[18] In fact, Galton tried to calculate the amount that an individual inherited from each of his ancestors. He concluded that it was ½ from the parents, ¼ from grandparents, ⅛ from great grandparents, and so on back. *Ibid.,* p. 136.

[19] For the life of Pearson, see E. S. Pearson, *Karl Pearson: An Appreciation of Some Aspects of His Life and Work* (Cambridge: Cambridge University Press, 1938). J. B. S. Haldane's "Karl Pearson," *New Biology,* No. 25 (January, 1958), pp. 7-26, is an excellent evaluation of Pearson's contributions.

[20] Quotation from Pearson in *Life, Letters and Labours,* I, 2.

[21] Pearson, *Karl Pearson,* esp. pp. 34-42.

²² Pearson, "On the Laws of Inheritance in Man," *Biometrika,* III (1904), 131-90.

²³ Especially, *National Life from the Standpoint of Science,* Eugenics Lecture Series, No. XI (Cambridge: Cambridge University Press, 1905).

²⁴ Summaries of Morel's thought are in Henry Maudsley, *Body and Mind* (rev. ed.; London: Macmillan and Co., 1873), p. 45; Havelock Ellis, *The Criminal* (2d ed.; London: Walter Scott, Ltd., 1897), pp. 32-33.

²⁵ The cephalic index is measured from the top of the head. It is the width of the head divided by the length and multiplied by 100.

²⁶ *Criminal Man: According to the Classification of Cesare Lombroso,* summarized by his daughter Gina Lombroso Ferroro (New York: G. P. Putnam's Sons, 1911), pp. 7ff.

²⁷ These findings by Lombroso are reported in Ellis, *The Criminal,* p. 83.

²⁸ Lombroso classified geniuses among the defectives. He was famous for his belief that genius was closely allied to insanity and other forms of defect.

²⁹ For a sketch of Lombroso's development, see Introduction by Maurice Parmelee in Lombroso, *Crime, Its Causes and Remedies* (Boston: Little, Brown, and Co., 1911), esp. pp. xii-xiii. Hans Kurella, *Cesare Lombroso: A Modern Man of Science,* trans. M. Eden Paul (London: Rebman Ltd., 1911), is chiefly a summary of criminal anthropology but contains much information on Lombroso's life. For Benedikt's findings, see *Anatomical Studies upon Brains of Criminals,* trans. E. P. Fowler (New York: William Wood and Co., 1881).

³⁰ For example, Samuel A. K. Strahan, *Marriage and Disease: A Study of Heredity and the More Important Family Degenerations* (London: Kegan, Paul, Trench, Trubner & Co., 1892), and Maudsley, *Body and Mind.*

³¹ *Inquiries into Human Faculty,* pp. 10-11; see also *Memories of My Life,* pp. 259-64.

³² See Wallace, "Human Progress: Past and Future," *Arena,* V (January, 1892), 145-59; E. Ray Lankester, *The Kingdom of Man* (New York: Henry Holt and Co., 1907), esp. pp. 31-41. It should be mentioned that Wallace became a bitter critic of the eugenics movement.

³³ In addition to publication in *Nature* in England, the speech was reprinted in *Pop. Sci. Mon.,* LX (January, 1902), 218-33, and in *Annual Report of the Board of Regents of the Smithsonian Institution* (1901), pp. 523-38, in the United States.

³⁴ "The Possible Improvement of the Human Breed under Existing Conditions of Law and Sentiment," *Essays in Eugenics* (London: Eugenics Education Society, 1909), p. 25.

³⁵ See, for instance, *Memories of My Life,* p. 311. The final chapter of his autobiography is a concise statement of his eugenics creed.

³⁶ "Restriction in Marriage" and "Eugenics as a Factor in Religion" in *Essays in Eugenics.*

³⁷ In establishing the fellowship, Galton carefully defined national eugenics as "the study of the agencies under social control that may im-

prove or impair the racial qualities of future generations either physically or mentally." The definition was often used by later eugenists. *Life, Letters and Labours,* IIIA, 222.

[38] The development of the Eugenics Laboratory can best be followed in *Life, Letters and Labours,* IIIA, *passim.*

[39] Ellis set forth his eugenics creed in *The Problem of Race-Regeneration* (New York: Moffat, Yard & Co., 1911). Earlier, in *A Study of British Genius* (London: Hurst and Blackett, Ltd., 1904) he had extended Galton's study of *Hereditary Genius.* Ellis wrote innumerable essays on eugenics.

[40] The early activities of the Society can be followed in the *Eugenics Review.* See also *Life, Letters and Labours,* IIIA, *passim,* and C. P. Blacker, *Eugenics in Retrospect and Prospect,* Occasional Papers on Eugenics, No. 1 (London: Eugenics Society, 1950), pp. 19ff.

[41] Remarks in *Sociological Papers, 1904* (London: Macmillan & Co., Ltd., 1905), pp. 74 & 75. Shaw's fullest statement of his eugenic notions is probably his Preface to *Man and Superman.*

[42] *Parenthood and Race Culture: An Outline of Eugenics* (New York: Moffat, Yard and Co., 1909), pp. 238ff. In other respects Saleeby was typical of eugenics sentiment. He was convinced that "eugenics is going to save the world" (p. 211) and urged extending "to the unfit all our sympathy but forbidding them parenthood" (p. 30).

[43] The controversy, from Pearson's point of view, is summarized in *Life, Letters and Labours,* IIIA, esp. pp. 405-9.

[44] *Eugenics Review,* II (July, 1910), 91-92.

[45] The proceedings were published as *Problems in Eugenics: Papers Communicated to the First International Eugenics Congress* (London: Eugenics Education Society, 1912).

## CHAPTER III

[1] For a biographical sketch, see Edward M. Shepard, *The Work of a Social Teacher: Being a Memorial of Richard L. Dugdale,* Society for Political Education, "Economic Tracts," No. XII (New York: 1884).

[2] Samuel Hopkins Adams, in an amusing article on "The Juke Myth," *Saturday Review of Literature,* XXXVIII (April 2, 1955), 13, concluded that the Jukes "never existed otherwhere than in the brain of an amateur criminologist." Unfortunately much of the humor and criticism in the article depend upon misrepresentation and misquotation of Dugdale's study.

[3] *The Jukes: A Study in Crime, Pauperism, and Heredity* (4th ed.; New York: G. P. Putnam's Sons, 1910), pp. 69-70. Dugdale first published his study in *A Record and Study of the Relations of Crime, Pauperism and Disease* in Prison Association of New York, *Thirty-First Annual Report* (1875), pp. 130-83.

[4] *Ibid.,* pp. 65 & 55. Dugdale, unlike many later writers who used his study, was no dogmatist: "What I have here related, what I have elsewhere written, is purely tentative." From "Hereditary Pauperism," *NCCC* (1877), p. 95.

[5] *Ibid.,* p. 62. For further statements by Dugdale of his position, see "Origin of Crime in Society," *Atlantic Monthly,* XLVIII (October, 1881), 452-62; (December, 1881), pp. 735-46; XLIV (February, 1882), 243-51.

[6] I use the term pauperism as it was then used: not as a synonym for poverty but as a physical and mental deterioration of the individual rendering him unable or unwilling to care for himself. For example, Charles R. Henderson, *Introduction to the Study of the Dependent, Defective, and Delinquent Classes* (2d ed.; Boston: D. C. Heath & Co., 1901), p. 10.

[7] See Theodule A. Ribot, *Heredity: A Psychological Study of its Phenomena, Laws, Causes, and Consequences* (New York: D. Appleton & Co., 1875), p. 147; Eugene S. Talbot, *Degeneracy: Its Causes, Signs, and Results* (London: Walter Scott, Ltd., 1898), p. 46.

[8] B. O. Flower, "The Right of the Child Considered in the Light of Heredity and Prenatal Influence," *Arena,* XIII (July, 1895), 254. For examples still more farfetched, see Talbot, *Degeneracy,* pp. 56-61.

[9] For instance, Amos Warner, *American Charities: A Study in Philanthropy and Economics* (New York: Thomas Y. Crowell & Co., 1894), p. 120; Lester F. Ward, *Dynamic Sociology, or Applied Social Science* (New York: D. Appleton and Co., 1883), II, 549-50, 614-15.

[10] The Association of Medical Superintendents of American Institutions for the Insane was established in 1844, became the American Medico-Psychological Association in 1897, and in the 1920's became the American Psychiatric Association. The Association of Medical Officers of American Institutions for Idiotic and Feeble-Minded Persons, organized in 1876, became the American Association for the Study of the Feebleminded in 1906, and the American Association on Mental Deficiency in 1933. The National Prison Association, after some meetings in the early and middle 1870's, was permanently formed in 1884 and in 1908 became the American Prison Association. The National Conference of Charities and Corrections, originally a section of the American Social Science Association, began an independent existence in 1874 and in 1917 became the National Conference of Social Work.

[11] Walter E. Fernald, "The Growth of Provision for the Feeble-Minded in the United States," *Mental Hygiene,* I (January, 1917), 38-39.

[12] Cited in Warner, *American Charities,* pp. 279-80. See also Harold Schwartz, *Samuel Gridley Howe, Social Reformer: 1801-1876* (Cambridge, Mass.: Harvard University Press, 1956), pp. 139-44.

[13] See Ernest Bicknell, "Feeble-Mindedness as an Inheritance," *NCCC* (1896), p. 221; Isaac N. Kerlin, "The Organization of Establishments for the Idiotic and Imbecile Classes," *NCCC* (1877), p. 20, and from 1884 on, any of the reports by the standing committee on the feebleminded before the National Conference of Charities and Correction.

[14] Quotations from Kerlin, *Idiotic and Feeble-Minded Children* (Boston, 1884), p. 15; Amos W. Butler, "A Notable Factor of Social Degeneration," *Proceedings of the American Association for the Advancement of Science* (1901), p. 339. A typical description is Martha Louise Clark,

"The Relation of Imbecility to Pauperism and Crime," *Arena,* X (November, 1894), 788-94.

One factor that caused, or at least confirmed, a belief in a close relation between feeblemindedness and crime was the concept of the moral imbecile that developed in the 1880's. While most feebleminded persons were believed to have an underdeveloped intellectual faculty and, in most cases, an underdeveloped moral faculty, the moral imbecile had only his moral faculty underdeveloped. Many institutions for the feebleminded had a few moral imbeciles committed to them, youths who were incorrigible, violent, sometimes sexually promiscuous. In the institutions they constituted a disrupting influence on their more docile fellow inmates. But the presence of such incorrigible youths and a belief that most feebleminded persons were likely to have an underdeveloped moral faculty gave a sort of scientific explanation to the belief that the feebleminded were a menace. See Arthur E. Fink, *Causes of Crime: Biological Theories in the United States, 1800-1915* (Philadelphia: University of Pennsylvania Press, 1938), pp. 213-17, 234-36.

[15] Stanley P. Davies, *Social Control of the Mentally Deficient* (New York: Thomas Y. Crowell Co., 1930), pp. 39-42; Albert Deutsch, *The Mentally Ill in America: A History of Their Care and Treatment from Colonial Times* (2d ed.; New York: Columbia University Press, 1949), pp. 351-53.

[16] For biographical information, see William Rhinelander Stewart, ed., *The Philanthropic Work of Josephine Shaw Lowell* (New York: The Macmillan Co., 1911), *passim.*

[17] *Ibid.,* p. 193. For descriptions of some of the cases she found in the almshouses, see Josephine Shaw Lowell, *et al.,* "Report of the Committee on a Reformatory for Women," in *Twelfth Annual Report of the New York State Board of Charities* (1879), pp. 289-92.

[18] *Ibid.,* chap. vii.

[19] *Ibid.,* chap. viii; also Deutsch, *Mentally Ill,* pp. 351-53.

[20] "Custodial Care of the Adult Feeble-Minded," *JPA,* I (December, 1896), 56 & 63.

[21] Especially the speech by Alexander Johnson, "Permanent Custodial Care," *NCCC* (1896), pp. 207-19. For the status of custodial care in 1890, see William B. Fish, "Custodial Care of Adult Idiots," *NCCC* (1891), pp. 203-21.

Epileptics ranked with the feebleminded in the proportion attributed to heredity; estimates of the proportion who were victims of heredity ranged up to two-thirds or higher. Hence many urged that they too be given custodial care and denied marriage. See William P. Letchworth, *Care and Treatment of Epileptics* (New York: G. P. Putnam's Sons, 1900), esp. pp. 10-12; also Dr. R. E. Doran, "A Consideration of the Heredity Factors in Epilepsy," *AmJI,* LX (July, 1903), 64-65.

[22] Pliny Earle, "The Curability of Insanity," *AmJI,* XXXIII (April, 1877), 504; also Earle, "The Curability of Insanity: A Statistical Study," *AmJI,* XLII (October, 1885), 179-209. For a discussion of the curability craze, see Deutsch, *Mentally Ill,* pp. 132-57.

²³ For example, *AmJI*, XLIII (October, 1886), 139; XXXI (July, 1874), 117.

²⁴ Deutsch, *Mentally Ill*, pp. 263-65 & 252-71, has a detailed discussion of the steps taken by the states to care for the incurable insane.

²⁵ See John P. Gray, "The Dependence of Insanity on Physical Disease," *AmJI*, XXVII (April, 1871), 377-408; Gray, "Thoughts on the Causation of Insanity," *AmJI*, XIX (October, 1882), 264-83; H. E. Allison, "On a General System of Reporting Autopsies in American Asylums for the Insane," *AmJI*, XLVI (October, 1889), 216-23.

²⁶ Dr. Charles E. Atwood, "Teachings of Recent Investigations into the Causation of Insanity," *AmJI*, XLVIII (January, 1892), 332. For a somewhat opposing view, see John P. Gray, "Heredity," *AmJI*, XLI (July, 1884), esp. p. 6.

²⁷ Jennie McCowen, "The Prevention of Insanity," *NCCC* (1883), p. 39.

²⁸ William G. Stearns, "A System of Obtaining and Recording Anthropological Data," *AmJI*, LIII (October, 1896), 256; Isaac Ray, in statement in *AmJI*, XXXVII (October, 1880), 169.

²⁹ William Krauss, "Heredity—With a Study of the Statistics of the New York State Hospitals," *AmJI*, LVIII (April, 1902), 607-23; Frederick L. Hills, "A Statistical Study of One Thousand Cases," *AmJI*, LVIII (July, 1901), 158.

³⁰ William Goddell, "Clinical Notes on the Extirpation of the Ovaries for Insanity," *AmJI*, XXXVIII (January, 1882), 295. See also, "Removal of Both Ovaries for Insanity," *AmJI*, XXXVIII (January-April, 1882), 477; Dr. E. D. Bondurant, "Two Cases of Oophorectomy at Cleveland Asylum," *AmJI*, XLIII (January, 1887), 364-65; Thomas G. Morton, "Removal of the Ovaries as a Cure for Insanity," *AmJI*, XLIX (January, 1893), 397-401.

³¹ Many of the best statements came after 1900. See G. Alder Blumer, "Presidential Address," *AmJI*, LX (July, 1903), 15; Charles P. Bancroft, "Presidential Address: Hopeful and Discouraging Aspects of the Psychiatric Outlook," *AmJI*, LXV (July, 1908), esp. pp. 10-11.

³² Thomas D. Crothers, ed., *The Disease of Inebriety from Alcohol, Opium and Other Narcotic Drugs* (New York: E. B. Treat & Co., 1904), p. v.

³³ Statement by Dr. Matthews in *ibid.*, p. 161.

³⁴ Crothers, "Heredity in Inebriety," *Journal of Heredity*, I (January, 1886), 53. See also the speech given by Dr. Jennie McCowen to the heredity meeting of the W.C.T.U. in Davenport, Iowa: "Heredity in Its Relation to Charity Work," *Journal of Heredity*, I (January, 1886), 50-51, and for a thorough discussion, Crothers, ed., *Disease of Inebriety*, chaps. xvi, xvii, & xviii.

³⁵ R. Osgood Mason, "The Curse of Inebriety," *Arena*, XXVI (August, 1901), 129.

³⁶ *Dictionary of American Biography*, II, 148-52.

³⁷ "On the Formation of a Deaf Variety of the Human Race," in *Mem-*

*oirs of the National Academy of Science* (Washington, D. C., 1884), II, 181 & 188.

[38] *Ibid.,* p. 217.

[39] *Ibid.,* p. 221. Quotation from Bell, *Marriage: An Address to the Deaf* (Washington, D. C.: Volta Bureau, 1891), p. 7. In *Facts and Opinions Relating to the Deaf from America* (London: Spottiswoode & Co., 1888), Bell presented to a Royal Commission the opinions of various American experts concerning the deaf. Chapter iii treats heredity.

[40] *Proceedings of the Third Convention of the National Association of the Deaf* (1889), p. 5. The differing opinions of experts can be seen in an exchange of views in *Science* from XVI (September 5, 1890), to XVII (February 6, 1891).

[41] Fay found the following percentages of deaf children in different types of marriages:

| | Per Cent of Children Deaf | |
| --- | --- | --- |
| | *If One Parent Deaf* | *If Both Parents Deaf* |
| Neither Parent with Deaf Relatives: | 2.4 | 1.0 |
| Both Parents with Deaf Relatives: | 20.8 | 21.0 |

See *Marriages of the Deaf in America* (Washington, D. C.: Volta Bureau, 1898), pp. 97 & 125.

[42] Quotations are from Brace, "Pauperism in the City of New York," *NCCC* (1874), p. 23. Brace's biography is given in Emma Brace, *The Life of Charles Loring Brace, Chiefly Told in his own Letters* (New York: Charles Scribner's Sons, 1894).

In *The Dangerous Classes of New York, and Twenty Years' Work among Them* (3d ed.; New York: Wynkoop & Hallenbeck, 1880), Brace described his work among the poor children of the city. His hope was to protect society from the dangerous classes, "classes with inherited pauperism and crime" (p. 25).

[43] The standard study is Frank B. Watson, *The Charity Organization Movement in the United States* (New York: The Macmillan Co., 1922). For a perceptive discussion of the motives and results of C.O.S., see Robert H. Bremner, *From the Depths: The Discovery of Poverty in the United States* (New York: New York University Press, 1956), pp. 46-57.

[44] Lowell, *Public Relief and Private Charity,* No. XIII of *Questions of the Day* (New York: G. P. Putnam's Sons, 1884), pp. 66 & 68. For further statements of her position, see *Philanthropic Work of Josephine Shaw Lowell,* chap. ix.

[45] "The Tribe of Ishmael: A Study in Social Degradation," *NCCC* (1888), p. 159.

[46] McCulloch, "Associated Charities," *NCCC* (1880), pp. 122-35. Many persons during the period saw a close connection between hereditary pauperism and charity. For example, Dugdale, "Hereditary Pauperism," p. 94; Dr. Jennie McCowen, "Heredity in its Relation to Charity Work,"

pp. 47-51; Dr. Luther, "Causes and Prevention of Pauperism," *NCCC* (1880), pp. 242-49.

[47] Warner, *American Charities: A Study in Philanthropy and Economics* (New York: Thomas Y. Crowell & Co., 1894), p. 74. Other texts that took much the same attitude toward social failure were Henderson, *Introduction to the Study of the Dependent, Defective, and Delinquent Classes* and, with somewhat less emphasis on heredity, Robert Hunter, *Poverty* (New York: The Macmillan Co., 1905), esp. pp. 66-105.

[48] Quotation in "Crime and Automatism," *Atlantic Monthly*, XXXV (April, 1875), 472. An excellent discussion of Holmes's views is George Boewe, *Heredity in the Writings of Hawthorne, Holmes, and Howells*, Unpubl. Doctoral Dissertation, University of Wisconsin, 1955, *passim*.

Fink, *Causes of Crime*, pp. 151ff, discusses the growing hereditarian emphasis in the study of crime.

[49] For a summary of the reformers' program, see Enoch C. Wines, "Report of the Executive Committee," in National Prison Association, *Transactions* (1874), pp. 45-53. The best secondary account of prison reform is Blake McKelvey, *American Prisons: A Study in American Social History Prior to 1915* (Chicago: University of Chicago Press, 1936), pp. 48-92.

[50] Brockway, "The Incorrigible Criminal: What is He and How Should He be Treated?" *NPA* (1884), pp. 105-12; discussion pp. 113ff.

[51] Moody, *Heredity, Its Relations to Human Development* (Boston: Institute of Heredity, 1882), *passim*.

[52] "Men are competent," said Noyes, "to choose in sexual intercourse whether they will stop at any point in the voluntary stages of it, and so make it simply an act of communion, or go on through to the involuntary stage, and make it an act of propagation." *Male Continence* (Oneida, N. Y., 1872), p. 8.

[53] Noyes, *Essay on Scientific Propagation* (Oneida, N. Y., n.d.), pp. 5 & 2. As early as the 1840's Noyes had favored scientific propagation, so his interest preceded his reading of Galton. See Noyes, *Male Continence*, p. 15.

[54] Hilda Herrick Noyes and George Wallingford Noyes, "The Oneida Community Experiment in Stirpiculture," *Eugenics, Genetics and the Family*, Scientific Papers of the Second International Congress of Eugenics (Baltimore: The Williams & Wilkins Co., 1923), I, 376.

[55] Theodore Noyes, *Report on the Health of Children in the Oneida Community* (Oneida, N. Y., 1878).

[56] The fullest of the many descriptions of the community is Robert A. Parker, *A Yankee Saint: John Humphrey Noyes and the Oneida Community* (New York: G. P. Putnam's Sons, 1935).

## CHAPTER IV

[1] I use the word "castration" for removal of the testes or ovaries, "sterilization" for the simple cutting of the fallopian tubes or *vas deferens*, and "asexualization" for either or both.

² For Morel, see Samuel Royce, *Deterioration and Race Education* (Boston: Lee and Shepard, 1878), esp. I, 80. See Dr. E. P. Fowler's translation of Benedikt, *Anatomical Studies upon Brains of Criminals* (New York: William Wood & Co., 1881); Benedikt's influence can be seen in Charles K. Mills, "Arrested and Aberrant Development of Fissures and Gyres in the Brains of Paranoiacs, Criminals, Idiots and Negroes," *Journal of Nervous and Mental Disease*, XIII (September & October, 1886), 1-32.

Early introductions of the Lombroso school were Arthur MacDonald, *Criminology* (New York: Funk & Wagnalls Co., 1893), esp. pp. 17-166; William Noyes, "The Criminal Type," *Journal of Social Science*, XXIV (April, 1888), 31-42; and Robert Fletcher, "The New School of Criminal Anthropology," *American Anthropologist*, IV (July, 1891), 201-36.

³ The best secondary account of the impact of criminal anthropology in the United States, especially on criminology, is Arthur E. Fink, *Causes of Crime: Biological Theories in the United States, 1800-1915* (Philadelphia: University of Pennsylvania Press, 1938), pp. 99-178.

⁴ Norris, *McTeague: A Story of San Francisco*, Vol. VIII of "Collected Writings" (Garden City: Doubleday, Doran & Co., Inc., 1928), p. 3; Nordau, *Degeneration* (from the 2d German ed.; New York: D. Appleton & Co., 1895), esp. pp. 13, 27, 31, 415-16.

⁵ Boies, *Prisoners and Paupers* (New York: G. P. Putnam's Sons, 1893), p. 266 & *passim;* McKim, *Heredity and Human Progress* (New York: G. P. Putnam's Sons, 1900), pp. 120, 65-66, & 168. Perhaps more influential than these two books was Eugene S. Talbot, *Degeneracy: Its Causes, Signs, and Results* (London: Walter Scott, Ltd., 1898).

In 1904 Dr. Henry Hatch, in a speech before the National Prison Association, suggested that the incurable insane and confirmed criminals might well be killed. The discussion was decidedly unfavorable. See "Crime and Criminals, and What Shall be Done with Them," *NPA* (1904), pp. 302-7, & 321-24.

⁶ Wey, "Criminal Anthropology," *NPA* (1890), pp. 274-90; remarks in *NPA* (1892), p. 238. Also Abraham Jacobi, "Brain, Crime and Capital Punishment," *NPA* (1892), pp. 175-205, and W. A. Corn, "Degeneration in Criminals as Shown by the Bertillon System of Measurement and Photographs," *AmJI*, LIII (July, 1896), 47-56.

⁷ See Henderson, *Introduction to the Study of the Dependent, Defective, and Delinquent Classes* (2d ed.; Boston: D. C. Heath & Co., 1901), pp. 229-36; and MacDonald, *A Plan for the Study of Man, Reference to Bills to Establish a Laboratory for the Study of the Criminal, Pauper, and Defective Classes*, Senate Document No. 400, 57th Cong., 1st sess., serial 4245 (Washington: G.P.O., 1902).

⁸ "A Study in Youthful Degeneracy," *Pedagogical Seminary*, IV (December, 1896), 233-40. See also Frances A. Kellor, *Experimental Sociology: Descriptive and Analytical* (New York: The Macmillan Co., 1901).

⁹ *The Criminal, His Personnel and Environment* (New York: The Macmillan Co., 1900), pp. 56, 101-16, and 138-41.

¹⁰ *Introduction to the Study of the Dependent, Defective, and Delinquent Classes* (2d ed.; Boston: D. C. Heath & Co., 1901), p. 252. Henderson described the instinctive criminal in *ibid.*, pp. 226-28.

¹¹ See Thomas Wilson, "Criminology," *Proceedings of the American Association for the Advancement of Science* (1900), pp. 294-300; Samuel G. Smith, "Typical Criminals," *Pop. Sci. Mon.*, LVI (March, 1900), 539-45; and Charles A. Drew, "Signs of Degeneracy and Types of the Criminal Insane," *AmJI*, LVII (April, 1901), 691-92.

¹² "Objections to the Indeterminate Sentence," *NPA* (1898), p. 168. Wines bitterly attacked McKim's book on *Heredity and Human Progress* in a speech on "Heredity and Human Progress," *NPA* (1900), pp. 187-94. For a detailed statement of Wines' views, see *Punishment and Reformation: An Historical Sketch of the Rise of the Penitentiary System* (New York: Thomas Y. Crowell & Co., 1895), *passim*.

¹³ J. H. Albert, "Barriers against Crime," *NPA* (1895), pp. 126 & 127. See also Graham Taylor, "Address," *NPA* (1894), p. 48.

¹⁴ Wilmarth, "Notes on the Anatomy of the Idiot Brain," *Proceedings of the Association of Medical Officers of American Institutions for Idiotic and Feeble-Minded Persons* (1885), pp. 323-28; "Notes on the Pathology of Idiocy," *ibid.* (1886), pp. 428-41; "Report on the Examination of One Hundred Brains of Feeble-Minded Children," *ibid.* (1890), pp. 56-66; and "Physical Anomalies of the Feeble-Minded," *JPA*, V (September, 1900), 1-3.

Psychiatrists also found stigmata among the insane: for instance, Adolf Meyer, "A Review of the Signs of Degeneration and of Methods of Registration," *AmJI*, LII (January, 1896), 344-63; Irwin H. Neff, "Some Cases Showing Possible Physical Signs of Degeneration," *AmJI*, LII (April, 1896), 545-50; William G. Stearns, "A System of Obtaining and Recording Anthropological Data," *AmJI*, LIII (October, 1896), 256-61; and Ales Hrdlicka, "A Few Words about Anthropometry," *AmJI*, LIII (April, 1897), 521-33.

¹⁵ Wilmarth, "President's Annual Address," *Proceedings of the Association of Medical Officers of American Institutions for Idiotic and Feeble-Minded Persons* (1895), p. 518, and Rudolph J. Vecoli, "Sterilization: A Progressive Measure?" *Wisconsin Magazine of History*, XLIII (Spring, 1960), 190-202.

¹⁶ Quotations from Fernald, "Care of the Feeble-Minded," *NCCC* (1904), p. 383, and "The Imbecile with Criminal Instincts," *JPA*, XIV (1909-1910), 35.

¹⁷ *Mental Defectives: Their History, Treatment and Training* (Philadelphia: P. Blakiston's Sons & Co., 1904).

¹⁸ Fink, *Causes of Crime*, pp. 188ff, summarized the views of various doctors on asexualization.

¹⁹ Hunter McGuire and G. Frank Lydston, "Sexual Crimes among Southern Negroes," *Virginia Medical Monthly*, XX (May, 1893), 122. See also, for instance, Robert Boal, "Emasculation and Ovariotomy as a Penalty for Crime and the Reformation of Criminals," *Transactions of the Illinois State Medical Society* (1894), p. 535.

[20] From a speech by Dr. William A. Hammond, reported in "Castration Recommended as a Substitute for Capital Punishment," *Journal of the American Medical Association,* XVIII (April 16, 1892), 499-500.

[21] Boal, *op. cit.,* p. 536.

[22] Frank S. Roby, "Criminal Law Reform," *NPA* (1907), pp. 191-92; also G. Frank Lydston, "Asexualization in the Prevention of Crime," *Medical News,* LXVIII (May 23, 1896), 576, and McGuire & Lydston, "Sexual Crimes among Southern Negroes," *op. cit.,* p. 123.

Dr. Jesse Ewell was still more blunt: "Castrate the criminal, cut off both ears close to his head and turn him loose to go where he will." In "A Plea for Castration to Prevent Criminal Assault," *Virginia Medical Semi-Monthly,* XI (January 11, 1907), 464.

[23] Lydston, "Asexualization in the Prevention of Crime," *op. cit.,* p. 575; see also Dr. Austin Flint, "The Coming Role of the Medical Profession in the Scientific Treatment of Crime and Criminals," *New York Medical Journal,* LXII (October 19, 1895), 48.

[24] *NCCC* (1899), p. 409; *JPA,* III (January, 1899), 194.

[25] Barr, *Mental Defectives,* pp. 189-90.

[26] Jessie Spaulding Smith, "Marriage, Sterilization and Commitment Laws Aimed at Decreasing Mental Deficiency," *JCL&C,* V (July, 1914), 365-66. See also Kate Gannett Wells, "State Regulation of Marriage," *NCCC* (1897), pp. 303-4; A. C. Rogers, "Recent Attempts at Restrictive Marriage Legislation," *NCCC* (1901), pp. 200-3. The later history of marriage regulation is given below, chap. ix.

[27] Barr, *Mental Defectives,* p. 190.

[28] *Ibid., Mental Defectives,* pp. 195-96, and "President's Annual Address," *JPA,* II (September, 1897), 8. A short time after Dr. Pilcher's experiment, Dr. Everett Flood, superintendent of the Hospital for Epileptics at Palmer, Massachusetts, castrated at least twenty-six youths. Apparently the chief reason for his action was curative, for "with 24 the cause for operating was epilepsy and persistent masturbation." Barr, *Mental Defectives,* p. 196.

[29] See C. F. Cave, "Report of Sterilization in the Kansas State Home for Feeble-Minded," *JPA,* XV (March and June, 1911), 123-25.

[30] Barr, "Results of Asexualization," *JPA,* IX (June, 1905), 129.

[31] For a history of the two operations, see E. S. Gosney and Paul Popenoe, *Sterilization for Human Betterment: A Summary of Results of 6,000 Operations in California, 1919-1929* (New York: Human Betterment Foundation, 1930), pp. 71ff.

[32] J. H. Kellogg, *Plain Facts for Old and Young* (new ed.; Burlington, Iowa: I. F. Segner, 1891), pp. 339-41.

[33] Sharp, "Rendering Sterile of Confirmed Criminals and Mental Defectives," *NPA* (1907), p. 178. By 1907 Dr. Sharp had operated on 223 inmates of the Reformatory.

[34] *Ibid.,* p. 180. See also "The Severing of the Vasa Deferentia and Its Relation to the Neuropsychopathic Constitution," *New York Medical Journal,* LXXV (March 8, 1902), 413.

[35] Dr. A. J. Ochsner, Surgeon in Chief of Augustana Hospital in Chicago, pointed out: "Castration has been recommended as a punishment for certain crimes, and has been practiced without legal sanction in many cases. Whenever and wherever this has been advocated, it has met with the strongest possible opposition, because it practically destroys the possibility for the future enjoyment of life." But vasectomy would leave the person normal while striking at hereditary defectives. See "Surgical Treatment of Habitual Criminals," *Journal of the American Medical Association*, XXXII (April 22, 1899), 867-68. See also Dr. Daniel R. Bower, "Medical Aspects of Crime," *Journal of the American Medical Association*, XXXII (June 10, 1899), 1282-87.

[36] "Asexualization of Criminals and Degenerates," *Michigan Law Journal*, VI (December, 1897), 289-316; Barr, *Mental Defectives*, p. 195; Harry H. Laughlin, *Eugenical Sterilization in the United States* (Chicago: Psychopathic Laboratory of the Municipal Court of Chicago, 1922), p. 36.

[37] Sharp, "Rendering Sterile of Confirmed Criminals and Mental Defectives," *op. cit.*, p. 180; Laughlin, *Eugenical Sterilization*, p. 15.

[38] "Rendering Sterile of Confirmed Criminals and Mental Defectives," *op. cit.*, p. 180. See also, Sharp, "The Indiana Plan," *APA* (1909), p. 36. The history of sterilization is continued in chap. ix below.

[39] For statements of the Anglo-Saxon creed, see Josiah Strong, *Our Country, Its Possible Future and Present Crisis* (New York: Baker & Taylor Co., 1885), and John Fisk, *American Political Ideas, Viewed from the Standpoint of Universal History* (New York: Harper & Bros., 1885). An excellent secondary account of Anglo-Saxon racism in America is Richard Hofstadter, *Social Darwinism in American Thought* (rev. ed.; Boston: Beacon Press, 1955), chap. ix. The impact of racism on historians is in Edward N. Saveth, *American Historians and European Immigrants, 1875-1925* (New York: Columbia University Press, 1948).

[40] For early southern racism, see William Sumner Jenkins, *Pro-Slavery Thought in the Old South* (Chapel Hill: University of North Carolina Press, 1935), chap. vi; William Stanton, *The Leopard's Spots: Scientific Attitudes Toward Race in America, 1815-1859* (Chicago: University of Chicago Press, 1960). A brief but excellent discussion of southern attitudes after the Civil War is Comer Vann Woodward, *The Strange Career of Jim Crow* (rev. ed.; New York: Oxford University Press, 1957). The alleged increase of crime and insanity is in William F. Drewry, "Care and Condition of the Insane in Virginia," *NCCC* (1908), p. 312 and Walter F. Willcox, "Negro Criminality," in Alfred Holt Stone, *Studies in the American Race Problem* (New York: Doubleday, Page & Co., 1908), pp. 443-75.

[41] For racist statements, see for instance John R. Commons, *Race and Immigrants in America* (New York: The Macmillan Co., 1908); William Hannibal Thomas, *The American Negro* (New York: The Macmillan Co., 1901); and R. W. Shufeldt, *The Negro, A Menace to American Civilization* (Boston: Richard G. Badger, 1907).

[42] Shufeldt, *The Negro*, p. 9, and Edward A. Ross, "The Causes of

Race Superiority," *Annals of the American Academy of Political and Social Sciences,* XVIII (July, 1901), 85.

43 For imperialist arguments, see Hofstadter, *Social Darwinism,* chap. ix; Julius Pratt, *Imperialists of 1898* (Baltimore: Johns Hopkins Press, 1936); also Christopher Lasch, "The Anti-Imperialists, the Philippines, and the Inequality of Man," *Journal of Southern History,* XXIV (August, 1958), 319-31. For oriental immigration, see Elmer C. Sandmeyer, *The Anti-Chinese Movement in California,* Vol. XXIV of Illinois Studies in Social Sciences (Urbana: University of Illinois Press, 1939), and Richard Austin Thompson, *The Yellow Peril, 1890-1924,* Unpubl. Doctoral Dissertation, University of Wisconsin, 1957.

44 John Higham in *Strangers in the Land: Patterns of American Nativism, 1860-1925* (New Brunswick, N. J.: Rutgers University Press, 1955), provides the indispensable study of the motives that led to racist thinking. For changing views of New Englanders, see Barbara Miller Solomon, *Ancestors and Immigrants: A Changing New England Tradition* (Cambridge: Harvard University Press, 1956). Anti-foreign feeling before the Civil War is in Ray A. Billington, *The Protestant Crusade, 1800-1860: A Study of the Origins of American Nativism* (New York: The Macmillan Co., 1938).

45 Quotation from Hjalmer H. Boyesen, "Immigration," in *National Perils and Opportunities* (New York: Evangelical Alliance, 1887), p. 57. A typical view was James H. Stoller, "Human Heredity," *Pop. Sci. Mon.,* XXXVII (July, 1890), 359-60. See also Higham, *Strangers,* pp. 20-34.

46 Mayo Smith, *Emigration and Immigration* (New York: Charles Scribner's Sons, 1890), p. 77. For his background and ideas, see Solomon, *Ancestors,* pp. 77-81.

47 Quotation from Walker, "Immigration and Degradation," *Forum,* XI (August, 1891), 642. For the development of Walker's views, see Solomon, *Ancestors,* pp. 69-77. For support of Walker, see L. C. Marshall, "Race Effects of Immigration," *NCCC* (1906), 314-24; Robert Hunter, *Poverty* (New York: The Macmillan Co., 1905), 300-17. A criticism is Maurice Fishberg, "Ethnic Factors in Immigration—A Critical View," *NCCC* (1906), pp. 304-14.

48 For the impact of the new immigration, see Higham, *Strangers,* pp. 64-67, 87-96, 110.

49 Ripley, *The Races of Europe* (London: Kegan, Paul, Trench, Trübner & Co., 1899), esp. pp. 103ff. European racist theories are summarized by Jacques Barzun, *Race: A Study in Modern Superstition* (New York: Harcourt, Brace and Company, 1937); see also T. K. Penniman, *A Hundred Years of Anthropology* (2d ed. rev.; London: Gerald Duckworth & Co., 1952).

50 Solomon, *Ancestors,* chaps. v, vi, & vii, provides an excellent history of the League; see also Higham, *Strangers, passim.*

51 Prescott F. Hall, *Immigration and Its Effect upon the United States* (New York: Henry Holt and Co., 1906), pp. 146-69, argued that the immigrants were sources of crime, insanity, disease, and pauperism. Early laws are in *Immigration Legislation,* Vol. XXXIX of Reports of the Im-

migration Commission, serial 5879 (Washington: G.P.O., 1911), pp. 5-144.

An 1875 bill excluded prostitutes, but was directed primarily at the Chinese and was little enforced against Europeans.

[52] *Immigration:* Speech of Hon. Henry Cabot Lodge of Massachusetts in the House of Representatives, Thursday, February 19, 1891 (Washington, 1891), p. 4. Lodge's racism is treated in Solomon, *Ancestors*, 111-19, and Saveth, *American Historians*, 51-64.

[53] For the success of the bills and the general course of American nativist and racist thought, see Higham, *Strangers, passim.*

CHAPTER V

[1] Galton first used the word eugenics in *Inquiries into Human Faculty* in 1883. The first use that I have found in America was in George J. Preston, "Hereditary Disease and Race Culture," *Pop. Sci. Mon.*, XXIX (September, 1886), 641. Thereafter I found no mention until the twentieth century.

[2] Many of his articles were reprinted in this country; for instance "On the Causes which Operate to Create Scientific Men," *Pop. Sci. Mon.*, III (May, 1873), 65-71; "The History of Twins, as Criterion of the Relative Powers of Nature and Nurture," *ibid.*, VIII (January, 1876), 345-57; and "Composite Portraits," *ibid.*, XIII (August, 1878), 460-69. See also "Sketch of Francis Galton," *ibid.*, XXIX (May, 1886), 117-21.

[3] What Weismann firmly rejected was the universal notion that damage or changes in the body could be passed on to the offspring through the germ cells. He did not deny that damage might, in rare instances, occur directly to the germ plasm. Poor nutrition or even alcohol in the blood, he admitted, might act directly on the germ plasm and therefore affect the offspring. He would have had no difficulty accepting the later discovery that mutations could occur through radiation damage.

For discussions of Weismann's theory, see Loren Eiseley, *Darwin's Century: Evolution and the Men Who Discovered It* (Garden City: Doubleday & Co., Inc., 1958), esp. pp. 216-21; E. S. Russell, *The Interpretation of Development and Heredity* (Oxford: Clarendon Press, 1930), pp. 39-54; Conway Zirkle, "The Knowledge of Heredity before 1900," *Genetics in the 20th Century*, ed. L. C. Dunn (New York: The Macmillan Co., 1951), pp. 53ff.

[4] Osborn, "The Present Problem of Heredity," *Atlantic Monthly*, LXVII (March, 1891), 354; for a similar view, see A. B. Richardson, "The Transmission of Acquired Variations," *AmJI*, XLVII (January, 1891), 402.

[5] Eugene S. Talbot, *Degeneracy* (London: Walter Scott, Ltd., 1898), pp. 46-56, and J. Arthur Thomson, *Heredity* (New York: G. P. Putnam's Sons, 1908), esp. pp. 207-39.

[6] (New York: Thomas Y. Crowell & Co., 1894), pp. 120-21. See also Lester F. Ward, "The Transmission of Culture," *Forum*, XI (May, 1891), 314.

[7] The rest of this book will be clearer if the reader has a rudimentary

understanding of Mendelian genetics. The reader is referred to a popular presentation such as L. C. Dunn & Th. Dobzhansky, *Heredity, Race and Society* (rev. ed.; New York: Mentor Book, 1946).

[8] Quotation from American Breeders' Association, *Proceedings*, II (1906), 11. See W. E. Castle, "The Beginnings of Mendelism in America," *Genetics in the 20th Century*, pp. 59-66. The history of the Association can best be followed in its *Proceedings* and *Reports*.

[9] For two excellent biographical sketches, see E. Carleton MacDowell, "Charles Benedict Davenport, 1866-1944; A Study of Conflicting Influences," *Bios*, XVII (March, 1946), 3-50; and Charles Rosenberg, "Charles Benedict Davenport and the Beginning of Human Genetics," *Bulletin of the History of Medicine*, XXXV (May-June, 1961), 266-276. Oscar Riddle's "Biographical Memoir of Charles Benedict Davenport," in National Academy of Sciences, *Biographical Memoirs*, XXV (1949), 75-110, is largely based on MacDowell's sketch.

[10] *Ibid.*, p. 8.

[11] In a letter to Major Leonard Darwin, April 9, 1927, C.S.H., Davenport declared: "Karl Pearson's attitude toward me has never been friendly since I became a Mendelian. He took the attitude that since I had ranged myself on the Mendelian side that [*sic*] I had ranged myself with his enemies." The Davenport-Pearson correspondence, C.S.H., shows their early cooperation and growing estrangement.

[12] MacDowell, *op. cit.*, pp. 17-24.

[13] The development of Davenport's research can be followed in his annual reports appearing in the Carnegie Institution of Washington, *Year Books*, 1905 on. His correspondence with Alexander Graham Bell, David Starr Jordan, and others shows how the heredity of man usurped his interests beginning in 1906.

[14] Harry H. Laughlin, *Eugenics Record Office, Report No. 1* (Cold Spring Harbor, 1913), pp. 9-10. Davenport's correspondence, especially with Goddard, Bell, and Jordan, records the formation of the committees.

[15] "Report of Committee on Eugenics," American Breeders' Association, *Report*, VI (1909), 94.

[16] Quotation from a statement by Davenport, C.S.H. See esp. the Davenport-Harriman correspondence, C.S.H., for the events leading up to the founding.

In 1912 a board of expert directors was formed to guide the research, with Alexander Graham Bell as chairman, plus Dr. William H. Welch (professor of pathology, Johns Hopkins), Dr. Lewellys F. Barker (Johns Hopkins University Hospital), Dr. Elmer E. Southard, Irving Fisher (Yale Economist), and Davenport as secretary and resident director.

[17] Davenport and Laughlin, in *How to Make a Eugenical Family Study*, E.R.O., Bull. No. 13 (Cold Spring Harbor, 1913), explained in detail how a family history should be made out. The Record Office provided the necessary forms.

[18] For early activities of the Office, see Laughlin, *Eugenics Record Office, Report No. 1*; also A. E. Hamilton, "Eugenics," *Pedagogical Semi-*

*nary,* XXI (March, 1914), 28-61. For counseling activities, see too A. E. Hamilton, "What to Say about Marriage?" *JH,* VII (February, 1916), 77-88.

[19] The development of the Record Office can be followed in the Carnegie Institution of Washington, *Year Books,* and in the Davenport-Harriman correspondence, C.S.H.

[20] See Davenport, "Heredity, Culpability, Praiseworthiness, Punishment and Reward," *Pop. Sci. Mon.,* LXXXIII (July, 1913), 39; also his "Euthenics and Eugenics," *Pop. Sci. Mon.,* LXXVII (January, 1911), 18.

[21] "Field Work an Indispensable Aid to State Care of the Socially Inadequate," *NCCC* (1915), p. 312, and "Eugenics and Charity," *NCCC* (1912), p. 281.

[22] Davenport, *The Trait Book,* E.R.O., Bull. No. 6 (Cold Spring Harbor, 1912), *passim.*

[23] *Heredity in Relation to Eugenics* (New York: Henry Holt & Co., 1911), pp. 58-64 & 80-82. For his major study along these lines, see "Inheritance of Temperament" in *The Feebly Inhibited,* Carnegie Institution of Washington, Publ. No. 236 (Washington, 1915).

[24] Quotation from Carnegie Institution of Washington, *Year Book, 1915,* p. 138. See *Nomadism, or the Wandering Impulse, with Special Reference to Heredity* in *The Feebly Inhibited,* Carnegie Institution of Washington, Publ. No. 236 (Washington, 1915); *The Feebly Inhibited: Violent Temper and Its Inheritance,* E.R.O., Bull. No. 12 (Cold Spring Harbor, 1915); Arthur H. Estabrook and Davenport, *The Nam Family, A Study in Cacogenics,* E.R.O., Memoir No. 2 (Cold Spring Harbor, 1912), pp. 66-68.

[25] Gregory Zilboorg, *A History of Medical Psychology* (New York: W. W. Norton & Company, Inc., 1941), pp. 447-64; Albert Deutsch, *The Mentally Ill in America: A History of Their Care and Treatment from Colonial Times* (2d ed.; New York: Columbia University Press, 1949), pp. 485-86.

[26] The progress can be seen in the recommended list of classifications adopted by the American Psychiatric Association, *AmJI,* LXXIV (October, 1917), 256-58.

[27] Especially, Myerson, "Psychiatric Family Studies," *AmJI,* LXXIII (January, 1917), 355-486, and "Psychiatric Family Studies: Second Paper," *AmJI,* LXXIV (April, 1918), 495-554; also Charles Ricksher, "Similar and Dissimilar Psychoses in Relatives," *AmJI,* LXXI (July, 1914), 133-48.

[28] For instance, Davenport and David F. Weeks, *A First Study of Inheritance in Epilepsy,* E.R.O., Bull. No. 4 (Cold Spring Harbor, 1911).

[29] Rosanoff & Florence I. Orr, *A Study of Heredity of Insanity in the Light of Mendelian Theory,* E.R.O., Bull. No. 5 (Cold Spring Harbor, 1911), 228 & 237.

[30] *Ibid.;* see also, Gertrude L. Cannon & Rosanoff, *Preliminary Report of a Study of Heredity in Insanity in the Light of Mendelian Laws,* E.R.O., Bull. No. 3 (Cold Spring Harbor, 1911).

In a later effort to bring his theory into line with the fact that off-spring tended to inherit the same mental disease as ancestors, Rosanoff suggested a hierarchy of dominance, with the gene for normal mental growth as most dominant and, in order of decreasing dominance, genes for manic-depressive psychosis, dementia praecox, and epilepsy. The various possible combinations among these genes allowed a wide range of intensities and types of mental illnesses. See "Dissimilar Heredity in Mental Disease," *AmJI,* LXX (July, 1913), 1ff.

[31] *Feeble-Mindedness, Its Causes and Consequences* (New York: The Macmillan Co., 1914), *passim.* The Davenport-Goddard correspondence, C.S.H., shows Davenport's influence upon Goddard's studies.

[32] "Psychiatric Family Studies," *op. cit.,* p. 359.

[33] For typical contemporary criticisms, see Augusta F. Bronner in *JCL&C,* VII (July, 1916), 311-13; H. C. Stevens, "Eugenics and Feeble-mindedness," *JCL&C,* VI (July, 1915), 190-97; William E. Castle, *Genetics and Eugenics* (Cambridge: Harvard University Press, 1916), 241-51; Edward L. Thorndike, "Individual Differences and their Causes," in Vol. III of *Educational Psychology* (New York: Teachers College, Columbia University, 1914), pp. 265-69.

[34] Heron, *Mendelism and the Problem of Mental Defect: A Criticism of Recent American Work,* Questions of the Day and of the Fray, No. 7 (Cambridge, 1913); also Pearson, *Mendelism and Mental Defect,* Questions of the Day and of the Fray, No. 9 (Cambridge, 1914). Davenport's major reply was *Reply to the Criticism of Recent American Work by Dr. Heron of the Galton Laboratory,* E.R.O., Bull. No. 11 (Cold Spring Harbor, 1914). The issue was debated in the press; see *NYT,* November 9, 1913, Pt. V, pp. 2-3, & January 4, 1914, Pt. V, p. 14.

[35] For typical examples, among many, see Paul Popenoe, "Heredity and Mind," *JH,* VII (October, 1915), 456-62; Popenoe & Roswell H. Johnson, *Applied Eugenics* (New York: The Macmillan Co., 1920), chap. iv; and interview with Davenport entitled "Breeding Just the Right People for any Vocation," *Denver Post,* March 15, 1914, C.S.H. For a more balanced view, see Samuel J. Holmes, *Studies in Evolution and Eugenics* (New York: Harcourt, Brace & Co., 1923), chap. vi.

[36] See *AmJI,* LXX (July, 1913), 232-40. For typical statements for eugenics, see Adolf Meyer, "Where Should We Attack the Problem of the Prevention of Mental Defect and Mental Disease?" *NCCC* (1915), 300-3; Carlos F. MacDonald, "President's Address," *AmJI,* LXXI (July, 1914), 1-12; Charles G. Wagner, "Presidential Address: Recent Trends in Psychiatry," *AmJI,* LXXIV (July, 1917), 1-14; and William A. White, "Eugenics and Heredity in Nervous and Mental Diseases," *Modern Treatment of Nervous and Mental Diseases,* ed. William A. White and Smith Ely Jelliffe (Philadelphia: Lea & Febiger, 1913), I, 17-55.

[37] See Lewellys F. Barker, "The Wider Field of Work of the National Committee for Mental Hygiene," *Mental Hygiene,* I (January, 1917), 5. A history of the National Committee is in Deutsch, *Mentally Ill,* chap. xv.

[38] The information on the college courses is from various sources, especially A. E. Hamilton, "Eugenics," *op. cit.,* p. 35. Information on Johnson is from the Johnson-Davenport correspondence, C.S.H.

[39] Davenport-Wiggam correspondence, C.S.H.; also *Eugenical News,* III (January, 1918), 5.

[40] Information on the Race Betterment Foundation from *Eugenical News,* III (May, 1918), 36; Russell Sage Foundation, *American Foundations for Social Welfare* (rev. ed.; New York, 1930), p. 38. See also the *Proceedings* of the First and Third Race Betterment Conferences.

[41] References to the Society are scattered through Davenport's correspondence. See Davenport to E. L. Thorndike, April 18, 1918, C.S.H.; also *Eugenical News,* III (July, 1918), 54.

[42] Davenport was elected president in 1913 and was followed in office by J. McKeen Cattell, an eminent psychologist; Adolf Meyer; Henry E. Crampton, zoologist; Madison Grant; Stewart Paton, psychiatrist; Irving Fisher; Lewellys Barker, distinguished physician at Johns Hopkins; Judge Harry Olson of Chicago; Albert Johnson, chairman of the House Committee on Immigration and Naturalization; and F. A. Woods.

The history of the Association can be followed in *Eugenical News* and in Davenport's correspondence, especially with Irving Fisher. See also a folder of Association correspondence and a typewritten history, C.S.H.

[43] Plans for the Congresses were discussed in Davenport's correspondence with Osborn, Grant, Bell, and Henry E. Crampton, C.S.H. The members of the committee to plan the 1921 Congress included Lewellys F. Barker, E. A. Hooton, Robert M. Yerkes, Stewart Paton, Raymond Pearl, and Bell.

[44] *Eugenical News, passim.*

[45] Quotation from Fisher to Davenport, June 22, 1913, C.S.H. The development and program of the Society can best be followed in the voluminous Davenport-Fisher correspondence, C.S.H. See also, *Eugenical News,* VIII (January, 1923), 5 (April, 1923), pp. 28-29, and (August, 1923), pp. 73-80.

## Chapter VI

[1] Quoted in *Tng. Sch. Bull.,* X (February, 1914), 160.

[2] Quotation from Tenney Frank, "Race Mixture and the Roman Empire," *American Historical Review,* XXI (July, 1916), 705. See also David Starr Jordan, *The Human Harvest* (Boston: Beacon Press, 1907), esp. p. 25.

[3] Charles B. Davenport, *Heredity in Relation to Eugenics* (New York: Henry Holt & Co., 1911), *passim.*

[4] Woods, *Mental and Moral Heredity in Royalty* (New York: Henry Holt & Co., 1906), p. iv, and *The Influence of Monarchs: Steps in a New Science of History* (New York: The Macmillan Co., 1913), p. viii. He applied this to America specifically in an article on "Heredity and the Hall of Fame," *Pop. Sci. Mon.,* LXXXII (May, 1913), 445-52.

[5] Walter F. Willcox, "The Nature and Significance of the Changes in

the Birth and Death Rates in Recent Years," *Publications of the American Statistical Association,* XV (March, 1916), 11.

⁶ Edward A. Ross coined the term "race suicide" for the declining birth rate of native stock compared to immigrant stock, but the term was widely used to describe the over-all decline in birth rate. See Ross, "The Causes of Race Superiority," *Annals of the American Academy of Political and Social Science,* XVIII (July, 1901), 67-89.

⁷ Roosevelt, "Social Evolution," in *The Works of Theodore Roosevelt* (New York: Charles Scribner's Sons, 1923-26), XIV, 111; "A Book-Lover's Holidays in the Open," *ibid.,* IV, 77. See also, Roosevelt, "Race Decadence," in *ibid.,* XIV, 151-66.

⁸ Roswell H. Johnson, "The Evolution of Man," *Pop. Sci. Mon.,* LXXVI (January, 1910), 49-70.

⁹ Frederick S. Crum, "The Decadence of the Native American Stock: A Statistical Study of Genealogical Records," *Publications of the American Statistical Association,* XIV (September, 1914), 218-19. See also S. J. Holmes & C. M. Doud, "The Approaching Extinction of the Mayflower Descendants," *JH,* IX (November, 1918), 296-300, and Walter F. Willcox, "Differential Fertility," *JH,* V (April, 1914), 141-48.

¹⁰ See Edward L. Thorndike, "The Decrease in the Size of American Families," *Pop. Sci. Mon.,* LXIII (May, 1903), 64; John C. Phillips, "A Study of the Birth-Rate in Harvard and Yale Graduates," *Harvard Graduates Magazine,* XXV (September, 1916), 25-34; Roswell H. Johnson, "Wellesley's Birth-Rate," *JH,* VI (June, 1915), 251-52, & "The Birth-Rate of College Women," *School and Society,* V (June 9, 1917), 678-80; Paul Popenoe, "Eugenics and College Education," *School and Society,* VI (October 13, 1917), 438-41; Theodore Roosevelt, "Birth Reform, from the Positive, Not the Negative, Side," in *op. cit.,* XXI, esp. 158-60.

¹¹ Cattell, "Families of American Men of Science," reprinted in *James McKeen Cattell, Man of Science,* ed. A. T. Poffenberger (Lancaster, Pa.: Science Press, 1947), I, 501.

¹² For typical discussions, see Sidney Webb, "Physical Degeneracy or Race Suicide?" *Pop. Sci. Mon.,* LXIX (December, 1906), 512-29; Warren S. Thompson, "Race Suicide in the United States," *Scientific Monthly,* V (July, 1917), 22-35 (August, 1917), 154-65 (September, 1917), 258-69; and Louis I. Dublin, "The Significance of the Declining Birth Rate," *Science,* XLVII, n.s. (March 1, 1918), 201-10. Paul Popenoe and Roswell Johnson in *Applied Eugenics* (New York: The Macmillan Co., 1918), 237-79, assembled and discussed the many statistics on the subject.

¹³ *The Human Harvest,* p. 104.

¹⁴ Wilhelmine E. Key, "Better American Families—IV," *JH,* XI (November-December, 1920), 358-63. Eugenists drew on Albert E. Winship's *Jukes-Edwards: A Study in Education and Heredity* (Harrisburg, Pa.: R. L. Ryers & Co., 1900), for their knowledge of the brilliant and influential descendants of Jonathan Edwards.

¹⁵ Woods, "Heredity and the Hall of Fame," *op. cit.,* pp. 445-52.

¹⁶ For example, Frederick H. Wines, "Is Crime Increasing?" *NPA* (1896), pp. 369-75; Roland P. Falkner, "Crime and the Census," *Annals*

*of the American Academy of Political and Social Science,* IX (January, 1897), 42-69; Charles A. Ellwood, "Has Crime Increased in the United States since 1880?" *JCL&C,* I (September, 1910), 378-85. For statistics on insanity, see F. B. Sanborn, "The Increase of Insanity," *NCCC* (1895), pp. 186-94; also *Report of the Commission to Investigate the Question of the Increase of Criminals, Mental Defectives, Epileptics and Degenerates* (Boston, 1911). Herbert Goldhammer and Andrew W. Marshall in *Psychosis and Civilization* (Glencoe, Ill.: The Free Press, 1949), concluded after careful study that the incidence of major psychoses of early and middle life had not increased during the previous century.

[17] R. B. Von Kleinsmid, "An Enquiry Concerning Some Preventions of Crime," *APA* (1915), p. 108.

[18] Quotation from Davenport, "The Eugenics Programme and Progress in its Achievement," in Morton A. Aldrich, *et al., Eugenics: Twelve University Lectures* (New York: Dodd, Mead and Co., 1914), p. 8. See Dublin, "The Significance of the Declining Birth Rate," *op. cit.,* 209-10.

In 1913 the physician who headed the Colorado State Board of Health undertook to promote eugenic marriages, and received applications from over fifty volunteers, only one of them a male. One applicant was a physical education teacher from Onondago, New York, who described herself as a "progressive western woman living in the East; good looking, of good figure and perfectly capable of doing all things wanted of her by a eugenic marriage." *NYT,* November 3, 1913, p. 1.

[19] Bell, "How to Improve the Race," *JH,* V (January, 1914), 1. For typical pleas, see "Francis Galton's Utopia," *Independent,* LIII (November 21, 1901), 2789-91, and George E. Dawson, *The Right of the Child to be Well Born* (New York: Funk & Wagnalls Co., 1912).

[20] Roosevelt to Davenport, January 3, 1913, C.S.H.; Roosevelt, "Birth Reform, from the Positive, Not the Negative, Side," *op. cit.,* XXI, 163.

[21] William N. Gemmill, "Genius and Eugenics," *JCL&C,* VI (May, 1915), 99.

[22] Edward L. Thorndike, "Eugenics: With Special Reference to Intellect and Character," *Pop. Sci. Mon.,* LXXXIII (August, 1913), 132-34; Frederick Adams Woods, "Good Qualities are Correlated," *JH,* X (February, 1919), 84-86.

[23] Elizabeth C. Billings, "Eugenics," *Survey,* XXXI (February 7, 1914), 597.

[24] John A. Ryan, *Family Limitation and the Church and Birth Control* (New York: Paulist Press [ca. 1916]), 17; see also Charles Bruehl, "Moral Aspects of Eugenics," *Homiletic and Pastoral Review,* XXVI (July, 1926), esp. 1017-18.

[25] Lawrence F. Flick, *Eugenics* (Philadelphia: John Joseph McVey, 1913), pp. 19 & 26.

[26] Dawson, *The Right of the Child,* 107; see also G. Stanley Hall, "Eugenics: Its Ideals and What It Is Going to Do," *Religious Education,* VI (June, 1911), 158.

[27] *NYT,* June 6, 1913, p. 10; also *ibid.,* June 7, 1913, p. 10, June 11, 1913, p. 8.

²⁸ For a discussion of Ward's ideas, see Richard Hofstadter, *Social Darwinism in American Thought* (rev. ed.; Boston: Beacon Press, 1955), pp. 67-84. The standard discussion of Ward is Samuel Chugerman, *Lester F. Ward, The American Aristotle* (Durham: Duke University Press, 1939). The author, however, had little understanding of the facts or history of genetics so that his discussion of Ward's views on heredity (398ff) is misleading and largely useless.

²⁹ Ward, *Applied Sociology* (Boston: Ginn & Company, 1906), pp. 113-16.

³⁰ Quotation from *ibid.*, p. 95. See Ward, *Pure Sociology* (New York: The Macmillan Co., 1903), 572ff & *passim.*

³¹ Ward in *American Journal of Sociology*, XII (March, 1907), 710. The discussion in *ibid.*, pp. 693-716, gives a cross-section of views of sociologists on the differential birth rate and on eugenics.

³² The issue was forcibly debated between Charles H. Cooley, a sociologist, and Frederick Adams Woods in *JH*, XI (February, 1920), 80-83. See also Herbert William Conn, *Social Heredity and Social Evolution, The Other Side of Eugenics* (New York: Abingdon Press, 1914); and Herbert Adolphus Miller, "The Psychological Limit of Eugenics," *Pop. Sci. Mon.*, LXXXIV (April, 1914), 390-96.

³³ Cattell, "Families of American Men of Science," *Pop. Sci. Mon.*, LXXXVI (May, 1915), 510-11 & 515. For discussion of Cattell's views, see Nicholas Pastore, *The Nature-Nurture Controversy* (New York: King's Crown Press, 1949), pp. 129-35.

³⁴ For complaints about the misuse of eugenics, see Roswell H. Johnson, "Eugenics and So-Called Eugenics," *American Journal of Sociology*, XX (July, 1914), 98-103; also C. B. Davenport, "The Eugenics Programme and Progress in its Achievement," *op. cit.*, pp. 1-2. On the Ohio group, see *JH*, VII (April, 1916), 189. The astrological side of eugenics is advocated in Ellis B. Guild, *The Science and Philosophy of Eugenics* (Kansas City: Burton Publishing Company, 1920), esp. pp. 167-84.

³⁵ See especially Jonathan Mayo Crane, "Reproduction of the Unfit," *American Journal of Eugenics*, I (July, 1907), 15-18; R. W. Shufeldt, "The Science of Stirpiculture," *ibid.* (October, 1907), pp. 193-96; [anon.], "The Opponents of Eugenics," *ibid.* (November, 1907), pp. 266-69; and editorial in *ibid.* (November, 1907), p. 271. The *American Journal of Eugenics* was the successor of *Lucifer.*

³⁶ For the close connection of sex education with eugenics, see the speeches on sex hygiene in *NCCC* (1912), pp. 275-79, 279-80, & 280-82; also G. Stanley Hall, "Eugenics: Its Ideals and What It Is Going to Do," *op. cit.*, pp. 152-59. The quotation is in Winfield Scott Hall, "The Relation of Education in Sex to Race Betterment," *Social Hygiene*, I (December, 1914), 79.

³⁷ For example, Herman G. Matzinger, "The Prevention of Mental Defect," *JPA*, XXIII (September, 1918, to June, 1919), 17.

³⁸ Frederick Peterson, "The Influence of Alcohol upon the Public Health," *Tng. Sch. Bull.*, VI (June, 1909), 52.
For discussion of the evidence on blastophthoria, see Michael F.

Guyer, *Being Well-Born*, pp. 167-82; J. E. Wallace Wallin, *Problems of Subnormality* (Yonkers-on-Hudson: World Book Co., 1917), pp. 444-53; Abraham Myerson, *Inheritance of Mental Diseases* (Baltimore: The Williams & Wilkins Co., 1925), pp. 298-320.

Of the prominent eugenists, Irving Fisher was most active for prohibition. See Fisher to Davenport, April 21, 1917, and further correspondence, C.S.H.; also Edward A. Ross to Fisher, December 20, 1915, and further correspondence in Ross Papers, W.H.S.

[39] George Nasmyth, *Social Progress and Darwinian Theory* (New York: G. P. Putnam's Sons, 1916), pp. 7-19, summarizes such views.

[40] Jordan, *The Days of a Man* (Yonkers-on-Hudson: World Book Co., 1922), II, 675. For biographical information, see also Edward McNall Burns, *David Starr Jordan: Prophet of Freedom* (Stanford: Stanford University Press, 1953), esp. pp. 1-37.

[41] *The Human Harvest;* also *The Blood of the Nation* (Boston: American Unitarian Association, 1910), and *War and the Breed: The Relation of War to the Downfall of Nations* (Boston: Beacon Press, 1915).

[42] D. S. Jordan & Harvey Ernest Jordan, *War's Aftermath: A Preliminary Study of the Eugenics of War* (Boston: Houghton, Mifflin & Co., 1914).

[43] *NYT*, July 25, 1915, Pt. IV, p. 6. See also Abraham Jacobi in *NYT*, January 23, 1916, Pt. IV, pp. 7-8; J. Arthur Thompson, "Eugenics and War," *Pop. Sci. Mon.*, LXXXVI (May, 1915), 417-27. For an English view, see Havelock Ellis, "War and Eugenics," *Essays in War-Time* (Boston: Houghton, Mifflin & Co., 1917), pp. 27-41. A dissenting view was Theodore Roosevelt, "Twisted Eugenics," in *op. cit.*, XIV, 167-78.

[44] Quotation from Sanger, "The Need of Birth Control in America," in *Birth Control, Facts and Responsibilities,* ed. Adolf Meyer (Baltimore: The Williams and Wilkins Co., 1925), p. 20. For her life, see Sanger, *Margaret Sanger, An Autobiography* (New York: W. W. Norton & Co., 1938); also Sanger, *My Fight for Birth Control* (New York: Farrar & Rinehart, Inc., 1931), pp. 3-88, and Lawrence Lader, *The Margaret Sanger Story and the Fight for Birth Control* (Garden City: Doubleday & Co., Inc., 1955), pp. 13-47.

[45] Victor Robinson, *Pioneers of Birth Control in England and America* (New York: Voluntary Parenthood League, 1919), *passim.*

[46] See especially, Sanger, *Margaret Sanger*, pp. 86-191.

[47] Mary Ware Dennett, *Birth Control Laws* (New York: Grafton Press, 1926), *passim.*

[48] Quotation from Ryan, *Family Limitation,* p. 5. See, for example, John M. Cooper, *Birth Control* (Washington: National Catholic Welfare Council, 1923), and Edward R. Moore, *The Case Against Birth Control* (New York: The Century Co., 1931).

In *Casti Connubii*, the Pope explained: "Any use whatsoever of matrimony exercised in such a way that the act is deliberately frustrated in its natural power to generate life is an offense against the law of God and nature, and those who indulge in such are branded with the guilt of a grave sin." *Five Great Encyclicals* (New York: Paulist Press, 1939), p. 93.

[49] For the campaign to change the laws, see Dennett, *Birth Control Laws, passim*. For Margaret Sanger's trials and tribulations, see her autobiography; also Lader, *Margaret Sanger Story*.

[50] He continued: "We had a lunatic fringe in the eugenics movement in the early days; we have been trying for 20 years to get rid of it and have finally done so. Let's not take on another fringe of any kind as an ornament." Copy of letter, Popenoe to Grant, April 14, 1928, C.S.H. See also copy of letter, Grant to Leon F. Whitney, April 15, 1928, C.S.H.

[51] Sanger, *Margaret Sanger,* p. 374.

[52] For example, Samuel J. Holmes, *Studies in Evolution and Eugenics* (New York: Harcourt, Brace & Co., 1923), p. 184; *Eugenical News,* II (July, 1917), 51 & (September, 1917), 73. Also Roosevelt, "Birth Reform, from the Positive, Not the Negative, Side," *op. cit.*

[53] For the opinions of these scientists, see *Birth Control:* The Proceedings of the First American Birth Control Conference (New York: Birth Control Review, n.d.); and Adolf Meyer, ed., *Birth Control, Facts and Responsibilities.*

[54] *Birth Control,* p. 158; *Eugenical News,* X (May, 1925), 58.

[55] Sanger, "Need for Birth Control in America," *op. cit., p. 15; see also William J. Robinson, *Birth Control or the Limitation of Offspring by Prevenception* (30th ed.; New York: Eugenics Publishing Co., 1927), esp. pp. 124-30.

[56] Davenport, *Heredity in Relation to Eugenics,* p. iii; Lewellys F. Barker in "Foreword" to *Eugenics: Twelve University Lectures,* p. xi. See also W. C. Rucker, "More 'Eugenic Laws,'" *JH,* VI (May, 1915), 219-26, and Alexander Graham Bell, "A Few Thoughts Concerning Eugenics," American Breeders' Association, *Report,* IV (1908), 208-14, & "Eugenics," in *ibid.,* V (1909), 211-14.

## CHAPTER VII

[1] Goddard & Helen F. Hill, "Delinquent Girls Tested by the Binet Scale," *Tng. Sch. Bull.,* VIII (June, 1911), 55; Mrs. E. Garfield Gifford & Goddard, "Defective Children in the Juvenile Court," *Tng. Sch. Bull.,* VIII (January, 1912), 133.

[2] J. E. Wallace Wallin, *Problems of Subnormality* (Yonkers-on-Hudson: World Book Co., 1917), p. 49. For a survey of systems in 1911, see *Provision for Exceptional Children in Public Schools,* U. S. Bureau of Education, Bull. No. 14, 1911 (Washington: G.P.O., 1911), pp. 42-65.

[3] The fullest secondary account of the alarmist period is in Stanley P. Davies, *Social Control of the Mentally Deficient* (New York: Thomas Y. Crowell Co., 1930).

[4] A sentimental history of the School is Joseph B. Byers, *The Village of Happiness: The Story of the Training School* (n.p., 1934). See also Goddard, "The Research Department," in Supplement to *Tng. Sch. Bull.* (December, 1907), pp. 1-10.

[5] *Mind*, XV (July, 1890), 373-80. The article had appended remarks by Galton.

[6] Histories of mental testing are Joseph Peterson, *Early Conceptions and Tests of Intelligence* (Yonkers-on-Hudson: World Book Company, 1925), and Frank N. Freeman, *Mental Tests: Their History, Principles and Applications* (rev. ed.; Boston: Houghton Mifflin Company, 1939). The former is best for the period through the development of the Binet tests, the latter for the period beginning with their introduction into the United States.

[7] The three scales are given in Peterson, *Early Conceptions*, pp. 172-75, 193-95, & 234-35.

[8] Goddard published a translation of the 1905 scale in *Tng. Sch. Bull.*, V (December, 1908), 3-10, and a translation of the 1908 scale in *ibid.*, VI (January, 1910), 146-55.

[9] Goddard, "Suggestions for a Prognostical Classification of Mental Defectives," *JPA*, XIV (September & December, 1909; March & June, 1910), 52.

[10] Goddard, "Four Hundred Feeble-Minded Children Classified by the Binet Method," *JPA*, XV (September & December, 1910), 18; also "Report of Committee on Classification of Feeble-Minded," *JPA*, XV (September & December, 1910), *passim*. The classification was more or less confirmed by Edmund B. Huey, who tested 1,300 inmates at Lincoln, Illinois, and found that only two reached the thirteen-year mental age; see "Retardation and the Mental Examination of Retarded Children," *JPA*, XV (September & December, 1910), 31-43.

[11] Goddard, "Two Thousand Normal Children Measured by the Binet Measuring Scale of Intelligence," *Pedagogical Seminary*, XVIII (June, 1911), 232-59. His revision was published as "A Revision of the Binet Scale," *Tng. Sch. Bull.*, VIII (June, 1911), 56-62.

[12] Goddard, "The Binet Measuring Scale of Intelligence: What it is and How it is to be Used," *Tng. Sch. Bull.*, XI (October, 1914), 87; Goddard & Hill, "Delinquent Girls," *op. cit.*, p. 55.

[13] Goddard, "The Binet Measuring Scale of Intelligence," *op. cit.*, p. 88.

[14] For instance, Augusta F. Bronner, "Mental Attitude Affecting Results in Psychological Tests," *APA* (1915), pp. 325-42.

[15] A brief history of the various revisions is in Freeman, *Mental Tests*, esp. pp. 92-112. A detailed contemporary comparison of the strengths and weaknesses of the various revisions is Warren W. Coxe, "Grading Intelligence by Years and by Points," *JCL&C*, VII (September, 1916), 341-65.

[16] Terman, *The Measurement of Intelligence* (Boston: Houghton Mifflin Company, 1916), was a manual for administering the tests.

[17] See, for instance, Dr. James W. Milligan, "Mental Defectives among Prisoners," *NPA* (1906), pp. 195-204, and Dr. Henry E. Allison, "Defective Inmates of Penal Institutions," *NPA* (1904), pp. 292-302.

[18] Summaries of many of the tests of delinquents may be found in Wallin, *Problems of Subnormality*, pp. 123-90, and James B. Miner, *De-*

*ficiency and Delinquency* (Baltimore: Warwick & York, 1918), pp. 128ff. Also J. E. Wallace Wallin, *Mental Deficiency* (Brandon, Vt.: Journal of Clinical Psychology, 1956), pp. 77-104.

[19] C. S. Bluemel, "Binet Tests on Two Hundred Juvenile Delinquents," *Tng. Sch. Bull.*, XII (December, 1915), 193.

[20] Healy, "The Mentally Defective and the Courts," *JPA*, XV (September & December, 1910), 44-57; Healy, "Mental Defects and Delinquency," *NCCC* (1911), pp. 59-65.

[21] *Individual Delinquent* (Boston: Little, Brown & Co., 1922), p. 447.

[22] Hickson, "The Defective Delinquent," *JCL&C*, V (July, 1914), 397-403.

[23] E. J. Emerick, *Problem of the Feeble-Minded*, Ohio Board of Administration, Publ. No. 5 (1915), pp. 4-6.

[24] Haines, *Mental Examination of Juvenile Delinquents*, Ohio Board of Administration, Publ. No. 7 (1915), p. 4. For the work of the Bureau, Haines, "The Ohio Plan for the Study of Delinquency," *Pop. Sci. Mon.*, LXXXVI (June, 1915), 576-80.

[25] Williams & Terman, "Psychological Survey of the Whittier State School," in *Biennial Report of the . . . Whittier State School* (Whittier: 1914), esp. pp. 15-19 & 29ff. A study two years later showed about the same percentages; Williams "Intelligence and Delinquency: A Study of Two Hundred Cases," *JCL&C*, VI (January, 1916), 696-705.

[26] Fernald, "The Recidivist," *JCL&C*, III (March, 1913), 866-75.

[27] Anderson, "Feeblemindedness as Seen in Court," *Mental Hygiene*, I (April, 1917), 261.

[28] *Report of the Commission for the Investigation of the White Slave Traffic, So Called*, Mass. House Doc. No. 2281 (Boston, 1914), p. 29. A study of the red-light district of Richmond found 70 per cent of the prostitutes feebleminded; see *Mental Defectives in Virginia*, A Special Report of the State Board of Charities and Corrections to the General Assembly of 1916 (Richmond, 1916), p. 66.

[29] Clinton P. McCord, "One Hundred Female Offenders: A Study of the Mentality of Prostitutes and 'Wayward' Girls," *JCL&C*, VI (September, 1915), 389.

[30] For instance, Victor V. Anderson & C. M. Leonard, "Drunkenness as Seen among Women in Court," *Mental Hygiene*, III (April, 1919), 266-74; Charles B. Barnes, "Feeble-Mindedness as a Cause for Homelessness," *Tng. Sch. Bull.*, XIII (March, 1916), 3-15 & (April, 1916), 27-35; Jean Weidensall, "The Mentality of the Unmarried Mother," *NCCC* (1917), pp. 287-94; Lilian Carpenter Streeter, "The Relation of Mental Defect to the Neglected, Dependent, and Delinquent Children of New Hampshire," *NCCC* (1915), pp. 340-52.

[31] See Johnstone, "How Shall We Lift the Burden," *Tng. Sch. Bull.*, VIII (April, 1911), 19; Fernald, "What is Practical in the Way of Prevention of Mental Defect," *NCCC* (1915), p. 290; Terman, *Measurement of Intelligence*, p. 6; Goddard, "Two Thousand Normal Children Measured by the Binet Measuring Scale of Intelligence," p. 237; Key, *Feeble-Minded Citizens in Pennsylvania*, p. 37.

A contemporary discussion of the variations is in James B. Miner, *Deficiency and Delinquency,* pp. 47-81; see also Fred Kuhlmann, "Distribution of the Feeble-Minded in Society," *JCL&C,* VII (July, 1916), pp. 205-18.

[32] For discussions of the defective delinquent, see Henry H. Goddard, *The Criminal Imbecile: An Analysis of Three Remarkable Murder Cases* (New York: The Macmillan Co., 1915); Victor V. Anderson, "A Classification of Borderline Mental Cases amongst Offenders," *JCL&C,* VI (January, 1916), 689-95, and A. Warren Stearns, "A Survey of Defective Delinquents under the Care of the Massachusetts State Board of Insanity," *AmJI,* LXXII (January, 1916), 427-37.

[33] Miner, *Deficiency and Delinquency,* pp. 166-69; Augusta F. Bronner, "A Research on the Proportion of Mental Defectives among Delinquents," *JCL&C,* V (September, 1914), 561.

[34] For instance, Hastings H. Hart, "The Extinction of the Defective Delinquent: A Working Program," *APA* (1912), esp. p. 207.

[35] H. B. Hickman, "Delinquent and Criminal Boys Tested by the Binet Scale," *Tng. Sch. Bull.,* XI (January, 1915), 159.

[36] Henry H. Goddard, *The Kallikak Family: A Study in the Heredity of Feeble-Mindedness* (New York: The Macmillan Co., 1912), *passim.*

[37] *Ibid.,* pp. 69 & 60.

[38] Estabrook, *The Jukes in 1915,* Carnegie Institution of Washington, Publ. No. 240 (Washington, D. C., 1916), *passim.*

[39] *Ibid.,* p. 85.

[40] *Ibid.,* esp. pp. 78 & 84.

[41] Elizabeth S. Kite, "The 'Pineys,' " *Survey,* XXXI (October 4, 1913), 7-13, 38-40; Mary S. Kostir, *The Family of Sam Sixty,* Ohio Board of Administration, Publ. No. 8 (1916); Mina A. Sessions, *The Feeble-Minded in a Rural County of Ohio,* Ohio Board of Administration, Publ. No. 12 (1918), pp. 39-67; A. C. Rogers & Maud A. Merrill, *Dwellers in the Vale of Siddem* (Boston: Richard G. Badger, 1919).

[42] Arthur H. Estabrook & C. B. Davenport, *The Nam Family: A Study in Cacogenics,* Eugenics Record Office, Memoir No. 2 (Cold Spring Harbor, 1912); Florence Danielson & C. B. Davenport, *The Hill Folk: Report on a Rural Community of Hereditary Defectives,* Eugenics Record Office, Memoir No. 1 (Cold Spring Harbor, 1912); Anna Wendt Finalyson, *The Dack Family: A Study in Hereditary Lack of Emotional Control,* Eugenics Record Office, Bull. No. 15 (Cold Spring Harbor, 1916). An important European family was the Zero Family described to the American audience by Gertrude Davenport in "Hereditary Crime," *American Journal of Sociology,* XIII (November, 1907), 402-9.

[43] One of the earliest, most alarming, and most influential surveys was Anne Moore, *The Feeble-Minded in New York: A Report Prepared for the Public Education Association of New York* (New York: State Charities Aid Assoc., 1911). Other important surveys included: *Mental Defectives in the District of Columbia,* U. S. Dept. of Labor, Children's Bureau, Publ. No. 13 (Washington: G.P.O., 1913); *Report of the State Commission to Investigate Provision for the Mentally Deficient,* New York

Senate Document No. 42 (1915); Wilhelmine E. Key, *Feeble-Minded Citizens in Pennsylvania*, Public Charities Assoc. of Pennsylvania, Publ. No. 16 (Philadelphia, 1915); *Mental Defectives in Indiana:* Report of the Committee on Mental Defectives Appointed by Governor Samuel M. Rolston (Indianapolis, 1916); and Thomas H. Haines, *Mississippi Mental Deficiency Survey:* Report of the Mississippi Mental Hygiene Commission, 1919; cited in *Mental Hygiene*, IV (July, 1920), 682.

[44] The evidence for the widespread belief that the feebleminded, especially the women, were prolific was very scanty. The figure often cited was that childbearing feebleminded women had seven children each, as compared to about half that for normal women. Such a figure, even if true, leaves several important questions unanswered. What percentage of feebleminded women, as compared to normal women, have children? Many idiots and imbeciles are incapable, feebleminded women in institutions have little opportunity, and many outside institutions remain childless. Thus, if a far smaller percentage of feebleminded women have children, the feebleminded would not contribute more than their share to succeeding generations even if the few who bear children have large numbers. Another question is the relation of the family size of the feebleminded women to the family size of other women of the same economic and social class. At that time the size of the family tended to be larger in the lower social groups, to which, naturally, the feebleminded belonged. Hence, the large families might not be characteristic of feeblemindedness but of social class. A review of the literature on fecundity of the feebleminded is in Wallin, *Mental Deficiency*, pp. 1-25.

[45] For instance, Alexander Johnson & Margaret Johnson Lane, *The Menace of the Mentally Defective*, American Unitarian Assoc., Dept. of Social & Public Service, Bull. No. 37 (Boston, n.d.); and March 2, 1912, issue of *Survey*.

## CHAPTER VIII

[1] Quotations from Bernard Glueck, "Concerning Prisoners," *Mental Hygiene*, II (April, 1918), 180, and Riis, "The Bad Boy," *Proceedings of the First National Conference of Race Betterment* (1914), pp. 245 & 246. The best detailed discussion of the studies that undermined the myth is Stanley P. Davies, *Social Control of the Mentally Deficient* (New York: Thomas Y. Crowell & Co., 1930), esp. chaps. x-xviii.

[2] For instance, Fred Kuhlmann, "The Present Status of the Binet and Simon Tests of the Intelligence of Children," *JPA*, XVI (March, 1912), 114-19; Samuel C. Kohs, "The Practicability of the Binet Scale and the Question of the Borderline Case," *Tng. Sch. Bull.*, XII (January, 1916), 211ff; James B. Miner, *Deficiency and Delinquency* (Baltimore: Warwick & York, 1918), pp. 93ff.

[3] Healy, *The Individual Delinquent* (Boston: Little, Brown, and Co., 1915), p. 80.

[4] Wallin has written an interesting autobiography, *The Odyssey of a Psychologist* (Wilmington: Publ. by author, 1955).

5 Wallin, "Who is Feeble-Minded?" *JCL&C*, VI (January, 1916), 706-16. For somewhat similar conclusions, see Augusta F. Bronner, *A Comparative Study of the Intelligence of Delinquent Girls*, Teachers College, Columbia University, Contributions to Education No. 68 (New York, 1914). See also Walter E. Fernald, "The Diagnosis of the Higher Grades of Mental Defect," *JPA*, XVIII (December, 1913), 74.

6 Wallin debated his views with Samuel C. Kohs. See Wallin, "Who is Feeble-Minded?" *op. cit.*, 706-16; Kohs, "Who is Feeble-Minded?" *JCL&C*, VI (March, 1916), 860-71; Wallin, " 'Who is Feeble-Minded?' A Reply to Mr. Kohs," *JCL&C*, VII (May, 1916), 56-78; Kohs, " 'Who is Feeble-Minded?'—A Rejoinder and a Rebuttal," *JCL&C*, VII (July, 1916), 219-22; Wallin, "A Rebuttal," *ibid.*, pp. 222-26.

7 A history of events is Robert M. Yerkes, ed., *Psychological Examining in the United States Army*, National Academy of Sciences, Memoirs, XV (Washington, 1921), esp. 7-10 & 299-414. A brief description of the tests is in Frank N. Freeman, *Mental Tests: Their History, Principles & Applications* (rev. ed.; Boston: Houghton Mifflin Company, 1939), pp. 113-40.

8 Yerkes, ed., *Psychological Examining*, p. 99.

9 *Ibid.*, pp. 785-90.

10 *Ibid.*, p. 789.

11 Wallin, "The Concept of the Feeble-Minded, Especially the Moron," *Tng. Sch. Bull.*, XVII (May, 1920), 50. See also Carroll Thompson Jones, "The New Moron," *Tng. Sch. Bull.*, XVI (September, 1919), 76-80.

12 For example, Herman M. Adler & Myrtle Raymaker, "The Scope of the Problem of Delinquency and Crime as Related to Mental Defect," *JPA*, XXX (1924-1925), 56. The superiority of the criminal is reported in Carl Murchison, *Criminal Intelligence* (Worcester: Clark University, 1926), esp. pp. 41ff. A recent summary is J. E. Wallace Wallin, *Mental Deficiency* (Brandon, Vt.: *Journal of Clinical Psychology*, 1956), esp. pp. 97-99.

13 Margaret Wooster Curti's "The Intelligence of Delinquents in the Light of Recent Research," *Scientific Monthly*, XXII (February, 1926), written because there remained a widespread feeling that crime was closely related to mental defect, provided an excellent historical criticism of the testing movement.

14 J. Harold Williams and Lewis M. Terman, "Psychological Survey of the Whittier State School," in *Biennial Report of the . . . Whittier State School* (Whittier, California, 1914), p. 30.

Charles Goring's *The English Convict, A Statistical Study* (London: Wyman & Sons, 1913) was usually cited as the definitive refutation of criminal anthropology. Goring made detailed comparisons of 3,000 convicts with various groups of non-criminals. He found the criminals generally shorter and less healthy than the normal population but saw no basis for a physical criminal type.

15 For example, Paul E. Bowers in *APA* (1914), pp. 267-68.

16 For a balanced argument, typical of many such arguments, see Victor V. Anderson, "Mental Disease and Delinquency: A Report of a Spe-

cial Committee of the New York State Commission of Prisons," *Mental Hygiene,* III (April, 1919), 177-98.

[17] Healy, *Individual Delinquent,* p. 447.

[18] *Ibid., passim.*

[19] *Ibid., passim.*

[20] Healy, *Mental Conflicts and Misconduct* (Boston: Little, Brown & Co., 1917), p. 58.

[21] For development of tests for aptitudes and personality, see Freeman, *Mental Tests,* pp. 169-236. George S. Stevenson and Geddes Smith in *Child Guidance Clinics, A Quarter Century of Development* (New York: Commonwealth Fund, 1934), trace some of the factors in the new attitude.

[22] For instance, Edward H. Ochsner, "Difficulties Encountered in Securing a Commitment Law for the Feeble-Minded," *NCCC* (1916), pp. 235-39.

[23] E. R. Johnstone, "How Shall We Lift the Burden," *Tng. Sch. Bull.,* VIII (April, 1911), 19-22.

[24] Fernald, "After-Care Study of the Patients Discharged from Waverley for a Period of Twenty-Five Years," *Ungraded,* V (November, 1919); cited in *Mental Hygiene,* IV (July, 1920), 695.

[25] *Ibid., passim.*

[26] Wallace, "Parole of the Feeble-Minded," *JPA,* XXIII (September, 1918-June, 1919), 60-81.

[27] Bernstein in "Colony and Extra-Institutional Care for the Feeble-minded," *Mental Hygiene,* IV (January, 1920), 1-28, described his system in detail. Also Elizabeth E. Farrell, "Results of After-Care Work with Special Class Children," *JPA,* XXII (September, 1917); a detailed and thoughtful report was Victor V. Anderson, "A Study of the Careers of 321 Feeble-Minded Persons Who have been in the Special Classes and are now out in the Community," *JPA,* XXVII (1921-1922), 138-49.

[28] Discussion in *JPA,* XXIII (September, 1918-June, 1919), 98. In 1924, shortly before his death, Fernald looked back and reviewed the alarmist period in his speech on "Thirty Years Progress in the Care of the Feeble-Minded," *JPA,* XXIX (1923-1924), esp. 211.

[29] Discussion in *JPA,* XXIII (September, 1918-June, 1919), 130. In a speech in 1927 Goddard retracted virtually everything; see "Feeble-mindedness: A Question of Definition," *JPA,* XXXIII (1927-1928), 219-27.

[30] In 1921 they heard Charles Bernstein on "Colony Care for Isolation Defective and Dependent Cases," *JPA,* XXVI (1920-1921), 43-54; Mabel A. Matthews on "One Hundred Institutionally Trained Male Defectives in the Community under Supervision," *ibid.,* pp. 60-70; Inez F. Stebbins, "Social and Economic Rehabilitation of the Feeble-Minded Girl," *ibid.,* pp. 71-81; Earl W. Fuller, "Extra-Institutional Care of Mental Defectives," *ibid.,* pp. 82-89; Hohanna D. Lillyman, "The Parole System at the Wrentham State School," *ibid.,* pp. 103-7.

[31] In "Two Brothers," *Survey,* XXVII (March 2, 1912), 1863, Miss Kite admitted that "of this girl, history has nothing and tradition very little to tell" and "of her name or ancestry no trace can be found to-day."

[32] Goddard, *The Kallikak Family* (New York: The Macmillan Co., 1912), pp. 78 & 90.

[33] For contemporary criticisms, see H. C. Stevens, "Eugenics and Feeblemindedness," *JCL&C*, VI (July, 1915), 190-97; J. E. Wallace Wallin, *Problems of Subnormality*, pp. 423ff; and especially Abraham Myerson, *The Inheritance of Mental Diseases* (Baltimore: Williams & Wilkins Co., 1925), pp. 77ff.

Goddard defended the method of collecting the data in *The Kallikak Family*, esp. pp. 13-16. Miss Kite defended herself in an article on "Method and Aim of Field Work at the Vineland Training School," *Tng. Sch. Bull.*, IX (October, 1912), 81-87.

[34] Myerson, *Inheritance*, p. 64 & *passim*. Dr. E. E. Southard, after numerous autopsies at Waverley, reported in 1918 that "there is an extraordinarily high percentage of feeble-mindedness of a non-hereditary nature." See "Remarks on the Progress of the Waverley Researches in the Pathology of the Feeble-Minded," *JPA*, XXIII (September, 1918-June, 1919), 48. Another who stressed the menace earlier but environmental causes later was Max G. Schlapp in "Causes of Defective Children," *JH*, XIV (December, 1923), 387-97. Even Davenport admitted in "The Nature of Mental Defect," *JPA*, XXXI (1925-1926), 202, that "concerning the specific question of whether mental defect is inherited in Mendelian fashion, I am free to confess that I think that the subject deserves further study."

[35] *Ibid., passim.*

[36] Walter E. Fernald, "A State Program for the Care of the Mentally Defective," *Mental Hygiene*, III (October, 1919), 566-74; Frankwood E. Williams, "Essential Elements in any Plan for Community Supervision of Trained Mentally Defective Persons," *JPA*, XXIX (1923-1924), 51-55. Davies in *Social Control*, esp. pp. 169-381, described the development of the new program.

[37] Discussion in *JPA*, XXIII (September, 1918-June, 1919), 130.

[38] See Frankwood E. Williams in "Foreword" to Davies, *Social Control*, pp. 121-37.

[39] *Chicago Tribune*, November 21, 1922; cited in *Eugenical News*, VII (December, 1922), 135.

[40] See below, chap. xi.

## CHAPTER IX

[1] Joseph P. Byers, *The Village of Happiness: The Story of the Training School* (n.p., 1934), *passim*. Alexander Johnson, *Adventures in Social Welfare* (Fort Wayne: by author, 1923), pp. 391-92.

[2] See *Tng. Sch. Bull.*, XII (December, 1915), 183-86, and typewritten Minutes of the Board of Directors of the Committee on Provision, V.T.S. At a meeting in Mrs. Harriman's home in spring, 1914, Davenport, Harry H. Laughlin, Johnstone, Goddard, and others had lectured her on the feebleminded; see Davenport-Harriman correspondence, C.S.H.

[3] Johnson, *Adventures, passim*. Byers had been Commissioner of Charities and Corrections, became interested in the work of the Vineland

group, and agreed to direct the crusade. See *Tng. Sch. Bull.*, XII (December, 1915), 183-86.

⁴ Johnson, "Custodial Care," *NCCC* (1908), 336. See Byers, "A State Plan for the Care of the Feeble-Minded," *NCCC* (1916), 223-29.

⁵ From a 1916 report by Byers on progress in various states and a Report of the Executive Secretary, March 5, 1917, V.T.S. Johnson, *Adventures*, pp. 400-1; *Tng. Sch. Bull.*, XIV (September, 1917), 84-86.

⁶ From 1916 Report of activities of the Committee on Provision, Minutes of the Board of Directors, March 13, 1917, and Report of the Executive Secretary, March 5, 1917, V.T.S.; Johnson, *Adventures*, p. 406.

⁷ Robert D. Dripps, "A Review of the Campaign in Pennsylvania," *JPA*, XXII (March & June, 1918), 162-72; Wilhelmine E. Key, *Feeble-Minded Citizens in Pennsylvania*, Public Charities Assoc., Publ. No. 16 (Philadelphia, 1915); Report of Joseph P. Byers to the Board of Directors, January 4, 1916, V.T.S.

⁸ Johnson, *Adventures*, pp. 416-17; also files of Committee on Provision for late 1917 and 1918, V.T.S.

⁹ See Thomas H. Haines, *Mississippi Mental Deficiency Survey*, abstracted in *Mental Hygiene*, IV (July, 1920), 682-94; Victor V. Anderson, "Mental Defect in a Southern State: Report of the Georgia Commission on Feeblemindedness and the Survey of the National Committee for Mental Hygiene," *Mental Hygiene*, III (October, 1919), 527-65; *A Report of the Wisconsin Mental Deficiency Survey with Recommendations* (Madison, 1921).

¹⁰ Bureau of the Census, *Feeble-Minded and Epileptics in Institutions, 1923* (Washington: G.P.O., 1926), pp. 17 & 25.

¹¹ *Ibid.*, p. 26.

¹² For example, W. C. Rucker, "More 'Eugenic Laws,'" *JH*, VI (May, 1915), 219-23.

¹³ E. R. Johnstone claimed, "With sterilization in the discard, so to speak, the one thing we believe necessary is segregation—permanent custodial care." Minutes of the Executive Committee of the Committee on Provision, February 22, 1917, V.T.S.

¹⁴ Statement in *Report of the State Commission to Investigate Provision for the Mentally Deficient*, p. 178.

¹⁵ *APA* (1909), pp. 40-42.

¹⁶ *APA* (1909), pp. 41 & 48. The debate will be found on pp. 40-48 & 245-53. The debate broke out again the next year; see *ibid.* (1910), pp. 140-52. Concerning the Biblical quotation, cf. Christ's statement in Matthew 19:12, "and there be eunuchs which have made themselves eunuchs for the kingdom of heaven's sake."

¹⁷ Charles Bruehl, "Eugenical Sterilization," *Homiletic and Pastoral Review*, XXVI (August, 1926), 1130. In subsequent issues, the author carefully defined the Catholic opposition. See also Joseph Mayer, "Eugenics in Roman Catholic Literature," trans. Paul Popenoe, *Eugenics*, III (February, 1930), 43-51, for a summary of discussion within the Church. The Papal condemnation is in *Five Great Encyclicals* (New York: The Paulist Press, 1939), pp. 96-97.

[18] Joel D. Hunter, "Sterilization of Criminals," *JCL&C*, V (September, 1914), 514-39. The report also summarized the moral and legal arguments. For a subsequent report, see William A. White, "Sterilization of Criminals," *JCL&C*, VIII (November, 1917), 499-501.

[19] For example, Charles V. Carrington, "Sterilization of Habitual Criminals," *APA* (1908), pp. 176-77.

[20] *NYT*, June 21, 1914, p. 14. For a further statement of his views, see *Heredity in Relation to Eugenics* (New York: Henry Holt and Co., 1911), pp. 255-58.

[21] Harry H. Laughlin, *Scope of the Committee's Work*, E.R.O., Bull. No. 10A (Cold Spring Harbor, 1914), p. 16 & *passim*. For a highly critical review, see Henry B. Hemmenway, in *JCL&C*, V (September, 1914), 623-26.

[22] Laughlin, *The Legal, Legislative and Administrative Aspects of Sterilization*, E.R.O., Bull. No. 10A (Cold Spring Harbor, 1914). This and his later compendiums are indispensable sources for the history of the movement; see *Eugenical Sterilization in the United States* (Chicago: Psychopathic Laboratory of the Municipal Court of Chicago, 1922); and *Eugenical Sterilization: 1926* (New Haven: American Eugenics Society, 1926).

[23] Laughlin, *Eugenical Sterilization* (1922), pp. 446-47. Full text of the model law is in *ibid.*, pp. 446-51.

[24] See Chap. IV, pp. 48-50.

[25] See an excellent article by Rudolph J. Vecoli, "Sterilization: A Progressive Measure?" *Wisconsin Magazine of History*, XLIII (Spring, 1960), 190-202.

[26] *Ibid.*

[27] Laughlin, *Eugenical Sterilization* (1922), pp. 31-32; also A. W. Wilmarth, "The Practical Working out of Sterilization," *JPA*, XXIII (September, 1918-June, 1919), 22-24.

[28] *Ibid.*, pp. 15 & 21. Texts of laws are in *ibid.*, pp. 15-33.

[29] J. H. Landman, *Human Sterilization: The History of the Sexual Sterilization Movement* (New York: The Macmillan Co., 1932), p. 259.

[30] Laughlin, *Eugenical Sterilization* (1922), pp. 15-33.

[31] *Ibid.*, pp. 149-62, 243-53, 255-69, 311-20.

[32] *Ibid.*, pp. 164-77, 217-41, 292-311; *NYT*, June 21, 1915 & May 12, 1920.

[33] For legal criticisms of early laws, see Charles A. Boston, "A Protest against Laws Authorizing the Sterilization of Criminals and Imbeciles," *op. cit.*, pp. 326-57; Frederick A. Fenning, "Sterilization Laws from a Legal Standpoint," *JCL&C*, IV (March, 1914), 804-14.

[34] Landman, *Human Sterilization*, esp. pp. 80-93.

[35] For Gosney's life, see "The Human Betterment Foundation," *Eugenics*, II (March, 1929), 17-21. For that of Popenoe, see Introduction to Gosney and Popenoe, *Sterilization for Human Betterment* (New York: The Macmillan Co., 1930).

[36] Bound together in *Collected Papers on Eugenic Sterilization in Cali-*

*fornia,* intro. E. S. Gosney (Pasadena: Human Betterment Foundation, 1930).

[37] Gosney & Popenoe, *Sterilization,* p. xv & *passim.*

[38] *Ibid.,* esp. pp. 39-47. Several years later, Popenoe and Gosney, in *Twenty-eight Years of Sterilization in California* (Pasadena: Human Betterment Foundation, 1939), confirmed the optimism of the earlier report.

[39] With his usual great detail, Laughlin presented the entire case in *The Legal Status of Eugenical Sterilization,* Supplement to the Annual Report of the Municipal Court of Chicago [Chicago, 1930].

[40] Laughlin, *Legal Status,* 17 & *passim.* See July, 1925 annual report of Estabrook to Davenport, C.S.H.

[41] *Ibid.,* p. 52. To the charge that the law constituted class legislation, Holmes replied: "The law does all that is needed when it does all that it can, indicates a policy, applies it to all within the lines, and seeks to bring within the lines all similarly situated so far and so fast as its means allow. Of course so far as the operations enable those who otherwise must be kept confined to be returned to the world, and thus open the asylum to others, the equality aimed at will be more nearly reached." *Ibid.*

[42] A popular and optimistic advocacy of sterilization was Leon F. Whitney, *The Case for Sterilization* (New York: Frederick A. Stokes Co., 1934). The enforcement of the German law gave him confidence that "undoubtedly we shall now see a wave of popular sentiment sweep the world" (p. 138).

[43] Landman, *Human Sterilization,* esp. pp. 104-5; Moya Woodside, *Sterilization in North Carolina: A Sociological and Psychological Study* (Chapel Hill: University of North Carolina Press, 1950), pp. 9ff.

[44] *Ibid., passim.* As Woodside wrote, "The aims of the Board are primarily those of social welfare, especially the welfare of children. Eugenic considerations are ever present, . . . but it is realized that the reduction of future generations of defectives is a long-term and maybe Utopian goal." *Ibid.,* p. 19.

The book is an excellent summary of the motives and administration of sterilization in North Carolina.

[45] For experience with sterilization in various states, see F. O. Butler, "A Quarter of a Century's Experience in Sterilization of Mental Defectives in California," *AJMD,* XLIX (April, 1945), 508-13; for Minnesota, Phyllis Mickelson, "Can Mentally Deficient Parents Be Helped to Give Their Children Better Care?" *AJMD,* LIII (January, 1949), 516-34; for Virginia, W. I. Prichard, "Sterilization of the Mentally Deficient," *AJMD,* LIII (April, 1949), 542-46; Lewis C. Tune, "Kansas Sterilization Law as It Applies to the State Training School," *AJMD,* LV (January, 1951), 381-83; L. Potter Harshman, "Nineteen Years' Experience with a Special Sterilization Act in Indiana," *AJMD,* LV (January, 1951), 377-80; as well as Woodside, *Sterilization in North Carolina.*

[46] Landman, *Human Sterilization,* pp. 49 & 289. The figures are minimum, since some states kept poor records and since a few institutions preferred not to reveal the extent of sterilization being done.

[47] Human Betterment Association of America, *Sterilizations Reported in the United States to January 1, 1959* (New York, 1959). The sterilizations per 100,000 population in 1958 show that sterilization is now strongest in the South: North Carolina (7.0), Georgia (3.7), Virginia (2.9), North Dakota (1.4), and Mississippi (1.0). Only 13 persons were sterilized in California in 1957 and in 1958.

[48] For example, Laughlin, *Scope of the Committee's Work,* p. 47.

[49] Wallin, *The Odyssey of a Psychologist* (Wilmington: by author, 1955), p. 88.

[50] Davenport did publish an analysis of existing laws, with advice for future laws, in *State Laws Limiting Marriage Selection Examined in the Light of Eugenics,* E.R.O., Bull. No. 9 (Cold Spring Harbor, 1913).

[51] *Eugenical News,* VII (May, 1922), 61.

[52] See esp. the story of the Wisconsin law of 1913 in *NYT,* January 1, 1914, p. 1, and succeeding issues.

[53] Mary Laack Oliver, *Eugenic Marriage Laws of the Forty-Eight States* (Unpubl. Master's Thesis, University of Wisconsin, 1937), p. 27. Texts of the laws are in her appendices.

## CHAPTER X

[1] Fisher to Davenport, March 2, 1912, C.S.H.

[2] For instance, Prescott F. Hall, *Eugenics, Ethics and Immigration,* Immigration Restriction League, Publ. No. 51 [1908 or 1909].

[3] Davenport to Hall, May 20, 1911, C.S.H. For founding of the Immigration Restriction League, see Chap. IV, pp. 50-56.

[4] Since both the Eugenics Research Association and the American Genetic Association were outgrowths of the American Breeders' Association and since the immigration committees of both had the same membership, it is difficult to know whether there were two committees or one committee speaking for both parent bodies. At any rate, see "First Report of the Committee on Immigration," *American Breeders' Magazine,* III (1912), 249-55; "Second Report of the Committee on Immigration," *JH,* V (July, 1914), 297-300; and "War, Immigration, Eugenics," *JH,* VII (June, 1916), 243-48.

[5] A brief sketch of Boas' thought is in Nicholas Pastore, *The Nature-Nurture Controversy* (New York: King's Crown Press, 1949), pp. 136-42.

[6] *The Mind of Primitive Man* (New York: The Macmillan Co., 1911), also "Human Faculty as Determined by Race," *Proceedings of the American Association for the Advancement of Science,* XLIII (1894), 301-27. Another article that attacked racism in the 1890's was Charles H. Cooley, "Genius, Fame and Comparison of Races," republished in *Sociological Theory and Social Research* (New York: Henry Holt and Co., 1930), pp. 121-59.

[7] In fact, in an important study conducted in 1907 for the Immigration Commission Boas found that physically the children of immigrants tended to resemble a common American type. (The cephalic index of foreign born Jews over twenty was 83.0 and of foreign born Italians 77.7, but that of their American born children of the same age was 81.4 and

81.5 respectively.) Such findings cast doubt upon the unalterability of even physical differences among races. See *Changes in Bodily Form of Descendants of Immigrants,* Reports of the Immigration Commission, Vol. XXXVIII, serial 5663 (Washington: G.P.O., 1911).

[8] For views of anthropologists, see Wilson D. Wallis, "Moral and Racial Prejudice," *Journal of Race Development,* V (October, 1914), 212-29; John R. Swanton, "Some Anthropological Misconceptions," *American Anthropologist,* XIX (October-December, 1917), 459-70; Robert H. Lowie, "Psychology, Anthropology, and Race," *American Anthropologist,* XXV (July-September, 1923), 291-303.

[9] Statement by the Immigration Restriction League in *Statements and Recommendations Submitted by Societies and Organizations Interested in the Subject of Immigration,* Vol. XLI of Reports of the Immigration Commission, serial 5881 (Washington: G.P.O., 1911), pp. 106-7.

[10] Ross, *The Old World in the New* (New York: The Century Co., 1914), pp. 113, 145, 147-48, & 150. For similar cataloging of race traits, see John R. Commons, *Race and Immigration in America* (New York: The Macmillan Co., 1908); Prescott F. Hall, *Immigration, and Its Effect upon the United States* (New York: Henry Holt and Co., 1906), pp. 46ff.

[11] Broughton Brandenburg, "How Shall we Make Our Immigration Laws More Effective?" *NCCC* (1906), p. 300.

[12] Discussion of reversion by early geneticists are in J. Arthur Thomson, *Heredity* (New York: G. P. Putnam's Sons, 1908), chap. v; and Herbert E. Walter, *Genetics* (New York: The Macmillan Co., 1913), chap. viii.

[13] William Z. Ripley, "Races in the United States," *Atlantic Monthly,* CII (December, 1908), 755; Fairchild, *The Melting Pot Mistake* (Boston: Little, Brown, and Co., 1926), p. 123.

[14] Cited in *Eugenical News,* III (February, 1918), 14-15. See also interview of East in *NYT,* July 18, 1920, Sec. III, p. 8, and East, *Mankind at the Crossroads* (New York: Charles Scribner's Sons, 1923), pp. 125-45. A less extreme statement is Edwin G. Conklin, "Some Biological Aspects of Immigration," *Scribner's Magazine,* LXIX (March, 1921), 358.

[15] Samuel J. Holmes, *Studies in Evolution and Eugenics* (New York: Harcourt, Brace and Co., 1923), pp. 216ff; David Starr Jordan, *War and the Breed* (Boston: Beacon Press, 1915), p. 30; Boas, *Mind of Primitive Man,* pp. 260-62.

[16] *Studies in Evolution,* p. 218.

[17] *The Rising Tide of Color Against White Supremacy* (New York: Charles Scribner's Sons, 1920).

[18] *The Passing of the Great Race* (New York: Charles Scribner's Sons, 1916), pp. 5 & 80-81.

[19] *Ibid.,* pp. 15-16 & 193. See also Grant, "Discussion of Article on Democracy and Heredity," *JH,* X (April, 1919), 165.

[20] For example, Prescott F. Hall, "Aristocracy and Politics," *JH,* X (April, 1919), 166-68.

[21] *Science,* XLVIII (October 25, 1918), 419, and *JH,* VIII (January, 1917), 34. In a letter to Grant, February 10, 1917, and to Stoddard, May 10, 1922, C.S.H., Davenport praised their books highly. See also F. A. Woods, "A Review of Reviews," *JH,* XIV (May, 1923), 93-95.

[22] Brigham, *A Study of American Intelligence* (Princeton: Princeton University Press, 1923), esp. pp. 88-111, 120-21, 157-69, 180-83. See also Robert M. Yerkes, ed., *Psychological Examining in the United States Army,* National Academy of Sciences, *Memoirs,* Vol. XV (Washington: G.P.O., 1921), chap. vi.

[23] Rudolph Pintner in *Intelligence Testing: Methods and Results* (new ed.; New York: Henry Holt and Co., 1931), pp. 446-67, summarized the testing of immigrants to that time.

[24] Pintner, *Intelligence Testing,* p. 443. Summaries of the testing of Negroes to that date are in Joseph Peterson, *The Comparative Abilities of White and Negro Children,* Comparative Psychology Monographs, Vol. I, No. 5 (July, 1923), and Pintner, *Intelligence Testing,* pp. 432-45. Results of Army testing of Negroes in Yerkes, ed., *Psychological Examining,* chap. viii. See also Edward B. Reuter, *The Mulatto in the United States* (Boston: Richard G. Badger, 1918), esp. pp. 211 & 380ff.

[25] An indictment of immigrants as breeders of delinquency and dependency is Prescott Hall, *Immigration,* pp. 146-69. For more balanced discussions, see Hastings H. Hart, "Immigration and Crime," *NPA* (1896), pp. 204-7, and Grace Abbott, "Immigration and Crime," *JCL&C,* VI (November, 1915), 522-32; also Aaron J. Rosanoff, "Some Neglected Phases of Immigration in Relation to Insanity," *AmJI,* LXXII (July, 1915), 45-58, and Horatio M. Pollock & William J. Nolan, "Sex, Age and Nativity of Dementia Praecox First Admission to the New York State Hospitals," abstracted in *Mental Hygiene,* IV (January, 1920), 221-26.

[26] John Higham's *Strangers in the Land: Patterns of American Nativism, 1860-1925* (New Brunswick: Rutgers University Press, 1955), is the outstanding interpretation of the American nativist impulse.

[27] Ward to Ross, April 7, 1912, Ross Papers, W.H.S.

[28] For a highly critical review of the Commission's work, see Oscar Handlin, *Race and Nationality in American Life* (Garden City: Doubleday & Company, Inc., 1957), chap. v.

[29] Summary of the Commission findings are in the two volume *Abstracts of Reports of the Immigration Commission,* Reports of the Immigration Commission, Vols. I & II, serial 5865 & 5866 (Washington: G.P.O., 1911). Contemporary criticisms are Isaac A. Hourwich, *Immigration and Labor* (New York: G. P. Putnam's Sons, 1912), and Cyrus L. Sulzberger, "Immigration," *NCCC* (1912), pp. 239-49.

[30] Robert DeC. Ward, "Immigration after the War," *JH,* VIII (April, 1917), 151. For enactment of the law, see Higham, *Strangers,* esp. pp. 202-4.

[31] Higham, *Strangers,* pp. 194-307; also Robert A. Divine, *American Immigration Policy, 1924-1952* (New Haven: Yale University Press, 1957), esp. pp. 5-8; and Robert K. Murray, *Red Scare: A Study in Na-*

*tional Hysteria, 1919-1920* (Minneapolis: University of Minnesota Press, 1955).

[32] See Higham, *Strangers,* pp. 177-78, 307, 313-14; also Davenport-Laughlin and Davenport-Grant correspondence, C.S.H. Laughlin's annual reports to Davenport, C.S.H., summarize his activities for the House Committee. His more important testimony was *Biological Aspects of Immigration,* Hearings before the Committee on Immigration and Naturalization, 66th Cong., 2d Sess. (Washington: G.P.O., 1921); *Analysis of America's Modern Melting Pot,* Hearings before the Committee on Immigration and Naturalization, 76th Cong., 3d Sess., serial 7-C (Washington: G.P.O., 1923); *Europe as an Emigrant-Exporting Continent and the United States as an Immigrant Receiving Nation,* Hearings before the Committee on Immigration and Naturalization, 78th Cong., 1st Sess., serial 5-A (Washington: G.P.O., 1924), pp. 1231-1437.

[33] Divine, *American Immigration,* pp. 5-18.

[34] Charles W. Gould, *America, A Family Matter* (New York: Charles Scribner's Sons, 1922), pp. 162-63. For varying expressions of the racist view, see William McDougall, *Is America Safe for Democracy?* (New York: Charles Scribner's Sons, 1921); Clinton Stoddard Burr, *America's Race Heritage* (New York: National Historical Society, 1922); Gino Speranza, *Race or Nation: A Conflict of Divided Loyalties* (Indianapolis: The Bobbs-Merrill Company, Inc., 1923); Ellsworth Huntington, *The Character of Races* (New York: Charles Scribner's Sons, 1924).

[35] See Davenport-Osborn correspondence, C.S.H. Osborn's speech is "Address of Welcome," in *Eugenics, Genetics and the Family:* Scientific Papers of the Second International Congress of Eugenics (Baltimore: The Williams & Wilkins Co., 1923), I, 1-4. For the exhibition, see typewritten "Report of H. H. Laughlin for the Year Ending August 31, 1922," in Davenport-Laughlin correspondence, C.S.H.

[36] Evans, *The Menace of Modern Immigration* [Dallas, 1923], pp. 5 & 22.

[37] Higham, *Strangers,* pp. 312ff; Divine, *American Immigration,* chap. ii.

[38] Quotation from Grant, "Closing the Flood-Gates," *The Alien in Our Midst,* p. 23. See Lothrop Stoddard, *Re-Forging America* (New York: Charles Scribner's Sons, 1927), and Fairchild, *The Melting-Pot Mistake.*

[39] For example, Robert DeC. Ward, "Immigration and the South," *Atlantic Monthly,* XCVI (November, 1905), 611-17.

[40] Davenport, *State Laws Limiting Marriage Selection Examined in the Light of Eugenics,* E.R.O., Bull. No. 9 (Cold Spring Harbor, 1913), p. 32; Grant, *Passing of the Great Race,* p. 78.

[41] See Albert Ernest Jenks, "The Legal Status of Negro-White Amalgamation in the United States," *American Journal of Sociology,* XXI (March, 1915), 666-78.

[42] Grant, *Passing of the Great Race,* p. 56; Holmes, *Studies in Evolution,* p. 221.

[43] *Eugenical News,* IX (May, 1924), 48. See Grant to Davenport, April 8, 1924, and enclosures with the letter, C.S.H.

[44] A comparison of the laws as given in Jenks, *op. cit.,* pp. 673-78, with digests in M. F. Ashley Montagu, *Man's Most Dangerous Myth: The Fallacy of Race* (3d ed.; New York: Harper & Brothers, 1952), pp. 302-8, shows very little change.

## CHAPTER XI

[1] Especially Goddard, *Feeble-Mindedness, Its Causes and Consequences* (New York: The Macmillan Co., 1920), chaps. i & x.

[2] F. A. Woods, "Democracy and the Human Equation," *JH,* XII (May, 1921), 208.

[3] "Nature or Nurture?" *JH,* VI (May, 1915), 227.

[4] Conklin, "Some Biological Aspects of Immigration," *Scribner's Magazine,* LXIX (March, 1921), 354; East, *Heredity and Human Affairs* (New York: Charles Scribner's Sons, 1929), p. 300.

[5] *Psychology of the Normal and Subnormal* (New York: Dodd, Mead and Co., 1924), p. 238; see also Goddard, *Human Efficiency and Levels of Intelligence* (Princeton: Princeton University Press, 1920).

[6] Quotation in *An Introduction to Social Psychology* (15 ed.; Boston: John W. Luce & Co., 1923), p. 20. For his debt to Galton, see "A Practical Eugenic Suggestion," *Sociological Papers, 1906* (London: Macmillan and Co., Ltd., 1907), pp. 55-80. His ideas are treated in Nicholas Pastore, *The Nature-Nurture Controversy* (New York: King's Crown Press, 1949), pp. 47-55, and Gardner Murphy, *Historical Introduction to Modern Psychology* (rev. ed.; New York: Harcourt, Brace and Co., 1949), pp. 403-6.

[7] See McDougall, *Is America Safe for Democracy* (New York: Charles Scribner's Sons, 1921), *Ethics and Some Modern World Problems* (New York: G. P. Putnam's Sons, 1924), *The Indestructible Union* (Boston: Little, Brown, and Co., 1925).

[8] Wiggam, *The New Decalogue of Science* (Indianapolis: The Bobbs-Merrill Company, Inc., 1923), p. 187; Stoddard, *The Revolt Against Civilization* (New York: Charles Scribner's Sons, 1922), *passim.*

[9] This and the next paragraph are based on several programs for research and on the voluminous correspondence involved in drawing up the programs. See especially a 1925 *"Summary* of Suggestions Made in Response to Inquiry Sent out by the *Committee on Research* of the *Eugenics Committee of the United States of America* Asking for Such Suggestions" and a 1928 "Problems of Eugenical Research," C.S.H.

[10] Thorndike, "Edward Lee Thorndike," in *A History of Psychology in Autobiography,* ed. Carl Murchison (Worcester: Clark University Press, 1936), III, 263-70. An excellent critical study of Thorndike's educational thought is Merle Curti, *The Social Ideas of American Educators* (New York: Charles Scribner's Sons, 1935), pp. 459-98.

[11] He summarized his twin studies in "Individual Differences and their Causes," Vol. III of *Educational Psychology* (New York: Teachers College, Columbia University, 1914), pp. 247-51; see also "Eugenics: With Special Reference to Intellect and Character," *Pop. Sci. Mon.,* LXXXIII (August, 1913), p. 131.

[12] Quotation from *ibid.*, p. 143. See Thorndike, *The Original Nature of Man*, Vol. I of *Educational Psychology* (New York: Teachers College, Columbia University, 1913).

[13] Terman, "Lewis M. Terman," in *A History of Psychology in Autobiography*, II, 331. For further sketch of Terman's life, see Pastore, *Nature-Nurture*, pp. 85-95. For his early studies of genius, see "The Mental Hygiene of Exceptional Children," *Pedagogical Seminary*, XXII (December, 1915), 529-37; "The Intelligence Quotient of Francis Galton in Childhood," *American Journal of Psychology*, XXVIII (April, 1917), 209-15; *Intelligence of School Children* (New York: Houghton Mifflin Company, 1919), pp. 165-267.

[14] *Genetic Studies of Genius* (5 Vols.; Stanford: Stanford University Press, 1925-1959), *passim*.

[15] *Genetic Studies*, I, 111.

[16] Henry H. Goddard, *School Training of Gifted Children* (Yonkers-on-Hudson: World Book Company, 1928), p. 29; Hollingworth, *Gifted Children, Their Nature and Nurture* (New York: The Macmillan Co., 1926), esp. pp. 199 & 350ff.

[17] Robert M. Yerkes, ed., *Psychological Examining in the United States Army*, Vol. XV of *Memoirs of the National Academy of Sciences* (Washington: G.P.O., 1921), pp. 819ff. For summary of intelligence of children and parental occupation, see Rudolph Pintner, *Intelligence Testing, Methods and Results* (new ed.; New York: Henry Holt & Co., 1931), pp. 513-19.

[18] Edgar Sydenstricker and Frank W. Notestein, "Differential Fertility According to Social Class," *Journal of the American Statistical Association*, XXV (March, 1930), 25. For an earlier study, see Hornell Hart, "Occupational Differential Fertility," *Scientific Monthly*, XIX (November, 1924), 527-32; for a later study, Clyde V. Kiser, "Fertility of Social Classes in Various Types of Communities of the East North Central States in 1900," *Journal of the American Statistical Association*, XXVII (December, 1932), 371-82.

[19] East, *Mankind at the Crossroads* (New York: Charles Scribner's Sons, 1923).

[20] Ross, *Standing Room Only?* (New York: Century Co., 1927), esp. pp. 234-36 & 271; Thompson, *Population Problems* (New York: McGraw-Hill Book Co., Inc., 1930), chaps. xx & xxi. For other moderate discussions, see Edward B. Reuter, *Population Problems* (Philadelphia: J. B. Lippincott Co., 1923), chaps. xv & xvi; Raymond Pearl, *The Biology of Population Growth* (New York: Alfred A. Knopf, Inc., 1925), esp. pp. 169ff.

[21] Morgan's important report on the fruitfly work was *The Physical Basis of Heredity* (Philadelphia: J. B. Lippincott Co., 1919).

[22] East, *Heredity and Human Affairs*, pp. 226ff & 104ff.

[23] For racism, see O. F. Cook, "American Race Problems," *JH*, XVIII (November, 1927), 465-73. For the other articles, see William M. Clay and E. Mead Wilcox, "Five Generations of an Inferior Family," *JH*,

XVIII (March, 1927), 121-23; William J. Tinkle, "Heredity of Habitual Wandering," *JH*, XVIII (December, 1927), 548-51.

24 Jennings, *Prometheus, Or Biology and the Advancement of Man* (New York: E. P. Dutton & Co., Inc., 1925), p. 7.

25 *Ibid.*, pp. 54-55.

26 *Ibid.*, pp. 26 & 85. For a similar view by an eminent geneticist and former eugenist, see Raymond Pearl, "The Biology of Superiority," *American Mercury*, XII (November, 1927), 257-66. Jennings later greatly expanded his discussion in a very influential book on *The Biological Basis of Human Nature* (New York: W. W. Norton & Co., Inc., 1930).

27 E. Carleton MacDowell, "Charles Benedict Davenport, 1866-1944: A Study of Conflicting Influences," *Bios*, XVII (March, 1946), 31-34. See Davenport, *Body-Build and its Inheritance*, Carnegie Institution of Washington, Publ. No. 329 (Washington, 1923), and "The Nature of Hereditary Mental Defect," *JPA*, XXXI (1925-26), 196-202.

28 Quotation in Davenport and Steggerda, *Race Crossing in Jamaica*, Carnegie Institution of Washington, Publ. No. 395 (Washington, 1929), p. 471. Jennings, in *Biological Basis of Human Nature*, pp. 283-86, adopted Davenport's conclusion. Castle criticized such views in "Race Mixture and Physical Disharmonies," *Science*, LXXI (June 13, 1930), 603-6.

29 Davenport to Darwin, January 3, 1922, and June 3, 1929, C.S.H. For other expressions of caution, see Davenport to Albert E. Wiggam, November 23, 1920; Davenport to Frederick Osborn, February 10, 1930, February 14, 1930, and February 24, 1930, C.S.H.

30 Quotation in Watson, *Behaviorism* (New York: W. W. Norton & Co., Inc., 1924), p. 74. General discussions of behaviorism are in Murphy, *Modern Psychology*, chap. xviii, and Pastore, *Nature-Nurture*, pp. 171-75.

31 Quotation from Charles W. Burr, "A Criticism of Psychoanalysis," *AmJI*, LXXI (October, 1914), 241; see too Charles G. Wagner, "Presidential Address: Recent Trends in Psychiatry," *AmJI*, LXXIV (July, 1917), 10-14.

32 Quotation from *The Mind of Primitive Man* (New York: The Macmillan Co., 1911), p. 121. See Bronislaw Malinowski, *Sex and Repression in Savage Society* (New York: Harcourt, Brace & Co., Inc., 1927), pp. 135-280, and especially Ruth Benedict, *Patterns of Culture* (Boston: Houghton Mifflin Company, 1934), chaps. i & vii.

33 After the war, the American Genetic Association contacted numerous twins and devoted an entire issue of its journal to them; see *JH*, X (December, 1919). One of the best brief studies in the 1920's was H. J. Muller, "Mental Traits and Heredity," *JH*, XVI (December, 1925), 433-48. Gladys C. Schwesinger in *Heredity and Environment* (New York: The Macmillan Co., 1933), pp. 175-231, reviewed studies of twins to that time.

34 Newman, *et al.*, *Twins, A Study of Heredity and Environment* (Chicago: University of Chicago Press, 1937), pp. 72 & 344.

35 R. S. Woodworth analyzes twin studies in *Heredity and Environ-*

*ment: A Critical Survey of Recently Published Material on Twins and Foster Children* (New York: Social Science Research Council, n.d.), pp. 3-32.

[36] Early reports on foster children studies were Frank N Freeman, *et al.*, "The Influence of Environment on the Intelligence, School Achievement, and Conduct of Foster Children," and Barbara Stoddard Burks, "The Relative Influence of Nature and Nurture upon Mental Development," in *Nature and Nurture*, National Society for the Study of Education, 27th Yearbook (1928), Pt. I, pp. 103-218 & 219-316. Woodworth's discussion of various studies in *Heredity and Environment*, pp. 33-69, is excellent.

[37] The Fisher-Davenport correspondence, C.S.H., traces the development of the Society and shows their disagreement over Whitney's worth. For the Fitter Family Contests, see David Starr Jordan to Davenport, February 3, 1913, C.S.H.; *Eugenical News*, VII (October, 1922), 111; and "Fitter Families Again," *JH*, XVII (February, 1926), 68-69.

[38] See correspondence of Eugenics Research Association and a typewritten history, C.S.H.; also *Eugenical News, passim*.

[39] Frederick Osborn to author, May 26, 1959. The Davenport-Osborn correspondence, C.S.H., is interesting in showing the aims and relationship of the two men in 1928 and shortly thereafter.

[40] Osborn to author, May 26, 1959.

[41] Schwesinger, *Heredity and Environment, passim;* Lorimer and Osborn, *Dynamics of Population* (New York: The Macmillan Co., 1934), *passim*.

[42] Lorimer & Osborn, *Dynamics, passim*.

[43] *Ibid.*, esp. chap. xiii.

[44] Osborn to author, May 26, 1959.

## CHAPTER XII

[1] Frederick Osborn to author, May 26 and June 18, 1959.

[2] Davenport's last years are sympathetically described in E. Carleton MacDowell, "Charles Benedict Davenport, 1866-1944: A Study of Conflicting Influences," *Bios*, XVII (March, 1946), 34-37. Laughlin's unhappy position is clear in the Laughlin correspondence, C.S.H. For a description of the Institute, see *JH*, XXI (April, 1930), 173-74.

[3] Osborn to Albert F. Blakeslee, April 23, 1940, C.S.H.

[4] Hans Harmsen, "The German Sterilization Act of 1933," *Eugenics Review*, XLVI (January, 1955), 227-32. In *Into the Darkness: Nazi Germany Today* (New York: Duell, Sloan & Pearce, Inc., 1940), pp. 179ff, Lothrop Stoddard recorded his admiration for the German emphasis upon biological fitness and described a German sterilization hearing.

[5] Gerald Reitlinger, *The Final Solution: The Attempt to Exterminate the Jews of Europe, 1939-1945* (London: Vallentine, Mitchell, 1953); also Joseph Tenenbaum, *Race and Reich* (New York: Twayne Publishers, Inc., 1956).

[6] Frank Lorimer and Osborn, *The Dynamics of Population* (New York: The Macmillan Co., 1934), p. 140; Klineberg, *Negro Intelli-*

*gence and Selective Migration* (New York: Columbia University Press, 1935). Klineberg, ed., *Characteristics of the American Negro* (New York: Harper & Brothers, 1944), presented a summary of current scientific knowledge on many phases of the Negro.

[7] For example, M. F. Ashley Montagu, *Man's Most Dangerous Myth: The Fallacy of Race* (New York: Columbia University Press, 1942), chap. iii, and Gunnar Dahlberg, *Race, Reason and Rubbish,* trans. Lancelot Hogben (London: George Allen & Unwin Ltd., 1942), chap. xi.

[8] In 1938 the American Association of University Professors, American Anthropological Association, and American Psychological Association, and in 1939 the International Genetic Congress all took firm stands against racism and attacked Nazi doctrines. See Margaret Mead, *Race: Science and Politics* (New York: Modern Age Books, 1940), pp. 259-66.

[9] Stuart Omar Landry, *The Cult of Equality: A Study of the Race Problem* (New Orleans: Pelican Publishing Co., 1945), and Herman E. Talmadge, *You and Segregation* (Birmingham: Vulcan Press, 1956), esp. pp. 42-46.

[10] Statement about Goethe from reading numerous of his pamphlets and letters.

[11] On birth rate trends, see Wilson H. Grabill, *et al., The Fertility of American Women* (New York: John Wiley & Sons, Inc., 1958), esp. pp. 274-77 & 378-79.

[12] Osborn, *Preface to Eugenics* (rev. ed.; New York: Harper & Brothers, 1951), esp. chaps. viii & ix; also "Freedom of Choice for Parenthood, A Program of Positive Eugenics," *Eugenical News,* XXXVIII (June, 1955), 25-31.

[13] Muller, *Out of the Night* (New York: Vanguard Press, 1935), and Haldane, *Heredity and Politics* (New York: W. W. Norton & Co., 1938). See also Muller, "The Dominance of Economics over Eugenics," *Scientific Monthly,* XXXVII (July, 1933), 40-47.

[14] For example, Linus Pauling, *No More War!* (New York: Dodd, Mead & Co., 1958).

[15] Its founding and goals are described in H. J. Muller, "Progress and Prospects in Human Genetics," *American Journal of Human Genetics,* I (September, 1949), 1-18.

[16] Kallmann, *Heredity in Health and Mental Disorder* (New York: W. W. Norton & Company, Inc., 1953), p. 124.

[17] Sheldon C. Reed, *Counseling in Medical Genetics* (Philadelphia: W. B. Saunders Co., 1955), *passim.*

[18] *Eugenical News,* VII (May, 1922), 63; Reed, *Counseling in Medical Genetics,* pp. 1-5; Lee R. Dice, "Counseling Centers on Human Heredity in North America," *Eugenical News,* XXXVII (June, 1952), 32-34.

[19] For a discussion by heredity counselors of the implications of their calling, see report of the Heredity Counseling Symposium sponsored by the American Eugenics Society, printed in *Eugenics Quarterly,* V (March, 1958); also Amram Scheinfeld, "Changing Attitudes Toward Human Genetics and Eugenics," *Eugenics Quarterly,* V (September, 1958), 145-53.

[20] The most readable book is Reed, *Counseling in Medical Genetics.*

Some geneticists feel, however, that he occasionally draws broad conclusions on too little data. A popular account of heredity counseling is Irving and Frances Freilich, "Will Your Baby be Normal?" *Saturday Evening Post*, CCXXX (November 9, 1957), 145 *et seq.*

[21] Lionel S. Penrose, *The Biology of Mental Defect* (London: Sidgwick & Jackson Ltd., 1949), pp. 54-57 & 114-18.

[22] Jennings, "Health Progress and Race Progress," *JH*, XVIII (June, 1927), 272; also Muller, "Our Load of Mutations," *American Journal of Human Genetics*, II (June, 1950), 111-76.

[23] James V. Neel, "The Detection of the Genetic Carriers of Inherited Disease," in *Clinical Genetics*, ed. Arnold Sorsby (London: Butterworth & Co., Ltd., 1953), chap. iii.

[24] In *Out of the Night*, Muller suggested that artificial insemination might produce great geniuses and that this should be the most important goal of eugenics. More recently James F. Crow, in an article by Robert O'Brien, "Coming: Man-Made Men," *Esquire* (April, 1959), pp. 95-98, has advocated the same. In the 1920's J. B. S. Haldane predicted that sperm, egg, and embryo would someday all be grown to maturity outside the parents and that the eugenic possibilities of this dwarfed anything eugenists could hope to accomplish by sterilization or tampering with birth rates; see *Daedalus, Or Science and the Future* (London: Kegan Paul, Trench, Trübner & Co., Ltd., 1925), pp. 63-71.

[25] There has been much popular discussion of research on DNA; for instance, "Secret of Life," *Time*, LXXII (July 14, 1958), 50-54; Leonard Engel, "The Race to Create Life," *Harper's*, CCXXV (October, 1962), 39-45.

[26] For moderate modern statements about eugenics, see Curt Stern, *Principles of Human Genetics* (San Francisco: W. H. Freeman and Co., 1949), chap. xxiv; and Julian Huxley, *Evolution in Action* (New York: Mentor Book, 1953), chap. vi. The activities of the Society are from American Eugenics Society, *Five-Year Report: 1953-1957*, and letter of Frederick Osborn to author, May 26, 1959.

[27] *Eugenics Quarterly*, V (March, 1958), 62.

# Index